INDUSTRIAL WASTE TREATMENT

A modern industrial-waste-treatment plant.

INDUSTRIAL WASTE TREATMENT

by

EDMUND B. BESSELIEVRE

Member, American Society of Civil Engineers;
Chief Sanitary Engineer, International Sales,
The Dorr Company

McGRAW-HILL BOOK COMPANY, INC.

NEW YORK   TORONTO   LONDON

1952

INDUSTRIAL WASTE TREATMENT

Library of Congress catalog card number: 51-12586

II

THE MAPLE PRESS COMPANY, YORK, PA.

TO
H. W. B. and J. S. B.

PREFACE

There are as many industrial-waste problems as there are industries which discharge liquid effluents from their plants. Practically all wet-process industries produce a liquid which may be classed as an industrial waste. However, not all liquids discharged from all plants are pollutional. It is with those wastes which cause pollution of streams, with its concomitant nuisances, health hazards, etc., that we are concerned.

Industrial-waste treatment is a comparatively new science; that is, intelligent scientific thought and research have been applied to it only recently, particularly in the last decade. Industrial wastes have been treated in England and Germany for many years and in this country for about twenty years, but the earlier work did not envision some of the concepts which are now recognized as "musts" in any consideration of the treatment of a given liquid industrial waste.

Owing to the intensity with which American investigators apply themselves to a problem when the necessity for its solution is made apparent to them, the research done on industrial-waste treatment by individual engineers and chemists, by the research departments of a number of the technical schools, and also by private industrial concerns or groups has been tremendous; and the literature has become so voluminous that the author has personally prepared a bibliography on industrial waste and stream pollution which includes over 6,000 references. With this great mass of material covering all kinds of wastes which have existed in past years and new ones which have arisen since World War II, it is obviously impossible to include a comprehensive résumé of these data in one portable book. As a matter of fact, an entire book could be devoted to the treatment of a number of the more important classes of wastes.

There is, however, in the author's opinion, a need for a book that will act as a guide for those who are faced with an industrial-waste problem and do not know how to solve it. There are so many phases of this problem that affect not only the industrialist but also public welfare, municipal policy, etc., that a knowledge of these is necessary before a campaign of treatment can be undertaken.

The rules and regulations of the Federal government and the several states all enter into the solution of a problem; the methods and means of treatment that have been devised and found satisfactory must be studied. No empirical rule can be laid down for the treatment of any class of waste; local conditions make it necessary to devise a plant which is right for the particular waste under consideration, but this may not be the right one for a similar waste in the next town.

It is with this idea in view, to present the factors that enter into a waste problem and to guide those who have such problems along the proper lines to their solution, that this book is written. It is hoped that it will serve that purpose for engineers of plants, consulting engineers called in to advise industrialists, chemists, state and city health and public officials, and others. This book can also be used as a reference work for students who are now shaping their careers and wish to select some field which offers a future not now overcrowded.

Industrial-waste treatment is now considered a branch of sanitary engineering. It will always remain such a problem, but with increased activity throughout the world in preventing pollution and the increased nationalistic feeling in many countries which will cause the development of more industry, the treatment of wastes is bound to become a more and more specialized field.

The technician who solves an industrial-waste problem must not only be an engineer, he must also be a diplomat, a politician, and an economist.

My sincere appreciation is extended to Edward S. Cleary for his helpful review of the original text and his valuable suggestions.

Edmund B. Besselievre

Greenwich, Conn.
April, 1952

CONTENTS

CHAPTER 1

WHAT CONSTITUTES A WASTE PROBLEM?

Industrial wastes are the liquid discharges from an establishment that prepares any material or article for the market. They are the liquid wastes which in any way differ from the water supply received by the establishment and used by it in its operations.

Industrial wastes are the penalty paid by an industrial nation and are one of the inevitable problems connected with industrialism. They are the outcome of civilization and its demand for a high standard of living. Only the so-called "civilized" nations suffer from such wastes. The "backward" peoples, the tribes of Africa, who live close to nature with simple household amenities and who receive their food supplies direct from the land, are free from industrial-waste problems.

This, however, is not an argument against industry or for a return to that era when man required "but little here below." We have so long been indoctrinated in a civilized way of life that retrogression toward the simpler life of bygone ages is out of the question. We shall continue to have more products of civilization and to develop more and more industries to produce them. Therefore, we shall have to suffer the penalty of more and more industrial wastes.

Industrial plants produce a variety of waste products—solid materials left over from the product which do not (except by accident) go into our streams, gaseous wastes which pass into the atmosphere, and liquid wastes which pass into our streams and watercourses. In this analysis we are concerned only with the last-named: the liquid wastes.

A definition of what constitutes an industrial waste is necessary because not all liquid effluents from an industrial plant are wastes that contaminate or pollute our streams. Water which is used only for cooling purposes in combustion engines or around other machinery or in air conditioning, to which no deleterious substances have been added, or which has not been changed physically or chemically, is not a true industrial waste.

In this book we shall consider only those liquid plant effluents which contain substances or compounds that contaminate our streams and render them unsafe for use as sources of water supply or for recreation or navigation or which contain organic matter that decomposes in the stream and depletes the oxygen content to the degree where it interferes with the

1

use of the stream, destroys aquatic life, and is the source of obnoxious conditions to nearby residents.

For many years after the great industrial development of the United States and before our lumbermen began their denudation of our forests, our streams ran plentifully and water shortages were a rarity. The industries which established themselves along streams were not large, and their wastes did no noticeable damage. However, as population density increased in certain localities, owing primarily to concentrations of industry in those areas, the amount of pollution increased and, in turn, as the local demand for water increased, the streams were barely able to supply that demand. As the cities upstream grew and took water, the amount available for those lower down not only was lessened but was received in a polluted condition. The increase of industry which discharged its wastes into this same stream only added to the problem.

It would be ideal and in true relation to the conception of the law that everyone has a right to the waters of a stream if he were charged with the responsibility of returning to the stream the same amount and quality of water which he received. But this does not happen. A city will take out a certain quantity each day, use it and soil it with household and manufacturing discharges, and then return a certain amount to the stream, usually about 80 per cent of the amount originally taken out. The balance is definitely out of circulation, passing into steam in boilers or into the ground.

Thus it can be seen that a stream on which six or seven cities are situated, each taking out a definite amount and putting back only 80 per cent of that amount, will have a greatly reduced volume when it reaches the lowest city. Unless the cities above have all provided treatment for their sewage and their industrial wastes, the water becomes not only less and less in quantity but worse and worse in quality.

This situation has been the cause of litigation. Owing to the increasing demands for water supply by growing cities and the increase in industrial pollution of the streams, in recent years the health authorities of the several states have had to give the problem careful and serious study.

It is natural that an industrial plant will be located (1) where it may receive its raw materials at low cost, (2) where there is a ready local market for its product, (3) where there is an ample and cheap supply of water, (4) where ample cheap power is available, (5) where an ample supply of labor exists, and (6) where a stream exists into which its wastes may be discharged.

In the past it has been common practice for industries to consider item (6) as one of the most important; thus many industries throughout the country have located their plants on a stream with the basic idea that they could discharge their wastes into it without effort or further thought. This cannot be laid at the door of the industrialist as a selfish motive, but rather as a common practice to which no one gave much thought. In fact, an industrialist does not wish to trouble about or spend money on waste products any more than does the individual person wish to worry about his own sewage. It is bad enough to have to waste any material, but when it becomes necessary to spend money on that same waste product, a charge must be made against the cost of production of the goods made in the plant. This then becomes an added charge to the customers who purchase the product.

However, this condition was becoming more pronounced and the streams were becoming so polluted that they were unsuitable as sources of potable water without excessive expense on the part of the cities to purify the waters sufficiently for human use. The streams also could not be used as sources of water supply for industrial purposes or for cattle and other animals. They became clogged with the deposited solids carried along in the wastes. Channels were filled with decomposing solids, producing obnoxious odors. Navigation was interfered with, making it a costly and continuous operation of the Federal government and other stream-control agencies to keep these channels open by dredging. Recreation was restricted because the waters were so polluted with chemicals and noxious compounds that it was not safe or pleasant for people to bathe or swim in them.

It is true that a plant for the treatment of water can be devised that will make it possible to produce a safe drinking water from virtually any source, but it is now recognized that this is not a tenable premise on which to work. There is no justice in forcing a city to install an expensive water-treatment plant because some industries upstream are discharging their wastes into that stream. This puts an inequitable burden of taxation on the downstream people. It is considered the responsibility of every city, state, and industry to endeavor to eliminate pollution and to return the waters to the streams, if not in exactly the same quantity, at least in almost the same quality as the water they took from it.

Industrial plants are built for the purpose not only of producing an article which is in demand by the people but also of making a profit for the plant owners from the sale of that article. Anything which increases the cost of the article is reflected either in the ultimate price to the consumer or in the lessened profits available for the stockholders. If there is much competition in the line produced by a given industry, anything that tends to increase the cost of production of the article and increase the selling price makes it harder for that manufacturer to compete with others. His only recourse, to avoid lessened sales, is to take less profit.

To the stockholders who purchase the stock of the company as a means of income, this is not a welcome prospect and meets with decided objection. An industrialist, faced with the prospect of spending a sum of money, no matter how small, on a waste-treatment plant which must be operated daily at a cost, is reluctant to add this extra burden to his production charges. He evades it as long as possible. This policy of evasion has been one of the causes of the present situation, and the government has been forced to step in and provide legislation on state, regional, and Federal levels to compel the elimination or abatement of pollution by everyone found to be polluting a potable-water stream, which renders it unfit for drinking purposes, damages property, and interferes with recreation or navigation.

The several states have long endeavored to do this, but the laws have either been loosely framed or inadequately or improperly enforced, so that no concerted effort has been exerted and no great amount of work done. By a Federal law which provides for assistance to the states and to industry for the construction of proper plants and assistance in the preparation of the plans, a great step has been made toward that utopian day when all our streams, except those arbitrarily classified as receptacles for industrial wastes, will be restored to a condition where they are again available as sources of potable and industrial water with a moderate degree of treatment.

The wastes discharged from various factories are as numerous in their polluting values as are the establishments which produce them. In general, however, any waste discharge which contains any compound or chemical, bacterial, or biological ingredient which will deplete the oxygen content of the receiving stream or will add deleterious elements to it (which, would, if not removed, cause illness, distress, or annoyance to those who would use the stream for potable purposes) may be classed as an industrial-waste problem which must be ameliorated, corrected, or removed.

Wastes which tend to destroy or inhibit fish and vegetable life in a stream by the depletion of oxygen or the deposition of solids, acids, or alkalies are problems. Wastes which contain dangerous or obnoxious ingredients which would render the water unfit or toxic for use by cattle or on farms along the stream constitute a problem. Wastes containing large volumes of solid matters that settle out in the stream bed constitute another problem by interfering with navigation and the use of the stream for recreational purposes, particularly if these solids are organic in nature and tend to decompose and throw off objectionable odors. Wastes which contain high concentrations of acids or alkalies which would attack structures built along the stream banks, such as piers, docks, wharves, warehouses, or buildings constitute a waste problem. The same is true of wastes which contain substances toxic to plant life, which would destroy trees and other shrubs along the stream banks or in its vicinity. Wastes which contain substances not commonly found in natural waters, above a certain concentration, which would make it necessary for cities desiring to use the stream for a potable-water supply to install expensive and complicated purification plants to remove these ingredients can be considered waste problems.

Wastes which contain high concentrations of ingredients which interfere with the operation of sewer systems and sewage-treatment works may present problems which would require amelioration.

Therefore it can be seen that any liquid discharge from an industrial plant into a stream, which in any way interferes with the normal use of the stream by the residents of neighboring cities, or interferes with the processes of other industries, or affects in any way the life, health, and well-being of the people, lessening their comfort, pleasure, or profitable use of the stream, requires treatment to remove the destructive or polluting element.

Wars have accentuated these problems, and the advance of science and medicine has added materially to the complexity of wastes and to the roster of problems. For example, atomic-energy plants have added radioactive substances to their waste waters. The development of new medicinals, such as penicillin, streptomycin, and other antibiotics, has added new problems in reference to the wastes emanating from these plants. These wastes, toxic to human and animal life, must be prevented from entering streams. The synthetic-rubber industry developed new types and sources of wastes. Shell-loading factories, ammunition plants, photographic-supply companies, and vegetable-dehydration and powdered-milk plants and distilleries have produced new types of wastes which have in turn introduced new problems.

A given waste may constitute a major problem in one stream but may not be a serious problem in another. Much depends upon the stream, its use, its size, and the character of the water in it. Thus a plant established on the banks of a salt-water stream or on the edge of the sea need not consider the same degree of waste treatment as the same type of plant located on a small inland stream which is the sole source of water supply for a community. No rule can be laid down for the degree of treatment that will be required for any waste without a thorough understanding of the location of the plant, the stream into which it is proposed to discharge its wastes, the uses of that stream by others, the character of the water and its volume, and what effect the wastes will have in changing the characteristics of that water to the detriment of the other users. A proper study of a stream will naturally include a survey as to the ability of that stream to carry a certain pollution load without injury or serious oxygen depletion due to the ratio between the volume and character of the water and the type and volume of wastes that will or may be discharged into it. A large river with a great flow of water will naturally sustain a greater pollution load than a small stream, and this factor must be given careful consideration in arriving at logical treatment requirements.

No rule can be established which will permit anyone to say to a given plant owner, "You had better build your plant in a certain place because there you will be permitted to discharge your wastes without treatment." That desirable condition may momentarily exist, but future populations will probably concentrate near the point at which that factory discharges its wastes, making it necessary to provide for treatment of the wastes. Nor is it a safe rule for a plant owner to proceed on the basis that, as other industries are located on a certain stream and are discharging their wastes into it, it is a desirable location in which to build. Conditions can and frequently do change, and the owner of the proposed plant may later have to provide treatment for its wastes, whereas in another locality it might have been found less costly to provide for a lesser degree of treatment in the initial construction.

The industrialists of the nation now generally realize that it is a part of their responsibility to see that their own plant wastes do not cause deterioration and to improve the condition of the streams. The great majority of them now accept this as a basic factor and provide for the necessary works as an integral part of the initial plant construction. This is a sensible and humanitarian approach to the problem, and it usually results both in economies in initial cost and good will on the part of the people, the community officials, and the authorities of the local health department.

Bibliography

1. Winget, R. L., The Position of Industry in Stream Sanitation, Proceedings, First Annual Public Health Engineering Congress, 1948, University of Florida, Gainesville, Fla. Abstracted, *Sewage Works Journal*, vol. 21, No. 5, p. 943, September, 1949.
2. Powell, S. T., Creation and Correction of Industrial Wastes, *Industrial & Engineering Chemistry*, vol. 39, p. 565, 1947.
3. Hart, W. B., Waste Treatment Problems from the Viewpoint of Industry, *Sewage Works Journal*, vol. 20, No. 2, pp. 273–278, March, 1948.
4. Symons, G. E., Industrial Wastes—What Are They? Proceedings, Second Industrial Waste Conference, Extension Series 60, Purdue University, Lafayette, Ind., pp. 20–27, Jan. 10–11, 1946.
5. Wolman, A., Responsibility for Industrial & Municipal Wastes, *Sewage Works Journal*, vol. 19, p. 548, 1947.

6. Eldridge, E. F., Introduction to the Industrial Waste Problem, Paper, Twenty-second Annual Conference Michigan Sewage Works Association, Jackson, Mich., May 14–16, 1947.

7. Stevenson, W. L., The State vs. Industry or the State with Industry, Paper, Meeting American Institute of Chemical Engineers, Providence, R.I., June 23–26, 1925.

8. Better Municipal-industry Co-operation Needed, *Sewage & Industrial Wastes*, vol. 22, No. 1, p. 93, January, 1950.

9. Hedgepeth, L. L., Industry and Its Waste Treatment, Paper, Annual Meeting American Society Civil Engineers, New York, January, 1949.

10. Jacobs, H. L., The Industrial Approach towards Waste Treatment and Stream Pollution Abatement, Paper, Tenth Annual Water Conference Engineers Society of Western Pennsylvania, Pittsburgh, Pa., Oct. 17–19, 1949.

11. Devendorf, E., Industries Show Interest in Wastes Treatment, *Sewage & Industrial Wastes Engineering*, vol. 21, No. 3, p. 138, March, 1950.

CHAPTER 2

WHO STARTS A WASTE-TREATMENT PROBLEM?

An industrial plant which discharges into streams an effluent containing elements harmful to the water supply or injurious to health and comfort originates a potential waste problem from the moment its wheels start turning. However, if this plant can discharge its wastes untreated into a stream without complaint from any source, it seemingly does not constitute a problem. It only becomes so when someone makes a complaint against this discharge because of some real or assumed injury or damage that has been sustained owing to this method of disposal of untreated industrial effluent.

The problem may be caused by the complaint of a municipality that wastes are contaminating the stream from which it takes its water supply. The fact that this same municipality discharges its untreated sewage into that same stream or that it permits industries located within its own borders to discharge their untreated effluents into the same stream does not matter. Their water supply is being endangered by this raw discharge; therefore it must be stopped. This same municipality may have an adequate water-treatment plant which has been installed to purify the water of the stream to render it potable, but if it believes, or can show with reasonable accuracy, that any given industrial plant is discharging wastes that put an unusual burden on its water-treatment facilities, that municipality feels that it has a case against the offending plant.

A municipality which has a complete sewerage system into which an industry is discharging its wastes may claim that its sewer lines and structures are being damaged by acids, chemicals, or other ingredients in the industrial effluent, causing undue repair, replacement, or rebuilding of sewer lines at heavy expense to the people. The municipality may claim that the wastes are interfering with the processes and methods of its sewage-treatment plant, inhibiting biological or other processes which normally render the sewage safe for discharge into the stream, thus imposing an additional and unplanned-for load on the existing plant which results in more complex control or additional expense in the operation of the units. Therefore, an industry may be subjected to a demand for provision of treatment facilities before it begins operations.

The municipality may claim that the wastes of a certain industry,

8

because of a component which of itself might cause no damage to sewers or treatment-plant structures or methods, may, when combined with the industrial effluents of other establishments, cause chemical and physical combinations which will damage the structures or interfere with the operation of the plant. It may be shown that certain chemical wastes will cause precipitation or coagulation of solids while flowing through the sewers and that these will settle and cause obstructions, thus compelling the city to clean out these obstructions at intervals at considerable expense.

An industrial plant which uses the water of a certain stream in its process work may claim that the discharge of untreated wastes from an upstream factory renders the stream water unsuitable for its peculiar use and either necessitates the construction of an expensive treatment plant to render the water suitable or forces it to go to another and more expensive source of supply.

An instance of this type occurred in New Jersey some years ago. A large new textile plant was located on a small stream running through a public park. Realizing that the wastes could not be discharged untreated into this small stream (and also restrained by the local authorities), the management employed engineers to work out a method of treatment for these wastes. This was done successfully.

A paper mill which manufactured high-grade tissue was located a few miles below. This factory used the water from the same stream as their source of process water. As the tissue was mainly used for wrapping silver articles, it was essential that there be no trace of sulfur in the water; otherwise the paper would blacken the silver. This meant that the treatment of the textile wastes must be based on a method which added no sulfates to the water. This was done.

Naturally, the paper company turned out a waste of its own. Downstream from the paper mill was a woolen mill, also using the stream as a source of process water. The mill complained that the discharges of the paper company interfered with its processes. These three problems came to the same source for solution. It was possible to work out a solution for each which recognized the needs of the others, and methods of suitable treatment were formulated. The third plant, the woolen mill, discharged a waste full of grease, wool dirt, and detergents, and it was necessary, from a public-health standpoint, for it to install a treatment plant of its own to prevent pollution of the stream below, as the stream later became part of the water supply of a large district.

All three treatment plants went into operation at about the same time, and shortly thereafter the woolen mill made a complaint against the textile mill. This did not seem justified, as the textile plant was carefully operated and should not have been discharging an effluent containing any substance that would affect the woolen-mill process. An investigation was made. It was found that the textile-mill waste-treatment plant was blameless but that the same mill had a water-softening plant, using the zeolite process, and that this plant was discharging waste waters from the regeneration of the zeolites with salt directly into a branch of the same stream. No one had given a thought to the effect that this saline waste would have on the processes of another mill. Had the stream been one of considerable size, this condition probably would not have arisen, but owing to its small volume and the fact that each of the three plants mentioned was using a large proportion of the flow in their daily processes, the saline content was accentuated and did interfere with the woolen-mill operations.

In another instance, in Pennsylvania, a tannery was discharging a waste that was polluting a small stream which later ran through a neighboring town. This waste was highly colored. The tannery was compelled to install a treatment plant to remove the color. This was done successfully, but soon after the plant was put into operation, complaints arose that the stream was now as black as ink. Something more must be done. The investigation which followed showed that the waters of the stream had a high percentage of iron in solution and that while the tannery effluent was now clear it did still contain some tannic acid. When this tannic acid combined with the water containing iron in solution, a true ink was formed. The program then was to neutralize the tannic acid in the tannery wastes, which, when done, solved this problem.

Still another instance may be mentioned, also in Pennsylvania, of a small tannery treating sheepskins and turning out a heavy, greasy, colored waste into a small stream which flowed through a town. The complexity of the waste and its viscosity made this problem difficult to handle. Laboratory tests finally indicated a method of treatment which would remove the ingredients causing the complaint. Here again, when the plant went into operation, the first cause of complaint was removed, but when the effluent from the new plant combined with the water in the stream, a heavy milky cloud formed, which was worse in appearance than the former color. Investigation showed that this cloud was due to the wastes from a large laundry upstream which discharged a large volume of highly caustic wastes into the stream. The caustic meeting the tannery effluent combined with the acids in this waste and caused the milky cloud. The solution adopted was to construct a channel leading from the stream above the tannery and bring the caustic-laden stream water into the tannery waste-treatment plant. In this way the reaction occurred in the plant and the resultant cloud was precipitated and retained in the plant, so that the final effluent from the tannery discharge line was clear.

These instances are given to show some of the problems that can arise in the solution of an industrial-waste difficulty for one plant which may cause a more serious situation in another.

To revert to the causes of an industrial-waste problem. A small stream may run through a district which is a highly developed residential section. The water of this stream is not used for potable purposes by those living on its banks or by livestock. But because of the discharge of an industrial waste from a plant upstream, the water may be discolored, or have an odor, or have surface scum consisting of light solids. The residents of the section may complain about the condition on the basis that it is depriving them of the use and comfort of the stream as part of their enjoyment of life. On their political influence and on their status as heavy taxpayers may rest the decision of the municipality to cause the industrial plant to take measures to prevent further pollution.

A stream may pass through an agrarian section, where large stock farms are situated that utilize the stream to water stock. Pollution of this stream may cause the stockmen to complain that their animals are being endangered or poisoned by drinking this water. In South Carolina a case of this nature arose where the local cattlemen filed suit against a large textile mill because the mill was discharging an effluent containing a large quantity of sodium chloride. The cattle, drinking this salt water, immediately drank more and more of it and eventually died. The problem here was to reduce the sodium chloride content of the textile-mill effluent. As a means of working out a method which would be within the financial capacity of the mill (the then known means of sodium chloride reduction being very expensive), it was undertaken to ascertain how much salt a cow could absorb without injury. If the textile mill were to be required to remove all the salt, the treatment would be extremely costly; on the other hand, if it could be ascertained that waters containing a certain proportion of chlorides would still be safe for the cattle to drink, then the treatment required would be less costly as it would be necessary only to reduce the chloride content to the safety margin. Unfortunately at that time there was no information on this point, and the mill was advised to find another discharge point for its wastes. Since then the U.S. Public Health Service has established that a maximum of 250 ppm of chlorides in potable water is satisfactory for human consumption. Actually, the chloride content may go up as high as 400 to 500 ppm without danger, but above 250 ppm the taste of the salt becomes apparent and thus the water becomes unpalatable. In later years research in the synthetic resins produced a means for reducing the chloride content of waters at a lower cost than by other known methods, and had this method been developed at the time this problem arose, a reasonable solution might have been proposed. Since that time other studies have been made as to the amount of salt domestic animals can absorb.[1] *

A stream may be a favorite fishing ground for trout lovers. Factories located on such a stream may discharge wastes which either kill the fish or make it so obnoxious to them that they depart for cleaner waters. Trout are delicate organisms and are accustomed to living only in clear, clean streams. If these fishing grounds are destroyed by the wastes from a factory, the fishermen will put in a loud protest. The Izaak Walton League of America, a group interested in clean streams from the standpoint of sport, is very strong and well organized and has been able to work effectively in having such conditions remedied. This, of course, while it does not affect the demand for the particular factory to cease pollution of that stream, does bring up a very important question: Which is the more important to the economic life of that particular section—the factories or the fishermen?

A group of cities and the residents thereof may complain that industries located along the banks of a given stream, which has formerly been used for recreation—boating, bathing, etc.—and for picnics along its banks, are discharging so much waste into the river that it has become useless for these purposes. This was the case with the Passaic River in New Jersey, which in earlier years was a favored recreation center for the residents of the numerous cities nearby. Picnics were held in the groves along the stream, regattas and boat races were held weekly, and the stream was a popular bathing place. Gradually this section became the center of an important textile industry. The individual mills were located immediately adjacent to the riverbanks for two very good reasons: they could get their water supply from the river, and they could put their wastes back into it. Eventually, the mills themselves found that the river water was unsuitable for their purposes, and they combined and formed their own water company, taking water from the upper reaches of the same river. This, while a cure for their water problems, did not help the pollution in the river. As time went on, the pollution became so bad that no one cared to spend any time in the vicinity of the river. Its odor was notorious; the water was chocolate in color, with rainbow hues, and the acid fumes arising from it destroyed the paint on nearby buildings and even destroyed the piling of the docks and wharves.

The situation became so intolerable that measures were finally taken, resulting in the formation of The Passaic Valley Sewerage District, which

* Superscript numbers indicate references given in the bibliography at the end of the corresponding chapter.

constructed a large intercepting sewer along the bank of the river, into which all adjacent municipalities were required to discharge their sewage. This removed the sewage pollution but did not materially affect the industrial-waste discharges. To remedy this, the Sewerage District permitted an industry to discharge 10 per cent by volume of its untreated wastes into the sewer, provided that they were of such a nature as not to affect or destroy the sewer. The balance of the wastes could be discharged into the sewer or the river provided that proper treatment was employed. To build up the volume of flow in the river which had been depleted by taking the water out and then putting the sewage into the sewer, the industries were encouraged to put, as their 10 per cent quota, their worst and most difficult wastes into the sewer and to provide treatment for the larger volume of more easily treated wastes and discharge this treated effluent into the river. With this removal of the sewage and the treatment of the wastes, the Passaic River has again become a popular recreation ground, and boating and bathing are again possible.

Some industries, which discharge large volumes of solids in their wastes, may become liable for waste treatment because these solids eventually fill up the river bed and clog docks, wharves, etc., causing great expense for continuous dredging of the channel or wharf areas. If the solids discharged are of an organic nature, subject to decomposition, they may cause a serious depletion of the oxygen in the stream, giving rise to noxious odors and causing fish to leave it.

Such problems have become more and more serious with the higher standard of living, particularly in the United States. With more time on their hands, due to shorter work weeks, people not only have more leisure but also have more time to worry about their prerogatives. More recreation grounds are being provided annually. More attention is being given to sport. Public health is a greater concern. Industry is more subject to claims upon it for returning stream waters to their natural state or retaining them in usable condition. In the early days of this nation, industry was considered our strongest asset, and the combinations of industrial organizations were so strong that they could effectually combat claims of municipalities or individuals against them. By threats of moving elsewhere or closing down, with consequent unemployment, which in small towns with only one industry was a serious threat to the economy of the town, industries were able to stall or prevent action to compel waste treatment. Now, however, with the greater governmental powers for enforcing laws for the protection of health and comfort, the industries have come to see that they have a definite civic responsibility to others, not only because polluted water affects the general health of a district, but because their own employees, who reside in the vicinity, are affected by it.   Loss of time due to illness of workers, traceable to polluted water, could be a more serious operational cost than the daily cost of treating the wastes to prevent the offending pollution.   Only a large plant would have waste-treatment facilities for which the operating cost exceeded $100 per day.   With employees earning $20 to $24 per day each, the absence of only five or six daily would be a greater loss than the operating cost of the treatment works.

Still another factor which may cause an industry to treat its wastes is the sanitary program of a city.   Pollution of the stream by the sewage of the city may have caused the city to have plans prepared for a sewage-treatment plant.   This city may have one or many industrial plants whose wastes constitute a problem.   It is normally desirable to handle these wastes with the sewage of the municipality, but a study of them shows that some of them are of such a type that if received in their natural state they would seriously affect the processes to be used in the plant, causing inordinate expense for larger units, etc.   Thus, as the cost of the plant must be assessed against the entire community, it will be found more economical to require the industries to pretreat their wastes to such an extent that normal sewage-treatment methods and processes may be resorted to.   In general, while this might seem to impose a large burden on industry, it does not always have this result.   Industry is usually a large taxpayer in any community, and if, by insisting that its wastes be cared for by the municipality, it imposes a much larger burden of cost upon the city, not only will its own tax burden be increased but also that of each one of its employees who owns property in the same city.   This increase in the cost of living may result in a demand for higher wages by the employees.   The sum total of the extra taxes paid by the industry and the possible extra wages required for its workers may easily exceed the daily operating cost and fixed charges that would be incurred by the industry by the construction of a private treatment plant.   Other than this, as said before, is the intangible value of the good will that may be created by the industry by this acceptance of a civic responsibility.   It becomes a unit in the public spirit instead of a revolutionary against the established order.

Industrial-waste problems are created in many other ways, and it is difficult for an industry to foresee all the conditions that may arise which at some time may compel it to resort to treatment of its wastes to eliminate or abate some real or fancied problem of pollution or annoyance.   Any industry which plans to settle in a given locality should carefully investigate the local situation as to rules, regulations, laws, etc., which may cause it to install a treatment plant.   Also it should investigate the local usages of a stream which appears to be the potential point of discharge for its wastes. Balancing these factors in one locality against those in another may dictate the abandonment of one site for another where the regulations are less stringent. However, even this cannot be a permanent guarantee that at some future date a pollution problem may not arise at the selected point which will compel treatment. Times change, and laws are passed which change conditions.

In some communities in the past it was the rule to encourage industries to locate in these towns by making certain guarantees, such as remission of taxes for a certain period, guarantee of acceptance of the wastes by the municipality, or free sites. This has resulted in some serious conditions, as in Worcester, Mass., where an agreement was made with a local steel company which required the municipality to accept the wastes from the mill in its treatment works. This has been found to cause great difficulty and has been a source of continuous expense to the city. Any city is ill-advised to adopt such a program for the reason that the admittance of one industry on such a basis tends to set a precedent for future industries which may impose a severe and expensive burden on the city.

Industries are sometimes reluctant to discuss their initial plans with the authorities of the city selected as a tentative site for a new plant, feeling that if they do so property values in the section in which they plan to build will rise and they will be penalized by paying a higher cost for their land. This has happened, of course, but it is believed that in most cities today real-estate values are well established and the prospective location of an industry would cause little change. On the other hand a free discussion of its intentions with the authorities will usually prevent future misunderstandings and will show the industry just where it stands and for what it must provide.

Bibliography

1. Heller, V. G., The Effect of Saline and Alkaline Waters on Domestic Animals, Bulletin 217, Experimental Station Oklahoma A. & M. College, Stillwater, Okla., 1933.
2. Malin, H., Some Thoughts on Controlling Industrial Wastes, *Water & Sewage Works*, vol. 94, No. 3, p. 115, March, 1947.
3. National Round-up of Pollution Abatement Progress, *Sewage Works Engineering and Municipal Sanitation*, vol. 17, No. 19, p. 518, October, 1946; and No. 11, p. 587, November, 1946.
4. Simpson, R. W., Approaching an Industrial Waste Problem, *Sewage Works Engineering and Municipal Sanitation*, vol. 17, No. 9, p. 456, September, 1946.
5. Parran, T., Public Health Service and Industrial Pollution, *Sewage Works Journal*, vol. 19, p. 946, 1947.
6. A Report of Procedure for the Handling of Industrial Wastes, Committee on Industrial Wastes of the California Sewage Works Association, *California Sewage Works Journal*, vol. 17, 1945.

7. Wolman, A., State Responsibility in Stream Pollution Abatement, *Industrial & Engineering Chemistry*, vol. 39, p. 561, May, 1947.

8. Eldridge, E. F., Introduction to the Industrial Waste Problem, Paper, Twenty-second Annual Conference Michigan Sewage Works Association, Jackson, Mich., May 14–16, 1947.

9. Glace, I. M., and C. F. Broning, Pollution Control—By Whom? *Engineering News-Record*, vol. 122, No. 11, p. 380, Mar. 16, 1939.

10. Tobey, J. A., Legal Aspects of the Industrial Waste Problem, *Industrial & Engineering Chemistry*, vol. 31, p. 1320, November, 1939.

11. Palmer, C. L., Regulation of Industrial Usage of Municipal Sewers, *Sewage Works Journal*, vol. 19, p. 811, September, 1947.

CHAPTER 3

THE FIRST STEPS TO TAKE IN THE SOLUTION

The first step to take if you as an industrialist are notified by some authority that you must take steps to eliminate, alleviate, or abate a nuisance caused by the discharges from your factory is to consider the problem calmly and look into the justification of the complaint or request. Do not immediately threaten to shut down the plant and move elsewhere. You probably have too much at stake in your present location. Treatment of industrial wastes is not too costly if properly handled.

The next step is to see whether or not there is anything in the deed on your property or in the laws or precedents of the city which in any way obligates the city to take your discharges into its sewerage system and plant. This research is important as an early step in order that it can serve your expert advisers as a guide which will aid them in working out for you the most satisfactory method of treatment, from the standpoint both of the authority which compels you to do this and of the ultimate economy to you. You can readily appreciate what it would mean to accept blindly an order to install treatment works and to engage consultants to prepare plans only to have someone tell you later that you could have discharged your wastes into the city system with much less treatment and expense to you. This point is one which your legal advisers can find out for you. Of if you have your own engineer or prefer to engage an outside consultant, he can do this in consultation with the city authorities. They will usually be found most cooperative and will no doubt give you complete information on this point.

Occasionally a plant owner will try to put something over which will work a hardship on the city. An instance of this comes to the author's mind. A certain industry in a small town employed some member of practically every family in the town, paid heavy taxes, and provided a great proportion of the town income, besides having some of its employees on the town council. Notice was given to the industry by the state health authorities that it must install a waste-treatment plant to eliminate pollution of a small stream which became part of the source of water supply of a large city below. The industry felt that it had prescriptive rights in the city which made it more or less obligatory on the part of the town to handle the wastes. Engineers were called in who advised them what

17

treatment would mean and its cost. This entailed a considerable sum for the size of the factory. The next suggestion came from the owner of the plant in the form of a query as to whether his wastes could not be handled at the town sewage-treatment plant. Investigation showed that with a degree of pretreatment the wastes could be handled by the city plant if certain new plant units were installed to treat the wastes partially so that they would not inhibit the biological action in the plant. This pretreatment was of a chemical nature. The owner then proposed to the town officials that he would stand the cost of construction of the necessary new units to treat his wastes to the proper degree, provided that the town would assume the operating cost of the treatment itself. This seemed like philanthropy until someone on the town council studied the matter and found that by assuming the cost of treatment of the wastes the town would burden itself with a heavy daily charge for the operation of the new units which far exceeded the normal daily operating costs of the plant. They declined this gift, and the plant owner was obliged to install a complete waste-treatment plant at his own initial expense and pay the daily operating charges.

The third step, after notification of the need for treatment, is to request a hearing with the compelling authority or its engineer and together with your expert or consultant sit down and discuss the matter. Request the compelling authority to advise you definitely as to the degree of treatment that will be required. If your wastes are colored, how much color do they want removed? Complete color removal, in some cases, is very expensive. If the volume of water in the stream into which the wastes are to be discharged is such that when the wastes, partially decolorized, are mixed with this stream the remaining color will be entirely dissipated, the treatment costs will be materially lessened. Any industrial waste can be so treated as to reduce the final effluent to a clear, sparkling discharge which will be practically as good as any stream water into which it may be discharged. But this costs money. There is usually no intent on the part of any authority to make you expend more than is necessary to obtain a degree of treatment which is not actually required. Simple tests of the wastes, with various degrees of color removal, when mixed in the ratio which the wastes bear to the volume of water in the stream, will soon give the answer on this point.

If certain acids or alkalies in the wastes are the objectionable ingredients, these can usually be neutralized at a moderate cost. Frequently, by investigation of the wastes from neighboring factories it will be found that some of their wastes can be combined with those of your plant to cause mutual and natural neutralization and thus eliminate the purchase and use of a daily supply of chemicals.

If organic solids are the objectionable element, they can be removed relatively simply. Frequently they may be put into the local sewers and handled at the local sewage-treatment plant. In many cities this method has been employed, with the industry building several units at the town plant in which its wastes are pretreated before the effluent enters the municipal plant. In some cases the industrial-plant owner pays for these improvements and pays a charge for their operation. In other cases it is possible to arrange for the town to receive the wastes, treat them in the municipal plant, and charge the industry a certain sum for this service. This basis of handling is discussed fully in Chap. 12.

The main thing, however, is to discuss the problem frankly with the agency compelling treatment and ascertain just how far they wish you to go with treatment. All engineers know that industrial-waste treatment is a drain on the resources of an industry, for which usually there is little or no recompense, and although the general public health and comfort must be protected against harmful operators, nevertheless authorities seldom, if ever, wish to compel an industrial owner to spend more than is actually required. Frequently, by such a conference, it can be ascertained that, although a definite final degree of treatment may be required, it is not needed at the particular moment; and even though the manufacturer must present plans for a complete plant which will conform with the ultimate requirement, he may be permitted to construct only part of the plant. When, and if, the conditions occur which require the full degree of treatment, he can add further units later. This is frequently an important item, for in several instances, on streams which required complete treatment at one time, conditions changed so that later requirements were not so severe. Therefore, the industrial owner who had built the entire plant at once and later found he need operate only part of it was saddled with a useless investment.

Another step for the industrialist faced with a waste problem is to survey the possibility of making changes in plant processes which will eliminate much of the polluting wastes or will so reduce their volume and concentration that they will be less costly to treat and perhaps require a lessened degree of treatment.

Perhaps the most important step to take is to engage a consultant, an engineer, or an engineering organization to act for you in the solution of the problem. The fee for this expert advice and for the design of a proper plant, which is economically as well as physically suitable for your problem, will usually be a small percentage of the entire cost. The engagement of consultants who are known as experts in this field will save you money, as these men know all the angles, they know all the authorities, they know the laws on pollution, and they know the means of solving your particular problem.   They do not need to waste time studying a phase of engineering with which they are not normally acquainted, and they know where to go to get any information they need which will help them to solve the problem.   They will satisfy the authorities at not too great a cost to you.

Industrial wastes are frequently very complex, and while in many cases known and common methods and processes of treatment may be found successful, a complete knowledge of the limitations and advantages of the different recognized methods is required to be able to select that one which will best solve your problem.   In many cases industrialists have been approached with wonderful panaceas and have been unsuspecting guinea pigs for someone with a bright idea.   Many piles of scrap iron lying around in the yards of industrial plants represent good money thrown away on unsuccessful experiments.

This discussion is not intended, by any means, as an argument against research and the development of new and more economical methods of treatment of industrial wastes, but such research should be carried out by proper organizations, many of which are now functioning, through the apportionment of funds by an industry to one of these to carry out work on a given subject.   This is much better than spending a lot of money on a full-scale plant to be operated on an untried process which may be an utter failure.   Subsidizing a research laboratory or school to undertake the problem in a knowledgeable way usually not only gives you the answer at a relatively low cost but will bring added prestige to the research organization which has worked out this new idea.   In doing this, all the kinks and headaches in the process are ironed out in the beginning, and when the final report is made to you, a full-scale plant may be built with confidence in its success.   In building such a plant for an untried process without the necessary preliminary research the possibility arises that, if the plant does not work or if, in working out the bugs in the system, a bad effluent is turned out, fines or a lawsuit for damages may result.

Many of the larger industrial groups have now established their own research departments with competent engineers, chemists, biologists, and laboratory facilities to specialize in the solution of problems common and peculiar to the industry.   Such organizations have been set up by the pulp and paper industry, the milk industry, the brewery interests, and others and have developed valuable data on the character of the wastes of these industries and what may be done with them.   These organizations are usually supported by contributions from fellow members of the industry and are available for use by anyone in the industry.   By restricting their investigations and research to the problems of their own industry, they become expert in the peculiar reactions of the wastes under many varying conditions and are competent to advise a group member as to what he should do to eliminate a pollution problem. They do the experimenting at small individual cost per member, and they will build and operate the necessary pilot and experimental plants out of the common fund, working on new methods and processes which have promise.

Other large companies, having many plants and factories, such as the Du Pont Company, General Motors Corporation, Ford Motor Company, and others, have set up their own private research organizations which specialize in the treatment of the wastes of the particular company.

Other industries, faced with the solution of a waste problem and realizing their own lack of knowledge of the subject and the cost of the necessary investigation, place their problems in the hands of one of the technical schools which have experimental laboratories and plants. These schools, while primarily organized for the purpose of educating young men for a profession, have elaborate facilities for experimental work so composed that they can run moderate-scale tests upon almost any type of waste. An industry which has a problem which is out of the ordinary can place the solution in the hands of one of these institutions in the form of a fellowship or grant of funds. Some promising student will then be selected to carry out the investigation required under the guidance of the faculty who are in charge of the school and who are competent to map out a campaign toward the solution of the problem. The results produced by these special studies are usually very good, and because of the reputation of the men involved, the work is well received and highly regarded by the authorities who must pass on the efficacy of the solution proposed. In the meantime, the student who has been appointed to carry out the specific study becomes an expert in that phase of work and usually earns special credits or a higher degree. The thesis, written around the problem and its solution, becomes a valuable contribution to the literature of waste treatment.

Numerous large industrial concerns have adopted this procedure, not only because they are assured of an answer along correct lines, but because they in turn get some prestige from it by having set up a scholarship, fellowship, or foundation, which is useful advertising. Other than this, the cost of such a program is usually quite reasonable. Students who have worked on these problems in their course of training have later become valuable men in the field and have been absorbed by the industry on whose problem they worked.

Industrial-waste treatment is not a static science. With the introduction of new materials and products, among them new pharmaceutical products, synthetic materials, and atomic energy, new problems in pollution have been created which older methods do not handle efficiently. Modern and better methods must be devised to handle these new and complex wastes, and it cannot be better done than by the organized research elements, both public and private, which exist for that purpose.

Be wary of untried processes and methods which may sound enticing from the standpoint of low cost. While the art or science of industrial-waste treatment is relatively new, nevertheless a great many of the more commonly occurring problems have been satisfactorily solved and ways and means already exist and are known to the technicians. These men solve your problem quickly and economically; so do not be misled by glowing arguments for new magic compounds which will perform miracles. It has long been found that common and easily procured chemical compounds or combinations of these can assist in the economic solution of many problems. The best investigators will always endeavor to work out a solution for you that will employ to the best advantage the means most readily and economically procurable.

There is the added advantage, which is reflected back to the plant owner in lowered initial costs, that the common chemicals may usually be procured locally, whereas a proprietary compound must be obtained from the sole manufacturer. This means that, in order to have on hand a sufficient supply of this compound to ensure the continuance of the treatment day after day, a large stock must always be kept on hand. This, in turn, means provision of large storage areas or bins and a considerable investment in the stock of chemicals. If the proprietary chemical is one which is hygroscopic in nature, especial care must be taken to provide warm and dry storage places. Another expense is incurred by the ever-present danger of destruction or damage to this stock by leakage. On the other hand, the common coagulants, lime, alum, ferrous sulfate, and other salts, can be found readily. Consequently large stocks with their heavy capital investment need not be provided, lesser storage space is required, and no special heat or moisture precautions are necessary.

Furthermore, in connection with the proposed use of untried processes, the various state health agencies now exercise very definite control over the methods used. Plans for industrial-waste treatment must be made and presented to these officials and approved by them before any construction is permitted. They do not permit the use of untried processes and methods without having strong evidence before them of their practical value. Many of the states are now revising their codes of practice to agree with the rules and regulations provided by a conference of their chief engineers, and these rules contain the following pertinent statement as to the handling of new and untried processes:

New Processes and Methods and Equipment.

The policy of the reviewing authority is to encourage rather than obstruct the development of new methods and equipment for the treatment of sewage and wastes, but under no circumstances will experimental installations be permitted at the expense of any municipality. Any new development must have been thoroughly tested in a full-scale installation under competent supervision before approval of a plant utilizing this process or equipment can be issued, unless a municipality is amply protected by a performance bond so that in case of failure any expenditure of public money will be refunded. Where it is necessary to revise or rebuild permanent plant structures in order to accommodate other mechanical equipment after the original installation has been rejected, the performance bond shall include provisions to cover the cost of the installation.

Bibliography

1. Baffa, J. J., Regulating Wastes Discharges into Sewers, *Sewage Works Engineering*, vol. 20, p. 238, May, 1949.
2. Coblentz, M. H., The Industrial Waste Problem in Sanitation, *Sewage Works Journal*, vol. 5, No. 3, p. 523, May, 1933.
3. Industrial Waste Disposal, Manual, Manufacturing Chemists Association, Washington, D.C.
4. Waste Water. Industry Problem, *Business Week*, No. 966, Mar. 6, 1948, pp. 54–56, 61–63.
5. O'Connell, W. J., Effects of Sewage and Waste Disposal Practices in Industrial Operating Costs, Paper, Twentieth Annual Meeting Federation of Sewage Works Associations, San Francisco, Calif., July 21–24, 1947.
6. Eldridge, W. J., A Plea for Sound Economy in Stream Pollution Abatement, *Water & Sewage Works*, vol. 93, No. 12, p. 494, December, 1946.
7. Parker, L. T., Pollution Causes Damage, *Sewage Works Engineering and Municipal Sanitation*, vol. 17, No. 9, p. 463, September, 1946.
8. Industrial Wastes, an Important Factor in Process Planning, Chemical Engineering Report 107, August, 1945.
9. Gehm, H. W., Coordinated Industrial Waste Research, *Sewage Works Journal*, vol. 17, p. 782, 1945.
10. McKenzie, V., The U.S. Public Health Service Program in Industrial Waste Research, Paper, Fifth Industrial Waste Conference, Purdue University, Lafayette, Ind., Nov. 29–30, 1949.
11. Gehm, H. W., The Importance of Fundamental Research in Waste Treatment Problems, Proceedings, Third Industrial Waste Conference, Purdue University, Lafayette, Ind., pp. 61–64, 1947.
12. Check List for Reducing Industrial Waste Costs, *Modern Industry*, p. 48, December, 1949.
13. Agar, C. C., Stream Standards and Their Practical Application, *Sewage Works Journal*, vol. 21, No. 6, p. 1050, November, 1949.
14. Cleary, E. J., Industry's Stake in the Ohio River Pollution Abatement Program, Paper, TAPPI Meeting, New York, Feb. 21, 1950.
15. Jacobs, H. L., The Industrial Approach towards Waste Treatment and Stream Pollution Abatement, Paper, Tenth Annual Water Conference Engineers Society of Western Pennsylvania, Pittsburgh, Pa., Oct. 17–19, 1949.

16. Knowlton, W. T., Problems of Industrial Wastes from the Standpoint of Municipal Administration, *California Sewage Works Association Journal*, pp. 33–39, 1942.
17. Poole, B. A., Economies in Industrial Waste Treatment Plant Design, Proceedings, Second Industrial Waste Conference, Extension Series 60, Purdue University, Lafayette, Ind., pp. 114–120, January, 1946.
18. Stead, F. M., Public Health Aspects of Industrial Waste Disposal, *California's Health*, vol. 4, pp. 9–11, July 31, 1946.
19. Liquid Wastes: New Ways to Crack a Common Problem, *Modern Industry*, p. 44, December, 1949.
20. Tax Leniency May Encourage Industrial Waste Treatment, *Sewage Works Engineering and Municipal Sanitation*, vol. 16, p. 340, July, 1945.
21. Mohlman, F. W., Plain Talk about Industrial Wastes Recovery, *Sewage Works Engineering and Municipal Sanitation*, vol. 16, pp. 489–490, October, 1945.
22. Reinke, E. A., Disposal of Liquid Industrial Wastes from the Viewpoint of Governmental Agencies, *California Sewage Works Journal*, vol. 16, No. 1, p. 43, 1944.
23. Research Grants Available for Sewage-wastes Studies, *Sewage Works Engineering and Municipal Sanitation*, vol. 18, p. 481, September, 1947.
24. Cooper, J. E., An Industry Initiates a Waste Control Program, *Sewage Works Journal*, vol. 19, pp. 817–826, September, 1947.
25. Balmer, R. R., Company Administration and Technical Organization for Industrial Waste Control, *Sewage Works Journal*, vol. 21, pp. 268–273, March, 1949.

CHAPTER 4

THE PLACE OF THE ENGINEER OR SPECIALIST

In the previous chapter we pointed out the importance of engaging a recognized expert in the science of industrial-waste treatment.

Owing to the relative newness of this science, not many engineers have had experience in the solution of waste problems. It is true that any engineer or engineering firm engaged to advise an industrial owner on this important matter can, if without previous experience, secure an outside expert to advise them. In such cases, the person who is doing the constructive thinking on the matter is an invisible entity as far as the plant owner is concerned, and all information reaches him secondhand. It is essential for the person who is actually designing the plant to have first-hand information on many questions which arise in the solution of an industrial-waste problem. During conferences with the owner, the expert will be able to obtain answers to many of his questions as they arise in the discussion, and he will be able to ask further questions necessary to develop pertinent data and facts. This will eliminate the need for a third person and the relaying of information and will save much time for everyone concerned.

Considerable work in the solution of industrial-waste problems has been done not by engineering firms but by research men at various technical schools, by engineers and chemists employed by industry itself, and by one or more of the private organizations which have the facilities to study, test, and develop methods and plans for the correct analysis and solution of these problems.

Many large industrial plants have their own engineers who are familiar with the methods and processes employed in their plant, who are competent to present the pertinent data needed in the study of the problem, and who are willing and able to work with an expert to arrive at a sensible, practical, and economical solution with the least waste of time. Such an engineer can call upon an outside firm to do the actual designing of the plant or can engage one of the several organizations regularly engaged in industrial-waste treatment to work with him. The plant engineer can collect and supply the correct data on characteristics of the wastes, volumes, periodicity of flow, and so forth, which the designing engineer or the research organization will need to make the necessary studies and tests to arrive at a proper solution.

If the wastes represent the output of a new industry and are not common or ones for which no known method of treatment has been worked out, then it is the duty of the technician to make studies of these wastes, possibly calling upon one of the several commercial organizations equipped with a laboratory, other investigational facilities, and trained personnel to make tests on the wastes, in order to arrive at an economical solution.

The laboratory experts which do this work must of course be furnished with complete information on the character of the wastes, with analyses, if such are available, to enable them to study various reactions. With their extensive knowledge, gained through handling many such problems, the experts are usually able to determine quickly what can be done with a given waste.

A detailed report should be made, outlining the test work done and the methods used and a suitable way recommended of handling the wastes to produce the desired results. Such organizations frequently can take these reports, resolve them into coordinated plans for complete plants, and place them before the consultants and the plant owner in sufficient detail to enable him to present them in turn to the health authority for study.

Experimental work on industrial wastes is expensive and requires considerable time to accomplish a worth-while result. Test-tube demonstrations are not the answer to most problems and serve mainly as a guide to large-scale tests. If these tests were carried out on the premises of an industrial plant, considerable expense would be involved in setting up a demonstration plant which, when the test work was completed, would be discarded. The money invested would be a total loss. On the other hand, an organization specializing in this type of work would have the large-scale units available in which, if it were deemed essential, the more extensive work could be done. The industry would then have only the expense of the relatively small fee charged for the work and would have the satisfaction of knowing that the program was carried out under the control and guidance of experts in the field. An organization of this type, doing this class of work continuously, knows what to look for in any general waste problem and does not have to spend time on useless experimentation. Special testing techniques have usually been developed, which speed up the work and lead to logical and practical solutions.

Regardless of the type of adviser or expert called in, which is a question for the individual industrial-plant owner to decide, the main objective is a practical and economical answer to the problem. Much emphasis is placed throughout this book on economy. We have been taught that "the cheapest is not always the best," but at the same time we are encouraged not to waste. The true engineer who follows the precepts and ethics of his profession is one who always works for the interests of his clients or employers. It is his duty to study and survey the methods and means available and to decide which of these will produce the desired results at the lowest over-all cost. Industrial wastes can always be treated to produce a given result. However, there is a decided difference between arriving at a solution which may cost the industrialist a large sum or one which will produce the same result at less cost.

The first cost in an industrial plant is not so critical or important as are the operating costs, although naturally it must be given careful consideration. The interest and amortization charges on the initial investment must go into the general expenses of the business. But the operating charges, which are daily costs, are most important. A plant may be designed along simple lines and the initial cost may be low, but in order to achieve the results required the daily operating charges may be high. Let us assume that a plant will cost $50,000 to build. The interest charge on that sum at 5 per cent is $2,500 per year. With a useful life of 20 years, the amortization write-off adds another item of $2,500 annual cost. This plant employs a method of treatment which costs $1 per 1,000 gallons to carry out. The plant treats 100,000 gallons of wastes per day. Therefore the daily cost of treatment is $100, which, multiplied by 365, amounts to the sum of $36,500 per year. The total plant cost, chargeable to expense, is therefore $41,500 per year.

Take a different solution, worked out with the economic phase in mind. The same result is achieved. This plant costs $75,000 to build. On the same basis of interest on investment and amortization as used before, the total annual charge is $3,750 interest and $3,750 amortization, or a total of $7,500 annual fixed charges. But the treatment employed in this plant has been reduced in cost per unit per day so that the cost per 1,000 gallons of waste is only 45 cents. With 100,000 gallons of waste per day, the daily operating cost is $45 and the annual charge only $16,725. The total annual cost, therefore, fixed and operating charges, is only $24,225 as against the total of $41,500 for the other plant. It is assumed that the same amount of attendance will be required for each plant. Frequently, however, this is not the case. With the introduction and widespread use of mechanical handling of materials and the automatic control of operations, the modern plant will perhaps utilize these developments to the utmost degree, and it may require only the time and attention of one man to operate the plant. The older type of plant, which costs less to build, may require the constant attendance of several operators because of its design and its reliance on manual operations. The saving of labor alone for the modern, well-integrated, mechanically operated and controlled plant is an item of importance which would warrant considerable additional initial expenditure to obtain.

It is important that the consultant selected be familiar not only with waste-treatment practice and techniques but also with plant-production practice.   As mentioned in Chap. 3, it is frequently possible materially to reduce the volume and strength of an industrial waste by revisions of plant processes without substantially affecting the operation.   A complete waste study, therefore, should always include a procedure survey.

Bibliography

1. Eagles, R. E., Relation of Chemical Engineering to Sewage and Trade Waste Treatment, *Chemical & Metallurgical Engineering*, vol. 23, No. 10, p. 433, 1920.
2. Besselievre, E. B., Industrial Waste Treatment as a Chemical Engineering Problem, *Chemical & Metallurgical Engineering*, vol. 38, No. 9, p. 498, 1931.
3. Velz, C. J., Evaluation of Analytical Data in Relation to Stream Sanitation, *Water & Sewage Works*, vol. 96, No. 6, pp. 213–214, June, 1949.
4. Roetman, E. T., Industry Increases Demand for Sanitary Engineers, *Civil Engineering (ASCE)*, vol. 18, No. 2, pp. 40–42, February, 1938.
5. Tarman, J. E., Chemical Engineers Approach to Industrial Waste Problems, *Sewage Works Journal*, vol. 19, p. 139, 1947.
6. Sullivan, W. L., Engineering Methods Economically Combat Stream Pollution, *Chemical & Metallurgical Engineering*, vol. 35, p. 483, 1928.
7. On Making a Place for the Industrial Waste Man, Editorial, *Water & Sewage Works*, vol. 93, No. 11, p. 454, 1946.
8. Homack, P., The Consulting Engineer's Place in the Industrial Waste Problem, Paper, Thirty-fourth Annual Meeting New Jersey Sewage Works Association, Trenton, N.J., Mar. 23–25, 1949.
9. Fair, G. M., Sanitary Engineering in a Changing World, *Sewage & Industrial Wastes*, vol. 22, No. 1, p. 11, January, 1950.
10. Barnes, G. E., Engineering for Trade Waste Disposal and Treatment, Paper, Meeting American Institute of Chemical Engineers, Pittsburgh, Pa., Dec. 4–7, 1949.

CHAPTER 5

COOPERATION BETWEEN ENFORCING AGENCIES, INDUSTRIALIST, AND TECHNICIAN

In the early days of industrial-waste treatment and abatement of stream pollution, when little was known of the means and methods of treatment, it was common practice for enforcing agencies to issue arbitrary orders to an industry to cease pollution, with little or no guidance or information as to what to do. As waste treatment in many cases is a severe financial drain and an added expense to an industrial-plant owner, he either deliberately avoided the issue or stalled as long as possible.

Because this is an industrial nation, measures should not be taken that will destroy or cause industry to discontinue functioning at a profit. When it is no longer possible for an industry to operate with the hope of a moderate return on its investment in plant and equipment, there is no longer an incentive to continue.

As stated earlier, it is possible to so treat any industrial waste that an effluent may be turned out of the treatment plant which will be as good as, or perhaps even better than, the waters of the stream into which it is discharged. But in the fulfillment of this result the plant owner may have such heavy additional overhead that he can no longer afford to continue operating. This is tantamount to confiscation and tends toward the undemocratic practices of governments which we abhor and is distinctly un-American. The aim should be to help and encourage industry to attain a satisfactory result that will remove or abate the pollution in question at a cost that will not bankrupt the owners.

Fortunately, practically all our state health authorities, especially those in states which are highly industrialized, now realize that common sense should prevail in this matter and that they should not impose unfair or impossible demands on industry. The modern trend of all those interested in stream-pollution abatement, including the legislators responsible for the passage of new legislation for the enactment of requirements for nationwide abatement, is to realize the inherent rights of industry to function at a profit and not to instigate such stringent laws that this basic principle of American development will be destroyed.

In very few cases is there the necessity for rendering an industrial-waste effluent suitable for drinking water. In some cases, where an industry is located on a small stream which later is to be used as a source of potable-water supply by a downstream community, this criterion may be required. The industry should not be required to treat its waste to that extent, however, before it has had a fair opportunity to study its internal operations, under expert guidance, with the view of modifying its own operations to the extent that much of the polluting element may be removed by a change of method or by a substitution of elements entering into the product.

At any event, no matter what the pollution situation is, there should be a meeting of minds on the problem. No arbitrary demands should be made until the plant owner has been given a fair opportunity to discuss his problem with the authorities and show a willingness to comply with the law. If, after such leniency, he then does not indicate a desire to comply, the full extent of the law may be invoked. The average industrialist is ready to accept his responsibility to others and to take part in the discussions which will usually lead to an amicable solution, satisfactory to all. Modern business depends to a great extent upon the good will of its customers and neighbors, and if this feeling is destroyed by the arbitrary act of a plant owner in refusing to meet others halfway, he knows that he soon will see the result in the public reception and purchase of his merchandise which will materially affect his earnings. He is not likely to continue this attitude for long when the red ink begins to appear on his ledgers.

There are three parties to every industrial-waste problem: the state or other authority whose business is the protection of the public health and whose effort must be to prevent pollution of streams; the industrial-plant owner whose wastes are causing the problem; the engineer or consultant who may be called in to assist the industrialist in solving the problem.

When a waste problem is discovered, the first step should be for the health authority, within its powers and jurisdiction, to notify the industry in question of the existence of the pollution and that steps must be taken to eliminate or abate this condition. In this notification a reasonable time limit should be given during which, at the suggestion of the health authority, a joint meeting can be held to discuss a sensible program that may be agreeable to both parties.

Having been served with such a notification, the industrial-plant management should immediately arrange to obtain the necessary engineering or technical advice to enable them to study their wastes properly and to design a plant for their treatment which will satisfy the health authority.

After the engineer or technician has had an opportunity to make a thorough study of the situation, the industrial owner should then request an interview with the engineering department of the health authority or with some competent official. At this conference the industrialist, his engineer, and the health authority should discuss the problem fully. All the cards should be laid on the table. The health authority should state what, in his opinion, is needed to remedy the pollution condition and, if he has had previous experience in the treatment of the same sort of wastes, offer a suggestion as to a successful method.

If, on the other hand, he does not know of a proper or satisfactory method of treatment, he should then state definitely what type of effluent should be turned out, whether it must be equal to a potable-water standard, free of color, or equal to the existing water in the stream. If he can, he should state just what degree of treatment will be required. These facts give the industrialist and his engineer firsthand knowledge of the needs of the case and give the technician something to work on, which, with his knowledge of the character of the wastes, will usually assist him in developing or adopting the right treatment.

As mentioned in Chap. 4, if a laboratory or research organization is consulted by the plant owner they should supply him with several samples of the effluents to be expected from several stages of treatment. These samples, exhibited to the health authority, will usually result in the selection by the official of the one which is between the least and the most costly and which, by its appearance and constituents, convinces him that it will eliminate the basic complaint.

Where several such samples of treated wastes, each representing a different degree and cost of treatment, were placed before a health official, the author does not recall any instance where the official selected the most expensive method of treatment. A visual method simplifies the problem enormously, and if the problem is one for the dissipation of color, the authority can readily see, by looking at a sample of the treated waste, that a given treatment will produce a result which, when the effluent is diluted with the water of the stream, will eliminate the color nuisance.

With these basic data and the selection of a type of effluent by the health authority, the engineer can design a plant and get the work under way. The health authority does and should reserve the right to require additional treatment at any future time if the treatment proposed does not perform to his satisfaction, if it does not remedy the trouble, or if the condition of the stream changes, requiring a greater degree of treatment.

If the stream into which a waste is discharged is already polluted, the health authority should recognize this and should not compel an industry (whose wastes when treated will not increase the existing pollution) to install a plant which will, at great expense, produce an effluent better than the average condition of the stream unless, however, the particular waste contains some element dangerous to humans or animals or unless there is a general clean-up campaign in which all industries contributing polluting wastes to that stream are to be compelled to participate. All industrial-plant owners are usually willing to meet the health authorities at least halfway, but they do not relish being required to do the unnecessary. It should not be the principle of any health authority to compel an industry to do more than meet the actual requirements. With this cooperative attitude, much more will be accomplished and more pollution abated than if the authorities maintain an arbitrary stand and the industries or their group association generally resist the program.

The logical program for any state to follow is to make a survey of all the streams in that state and classify them according to their present use, their possible future use, and their present condition. If a certain stream is likely to be needed for potable-water supplies for a number of communities, then that stream should be classified as such and general notice should be given of the decision so that industrialists searching for a site for a new plant and knowing that wastes from their plant might adversely affect that stream would not purchase property adjacent to it. Otherwise, they would later learn, after much capital had been spent, that they must install an expensive waste-treatment plant to render their wastes suitable for discharge into the stream. With such warning, they could look elsewhere for a site which would not entail the same expense for treatment.

Likewise, if a certain stream is already polluted with industrial wastes to the extent that it is not suitable for potable purposes and the trend of industry is toward that stream, requirements should be set up that would advise industry what extent of treatment, if any, would be required if it locates on that stream.

After all investigations have been made and a suitable type of treatment is developed, the industrial-plant owner should obtain the approval of the health authority for the plant. This is advisable because, as stated elsewhere, in some states methods of an unproved or experimental nature are not generally approved and reservations may be made which may later entail additions or alterations at an added cost. If possible, where new methods are recommended, the report accompanying the plans of the plant should include a complete description of the method proposed and, if possible, references to articles or other available information that may have been written or published about that particular method. The health authorities will then be able to scan these references and determine whether or not the method is practical, is likely to be successful, and meets the needs of the particular problem.

In many cases new methods may be rejected by the health authority because of lack of knowledge of their operation. Therefore, if an untried method is proposed, the more complete the data accompanying the plan are, the greater the assurance of success in obtaining approval will be. In some cases, testing laboratories recommend the use of coagulants or chemicals which differ from those formerly used in similar cases. A full statement of these chemicals, their value as coagulants or precipitants, and their availability for use should be given so that the health engineers may be appraised of these facts and may readily determine the practicability of the use of that material.

If the plant owner is financially unable to undertake the expense of constructing the plant at once, he should so state, as under the new Federal Stream Pollution Law means are provided to assist him in carrying out the program.

Bibliography

1. Wolman, A., State Responsibility in Stream Pollution Abatement, *Industrial & Engineering Chemistry*, vol. 39, pp. 561–565, May, 1947.
2. Devendorf, E., Industries Show Interest in Wastes Treatment, *Sewage & Industrial Wastes Engineering*, vol. 21, No. 3, pp. 138–139, March, 1950.
3. Mohlman, F. W., Waste Disposal as a Factor in Plant Location, Paper, Meeting, American Institute of Chemical Engineers, Pittsburgh, Pa., Dec. 4–7, 1949.
4. Nelson, F. G., Should Industries Pre-treat Their Wastes? *Sewage Works Engineering and Municipal Sanitation*, vol. 19, pp. 451–452, September, 1948.
5. McDill, B. M., An Approach to Industrial Wastes Treatment Problems, Paper, Twenty-second Annual Meeting Ohio Sewage and Industrial Wastes Treatment Conference, Dayton, Ohio, June 23–25, 1948.
6. Danse, L. A., Industry's Responsibility in Waste Treatment, Paper, Twenty-second Annual Meeting Ohio Sewage and Industrial Wastes Treatment Conference, Dayton, Ohio, June 23–25, 1948.
7. Hess, R. W., Cooperation—Key to Industrial Wastes Problem, *Sewage Works Engineering and Municipal Sanitation*, vol. 20, pp. 241–242, 257, May, 1949.

CHAPTER 6

FACTORS IN THE SOLUTION OF A WASTE PROBLEM

An industrial-waste problem cannot be solved by simply calling in an expert, having him design a plant, building and putting it into operation, and then forgetting it. A great many other factors that enter into such a problem require mature consideration, study, discussion, and diplomacy and persuasion between the industrial-plant owner, the expert, and the local and other officials.

Each municipality, each section of the country has different ideas about the use of its streams, its rights and privileges, and its acceptance or reluctance to have industry in its locality. Therefore, no general set of rules can be laid down, nor can a complete list of factors be set up that can be followed in all localities. The endeavor in this chapter will be to outline many of the factors that concern the industrial-plant owner who is confronted with a waste-treatment problem.

Pollutional Factors

1. The type of pollution.
    a. Color
    b. Bacterial.
    c. Oxygen depleting.
    d. Toxic.
    e. Odorous.
    f. Destructive to animal and vegetable life.
    g. Deposits of solids.
2. The degree of treatment that must be given.
    a. Complete treatment to turn out a water-white, crystal-clear effluent.
    b. Removal of color or other single constituent.
3. Are other industries discharging into the same stream?
    a. What wastes are they discharging?
    b. Of what types are their wastes?
    c. Are they taking steps to eliminate pollution?
4. Present condition of the stream, to determine a reasonable degree of treatment.
5. Future use of stream to determine the possible ultimate degree of treatment to be planned for in the plant design.

6. Restrictions to be placed on further discharge of wastes into the stream by other present or future industries.
7. Possible trend toward classification of the stream for future use, which may help to establish the ultimate degree of treatment.
8. Elimination of other industrial wastes which may be more harmful than yours and may indicate the need for a lesser degree of treatment in your plant.
9. General policy of state health department toward elimination of pollution by industrial wastes.
   a. General policy
   b. Definite policy as to stream involved.

Public-policy Factors

1. Desire of local citizens to have a clean stream.
2. Cooperation of local officials with residents versus industrial-plant owners.
3. General attitude of residents toward industry in their particular section or in the city in general.

Public-expediency Factors

1. Is the city obligated to take industrial wastes into its sewerage system?
2. Has the city in the past established a precedent by accepting those of other industries?
3. What is the general policy? If treatment of your wastes is demanded, will others, formerly accepted, be excluded?
4. Are the local sewers large enough in the vicinity of your plant to carry the extra load of your wastes? Or will expensive new construction be required? If so, who will pay for it—you or the city?
5. If the city is willing or obligated to accept your wastes, what will be the basis of the charge, if any?
6. Will your wastes be of such nature as to damage the pipes or structures of the sewerage system?
7. Are your wastes of such composition, strength, and quality as to be destructive or inhibitive of the processes and methods of treatment used in the local sewage-treatment works?
8. If they are inhibitive or destructive, what type of pretreatment plant will you be obliged to install to render them harmless to the plant processes?
9. Is the local sewage treatment, as now constituted, of a design and

degree that will adequately handle your wastes to remove the pollution for which you have been cited?

10. If the plant is not so constituted, what will be required to make it so, and who will pay for the additions—you or the city?

11. Is the present plant and its various units large enough to handle your wastes adequately, or will it need additional units? If new units are added, who will pay for them—you or the city?

12. If the city has not heretofore accepted industrial wastes into its sewerage system, is your industrial position likely to be valuable enough to the city's interests to encourage it to accept your wastes on a cooperative basis?

13. Is your industry sufficiently important in the employment and tax structure of the city so that the city officials will cooperate with you in lessening your treatment burden by
    a. Accepting your wastes for treatment in the city system at no cost to you?
    b. Accepting your wastes on the basis of a fair charge for handling?
    c. Treating your wastes in their plant at no cost?
    d. Adding the necessary additional plant units at their expense?
    e. Adding the additional plant units at your expense but agreeing to handle your wastes at no further cost?

14. If the city accepts your wastes and you agree to make one of the following payments, will the city in turn be willing to reduce the monthly or annual bill for such charges by the amount of the taxes you pay the city?
    a. To pay a fair charge for the handling and/or treatment.
    b. To pay for the construction of new plant units which may be required because of the character or quantity of your wastes.
    c. To pay for the operation of such new units as may be required and which are built at city expense.

This may seem an illogical claim, as your wastes are causing trouble and something must be done to remedy that condition. The city naturally is to be put to some expense to assist in remedying the trouble. On the other hand, you pay taxes which are used for the general administration of the city activities, salaries, police, fire protection, etc. It is only fair, therefore, that if you agree to pay for the extra cost occasioned by the treatment of your wastes (as you have taken some of the burden of taxes from the citizens for which they would have been charged if you had not agreed to pay this cost) the taxes you pay should be deducted from the total of the bill rendered for treatment of your wastes. This, of course, depends upon the general attitude of the city officials and the importance of your industry to the general welfare and advancement of the city.

Another factor to be taken into consideration is the investigation of measures that other industries in your same general neighborhood may be preparing to take, or would be prepared to take, were they to be required to do so. This is important because it frequently happens that when a number of industrial plants are situated in the same locality, although they may have totally different wastes, important economies in initial plant construction and individual operating costs may be made by the grouping of industries to build waste-treatment plants on a joint basis, each industry paying its proportionate part of the construction and operating costs. It is a known fact, in sanitary-engineering work, that a large plant will cost less per unit of volume handled than a small plant. Thus, if a number of small, individual plants are involved in an industrial waste-treatment program in a given locality, considerable economy will be achieved if these industries join, with a central administration, and build only one large plant. Further details concerning this point are discussed in Chap. 10.

These factors may seem to point toward a lessening of the cost to industry alone. This is true and should not be opposed or criticized too severely by public officials. The general welfare and strength of the United States are based upon its industrial activity. Many of our cities would not exist if it were not for the employment given to workers by industrial plants, by the taxes paid by them, and in many cases by the welfare programs and assistance to public health and public good so generously contributed by industrial owners. Therefore, when these industries are compelled to clean up a pollution problem, it is in the best spirit of American good will and cooperation for the city officials to be willing to work out a program which will not overburden either the city or the industry. To say dictatorially to an industrial owner, "You must stop polluting the stream and must immediately build a treatment plant" will at once raise a curtain of protest. If the demand is too strongly insisted upon and enforced by litigation without previous round-table discussions of the rights and privileges of both parties, the plant owner may relocate his industry elsewhere.

Many of the factors listed naturally will be impossible to achieve and may not be desirable for a given case, but a quick survey of local feelings and knowledge of precedent and public policy can be speedily obtained and will furnish an answer to many of the questions.

A program of industrial-waste treatment which is carefully thought out after serious consideration of all the factors involved is more likely to be carried to a successful, quick conclusion than one in which the authorities refuse to discuss the matter and compel an industry to accede to their demands, regardless of the sums required or the possible effect on the industry and the welfare of the city.

It is just as much to the benefit of the local authorities to be willing to discuss the points brought out in this chapter with an industrial-plant owner as it is for the owner and right-minded, far-seeing authorities, Federal, state, or local, to be willing to consider fairly and justly any of these points which may fall under their jurisdiction.

Bibliography

1. Brown, C. V., Classification and Treatment of Industrial Effluents, *Public Works*, vol. 68, No. 12, pp. 40–42, 1937.
2. Mohlman, F. W., Are Industrial Wastes Always Liabilties? *Chemical & Metallurgical Engineering*, vol. 45, p. 200, 1938.
3. Regulating Industrial Wastes Discharged to City Sewers, *The American City*, vol. 52, No. 11, pp. 91–93, November, 1937.
4. Mahlie, W. S., Industrial Wastes as an Administrative and Financial Problem of Cities, Proceedings, Twenty-fourth Texas Water Works and Sewage Short School, College Station, Tex., Feb. 9–13, 1942.
5. Croft, H. P., The Discharge of Industrial Wastes from a Public Health Standpoint, Proceedings, Fifty-fourth Annual Meeting New Jersey Public Health and Sanitary Association, Princeton, N.J., Dec. 7–8, 1928.
6. Waring, F. H., Sewage and Industrial Waste Problems Resulting from Population Concentration, *The American City*, vol. 1, No. 5, p. 73, May, 1935.
7. Better Municipal—Industry Co-operation Needed, *Sewage & Industrial Wastes*, vol. 22, No. 1, p. 93, January, 1950.
8. Niles, A. H., Necessity for Proper Operation of Waste Treatment Plants, Paper, Third Annual Meeting West Virginia Sewage and Industrial Wastes Association, Wheeling, W.Va., Sept. 20–22, 1949.
9. Knowlton, W. T., Problems of Industrial Wastes from the Standpoint of City Administration, *California Sewage Works Journal*, vol. 16, No. 1, pp. 33–39, 1942.
10. Liquid Wastes: New Ways to Crack a Common Problem, *Modern Industry*, p. 44, December, 1949.
11. Mohlman, F. W., Plain Talk about Industrial Wastes Recovery, *Sewage Works Engineering and Municipal Sanitation*, vol. 16, pp. 489–490, October, 1945.
12. Report of Committee on the Limitation of Discharge of Industrial Waste into Sewers, *California Sewage Works Journal*, vol. 3, No. 1, pp. 78–95, 1930.
13. Martin, R., and W. S. Wise, Industrial Wastes Treatment by Co-operation, *Sewage Works Engineering and Municipal Sanitation*, vol. 19, pp. 60–62, 86–88, February, 1948.
14. Wood, C. P., Factors Controlling the Location of Various Types of Industry, Transactions, American Society of Civil Engineers, Paper 2306, 1947.
15. Riddick, T. M., The Formation of Basic Policies to Control the Discharge of Industrial Wastes into Sanitary Sewers, Paper, Meeting New York State Sewage Works Association, Niagara Falls, N.Y., June 4–5, 1948.
16. Gray, H. F., The Responsibility of the Municipality in the Industrial Waste Problem, *Sewage Works Journal*, vol. 17, No. 6, p. 1181, November, 1944.
17. The Factors Affecting Industrial Waste Treatment, *Sewage Works Engineering and Municipal Sanitation*, vol. 17, No. 5, pp. 264–266, May, 1946.

CHAPTER 7

THE INTERESTS CONCERNED IN INDUSTRIAL-WASTE PROBLEMS

The discharge of unusual quantities or concentrations of liquid wastes from an industrial plant frequently has effects which reach much further than the immediate sewerage system or its components of the municipality in which an industry is located. It may affect public health, public comfort, public convenience or expediency as well. For this reason a great number and variety of agencies interested in the enforcement of pollution regulations may be or will become concerned and will exert their powers and influence against an industry to compel it to abate a waste problem.

These agencies vary from private interests and associations to the top level of governmental agencies and enforcement bodies. They may be agencies charged with the responsibility for the use of natural resources, protection of public health, protection of fish and game, both from the standpoint of the sportsman and of the commercial fisherman or hunter, the abatement of nuisances of odor or of a visual character; port authorities charged with maintenance of channels and docks; and military authorities and private interests zealous in protecting and preserving their property rights and the recreational use of bodies of water. The number and title of these agencies vary in different states, but in general the list of departments, boards, commissions, and officials who may enter into a particular waste problem, is as follows:

Community or Municipal Level

1. Community or municipal health department or officer.
2. Community department of public works or its equivalent.
3. The community engineering department.
4. The community building department and inspectors.
5. The community department or bureau controlling the sewerage system.
6. The community department in charge of land bordering an important navigable stream.
7. The community treasury and tax departments.
8. The community or city planning boards.

County Level

In many localities a city is included within the borders of one county, but it is not infrequent that, where the city and county boundaries are synonymous, a waste problem may concern also those counties bordering the one in which the problem exists; therefore the agencies of those counties will also have a voice in the discussion. The following are some of the agencies of the county level which may have some jurisdiction over waste problems:

1. The county health department.
2. The county public works department.
3. The county engineering department.
4. County sanitary or sewerage districts, through which polluted streams may pass from their own to an adjacent county or municipality.
5. Districts or organizations for the control of streams to prevent floods.
6. County sewerage boards or organizations.
7. Public utility commissions, especially those concerned with electrical (hydroelectric) plants, where pollution of the water in a stream might affect the machinery in the power plant.
8. Drainage districts.
9. County planning commissions or boards.
10. Water-supply commissions.
11. Mosquito-control organizations.
12. Local sportsmen's organizations; fishing, boating, and bathing clubs and organizations.

State Level

1. The state department or board of health, with its general jurisdiction over the health of the state, and its engineering division, which is responsible for the approval of the design and operation of works for the elimination of pollution.
2. Antipollution agencies created under the new Federal legislation.
3. The fish and game and wildlife departments responsible for both commercial and recreational fishing, hunting, and conservation of wildlife.
4. The department of public works or other department which has jurisdiction over the use and resources of water in the state.
5. The state department which exercises jurisdiction over industrial activities.
6. The state department which controls state-owned lands, parks, public preserves, and recreation grounds.

7. The state department having jurisdiction over waterways passing through the state or entirely within it.

Regional Level

Since the recent increase in interest in the problem of industrial wastes and their effects on public health, a number of regional bodies have been created to control waste problems in public waters which form the boundary line between several states or into which streams from several states discharge. Each state concerned has a primary interest in the elimination or control of pollution in these common waters, and it is now accepted and common practice for these states to form joint bodies, in which each state has an equal voice, shares equally in the expense and responsibility, and cooperates to solve the joint problems in a manner acceptable to all. These joint bodies are usually administered by a board of directors or commissioners, the members of which are appointed by each of the component states or municipalities. This board usually appoints a manager or chief engineer who, with his staff, is responsible for carrying out the policies promulgated by the board or commission.

Numerous examples of this joint action now functioning can be mentioned.

1. The Tri-State Commission, with headquarters in New York City, which has jurisdiction over the waters around New York and is made up of representatives from the states of New York, New Jersey, and Connecticut.
2. Incodel, a joint board which has jurisdiction over the lower Delaware River and its tributaries and represents Pennsylvania, Delaware, New York, and New Jersey.
3. The Ohio River Valley Water Sanitation Commission, with jurisdiction over the Ohio River and tributary waters.
4. The Interstate Commission for the Potomac River Basin.
5. The New England Commission.

Lately, since the passage of the new Federal Anti-Pollution Bill by the Congress of the United States, new regional bodies have been formed under the provisions of this act, which have full and overlying control of the streams within certain areas. These organizations are usually located near watersheds of large streams and may embrace a large number of streams. They are administered by a governing body and managed by an engineer, who is selected for his knowledge of industrial-waste problems.

The regional offices set up under the National Water Pollution Control Program (Public Law 845) and the drainage areas controlled by them are as follows:

1. Boston, Mass., for the New England Area.
2. New York City for the North Atlantic Area.
3. Washington, D.C., for the Middle Atlantic Area.
4. Atlanta, Ga., for the Southeast Area.
5. Cincinnati, Ohio, for the Ohio-Tennessee Area.
6. Chicago, Ill., for the Great Lakes Area.
7. St. Louis, Mo., for the Upper Mississippi and Red River of the North Area.
8. Kansas City, Mo., for the Missouri River Area.
9. Little Rock, Ark., for the Southwest and Lower Mississippi Area.
10. Dallas, Tex., for the Western Gulf Area.
11. Boulder City, Nev., for the Colorado River Area.
12. San Francisco, Calif., for the California Area.
13. San Francisco, Calif., for the Great Basin Area.
14. Portland, Ore., for the Pacific Northwest Area.

This program is administered by a Water Pollution Control Advisory Board, created within the structure of the U.S. Public Health Service. The chairman of this board is the Surgeon General of the U.S. Public Health Service, and the board is composed of one representative each from the Department of the Army, the Department of Agriculture, the Department of the Interior, and the Federal Works Agency, and six other persons, not employees or officers of the United States government, who are appointed by the President of the United States. These six outside men include a recognized expert in sewage and industrial-waste disposal, a person specifically identified with wildlife conservation, a representative of municipal government, a representative of state government, and a representative selected from industrial life.

Still other forms of regional boards or associations are those formed locally for the purpose of protecting certain streams. These have jurisdiction over only one particular stream or its watershed. They are usually composed of representatives from the communities in the area and are organized to make rules and regulations governing pollution and its abatement or correction in that one stream. They exist in various parts of the country, such as the Raritan Valley District in New Jersey, for the Raritan River, and the North Jersey Water Supply District.

Government Level

1. The U.S. Public Health Service, which is concerned with pollution in interstate waters and navigable waters.
2. The War Department, which is concerned with obstructions to navigation, channels, etc., in interstate and boundary waters and with the effect of polluted streams on water supplies and recreational

interests for their camps, cantonments, forts, etc. The Navy Department is also concerned with preventing pollution of its docks, construction yards, berthing docks, etc., where acid or other wastes might damage the hulls of ships or render the water unsuitable for use for engine or boiler purposes.

3. The Engineer Corps, which has jurisdiction over interstate and boundary waters and in times of war exercises jurisdiction over waters bordering on army posts and camps where pollution might affect the potential or actual water supply of the post.

4. The Bureau of Reclamation, which is concerned with the building of dams, river-control works, etc., and is interested in the pollution of the water impounded in the reservoirs, which may be intended as recreational grounds for large numbers of people.

Private Level

This level comprises groups of landowners who may join forces to prevent the continuance of pollution on their lands or adjacent properties which creates a nuisance or potential danger to public health, animal life, or their enjoyment of the waters. These groups seldom have any actual authority or jurisdiction over the creator of the pollution, but they can frequently compel action by the authorities who have rights of enforcement. In many cases, private water companies can enlist sympathy for their efforts in compelling an industrial plant to cease pollution of a stream. Water consumers, because of the present need for more water and for the conservation of water, are jealous of their supplies and ready to act against any transgressor who is said to be affecting or damaging that supply in any way.

Now that the conscience of America is awakened to the dangers of industrial-waste pollution it is almost essential for any industrial group or entity to incorporate the treatment of polluting wastes into the initial construction plans. This is in itself an economy, as the total cost of a waste-treatment plant is usually a relatively small item in the total cost of a new industrial-construction program, and it is usually much easier to persuade the board of directors of a company to provide the small amount of money required for the waste plant when they are considering the over-all picture than it is to go before the board at a later date and ask for the necessary sum. It then becomes a major item of capital expense, whereas in the first stages it would be a minor item compared with the other expenses.

The call for the elimination or abatement of a waste-pollution problem is usually brought to the attention of the plant owner by some one of the bodies or organizations mentioned, and seldom does one plant owner hear from all of them.

As previously mentioned, several interstate compacts are functioning. These are mainly confined to the control of rivers and bodies of water east of the Mississippi River. They range in date of formation from 1936 to 1948. The first compact formed was known as the Interstate Sanitation Commission; it was organized in 1936 by the states of New Jersey, New York, and Connecticut to control the waters contiguous to the metropolitan district of New York. The second, formed also in 1936, is known as Incodel, from the official title Interstate Commission on the Delaware River, and comprises representatives from Delaware, Pennsylvania, New York, and New Jersey, all of which states have some part in the waters of the Delaware River. The next formed was the Interstate Commission on the Potomac River Basin, in 1941, with Maryland, West Virginia, Virginia, Pennsylvania, and the District of Columbia being represented. In 1947, the New England Interstate Water Pollution Control Commission was formed, composed of Connecticut, New York, Rhode Island, and Massachusetts. The most recently formed group is the Ohio River Valley Water Sanitation Commission, which represents Indiana, West Virginia, Pennsylvania, Illinois, New York, Ohio, Kentucky, and Virginia.

Scrutiny of these compacts shows that in several cases a state is a member of more than one group. This overlapping calls for concerted interest and conferences between the compact officials to assure that they coordinate their rules and regulations so that an industry working in a state which is a member of more than one group will have only one set of rules to follow.

Table 7-1 indicates the jurisdiction, the areas controlled, and other factors of these compact organizations.

In addition to these compact agreements, several other interstate agreements are also in force, controlling pollution in waters that affect the member states. Among these may be mentioned the following:

1. Great Lakes Drainage Basin Sanitation Agreement, formed in 1928 by Wisconsin, Minnesota, Illinois, Michigan, Ohio, Pennsylvania, New York, and Indiana, all of which states border on or have waters passing through them which enter the Great Lakes.
2. The Upper Mississippi River Drainage Basin Sanitation Agreement, composed of Minnesota, Iowa, Wisconsin, Illinois, and Missouri and formed in 1935.
3. The Interstate Sanitation Committee, recently formed and representing North Dakota, South Dakota, and Minnesota.

TABLE 7-1. INTERSTATE POLLUTION-CONTROL COMPACTS
(As of September, 1948)

Item	Ohio River Valley Water Sanitation Commission	Interstate Commission on Potomac River Basin	Interstate Sanitation Commission	Interstate Commission on Delaware River Basin	New England Interstate Water Pollution Control Commission
Signatory states	Ind., W.Va., Pa., Ill., N.Y., Ohio, Ky., Va. (8 states)	Md., W.Va., Va., Pa., D.C. (5 states)	N.Y., N.J., Conn. (3 states)	Del., N.Y., Pa., N.J. (4 states)	Conn., R.I., Mass. (3 states)*
Effective date	1948	1941	1936	1936	1947
Commissioners per state	3	3	5	5	5
Area, sq miles	154,880	14,500	....	13,000	13,926
Population in area	15,822,337	2,100,000	11,000,000	5,000,000	6,739,309
Functions	Issue orders regulating pollution	Coordinate; investigate, summarize technical data; act as adviser; agency; promote uniform legislation and practices	Substantially same as in Ohio River compact	Coordinate enactment of uniform state laws; develop and propose objectives; states exercise enforcement authority	Coordinate and advise; adopt water standards; classify streams; states exercise enforcement authority
Minimum treatment requirements	Removal of not less than 45% of suspended solids	None specified in compact; commission directed to recommend standards	Two classes of treatment specified, depending upon zone of carrying stream	Water specifications based on zone of carrying stream	None specified
Stream zoning	None specified	Preliminary zoning complete	Class A and B zones specified in compact	Compact specifies four zones	Compact authorizes zoning; tentative standards adopted
Special features	Consent of Congress given for other Ohio River states to become members	....	....	Program effectuated by terms of reciprocal legislative agreements not requiring ratification by Congress	Compact does not pertain to one basin but to all interstate waters among various states

* Eligible to join: Maine, Vermont, New Hampshire, and New York.

TABLE 7-2. STATE POLLUTION-CONTROL AGENCIES*

State	Does state law give an agency control over pollution? Yes or no	Date of law	Agency having control over water pollution	Other state agency sharing pollution control	Does law permit issuing orders and court action?	Are there any deficiencies in the law?	Remarks
Alabama	No	....	....	Water Improvement Advisory Commission			
Arizona	Yes	1943	State Dept. of Health	None	Yes	....	Special orders issued and enforced by state superintendent of health
Arkansas	Yes	1941	Fish and Game Commission	Water Pollution Control Commission, State Board of Health	Yes	....	
California	Yes	....	State Health Dept., Water Pollution Control Board	None	Yes		
Colorado	....				Yes	....	
Connecticut	Yes	1918	State Dept. of Health	State Water Commission Water Pollution Control	Yes	....	
Delaware	No	....			......		Bill to establish pollution-control agency vetoed by governor, May 5, 1947
Florida	Yes	1927	State Board of Health	None	Yes	....	Fine of not over $500 in any court of competent jurisdiction
Georgia	No			None			
Idaho	Yes	1889	Dept. of Fish and Game	Dept. of Mines and Minerals	Limited	Yes	Laws inadequate and out of date
Illinois	Yes	1929	Sanitary Water Board		Yes	....	Penalty, fine $100. Each day's continuance constituting separate offense
Indiana	Yes	1943	Stream Pollution Control Board	None	Yes		Penalty, fine $25–$100, also imprisonment for not over 90 days
Iowa	Yes	1925	State Dept. of Health	None	Yes	Not effective within 5,000 ft of contiguous waters	Penalty, fine not over $1,000 or imprisonment for failure to pay
Kansas	Yes	1907	State Board of Health	None	Yes		Penalty, fine $25–$100. Each day constitutes separate offense
Kentucky	Yes	1911	State Board of Health	Water Pollution Control Commission, Fish and Game Commission	Yes	Penalties not stated	
Louisiana	Yes	1940	Stream Control Commission	Dept. of Wildlife and Fisheries	Yes	....	Penalty, fine $25–$1,000, or imprisonment for 1 year, or both

State	Yes	Year	State Sanitary Water Board	Public Utilities Commission	Yes	No license to discharge wastes required for existing establishments	Attorney general may institute injunction proceedings to enjoin violation
Maine	Yes	1941	State Board		Yes	....	Penalty, fine to $500, or imprisonment to 90 days, or both
Maryland	Yes	1947	Water Pollution Control Commission	State Board of Health	Yes	....	Penalty, fine $25–$100, or imprisonment to 90 days, or both
Massachusetts	Yes	1945	Dept. of Public Health	Dept. of Conservation	Yes	....	Violation a misdemeanor, may cooperate with other states
Michigan	Yes	1929	State Stream Control Commission	Water Resources Commission	Yes	....	
Minnesota	Yes	1945	Water Pollution Control Commission	State Dept. of Health	Yes	No specific penalties provided	
Mississippi	Yes	1946	Game and Fish Commission	State Health Dept.	No		
Missouri	No	....					Regulation based on broad health powers of Division of Health and Conservation Commission
Montana	Yes	1945	State Board of Health		Yes	Yes	Stream pollution powers are vague. Various statutes prohibit pollution. Action may be brought by almost any official
Nebraska	No					....	
Nevada	Yes	1939	State Health Dept.	None	Yes	....	1947 legislation, if passed, will provide fine not exceeding $1,000 for each day of violation
New Hampshire	Yes	1947	New Hampshire Water Pollution Commission	State Dept. of Health	Yes		Not effective in Passaic Valley Sewerage District, Passaic River, Paterson to mouth
New Jersey	Yes	....	State Dept. of Health		Yes	Yes	
New Mexico	Yes	1903	State Dept. of Health	State Conservation Dept. Water Pollution Control Board	Yes	Yes, sources of pollution existing in 1903 exempt	Orders require approval by governor and attorney general. Varying fines provided
New York	Yes				No	Yes	
North Carolina	Yes	1945	State Stream Sanitation and Conservation Commission	State Board of Health Dept. of Conservation and Development		Yes	Committee to study stream pollution and make recommendations
North Dakota	Yes	1939	State Water Conservation Commission and State Health Dept.	None	Yes		
Ohio	Yes	1935	State Dept. of Health	None	Yes	Yes, exemptions re contiguous waters and mine wastes	Penalty, fine $100–$500 for each 30-day period. Law pertains to gross pollution
Oklahoma	Yes	....	State Board of Health	State Planning and Resources Board, State Corporation Commission	Yes	Yes	Penalty, fine $25–$100 for each day

* Arthur D. Weston, Federal Legislation on Water Pollution Control, Technical Association Papers, 31st series (Technical Association Pulp and Paper Industry), June, 1948, pp. 126–129.

TABLE 7-2. STATE POLLUTION-CONTROL AGENCIES.—(Continued)

State	Does state law give an agency control over pollution?		Agency having control over water pollution	Other state agency sharing pollution control	Does law permit issuing orders and court action?	Are there any deficiencies in the law?	Remarks
	Yes or no	Date of law					
Oregon	Yes	1938	Oregon State Sanitary Authority	None	Yes		Sanitary authority authorized to enter into interstate compacts for pollution control
Pennsylvania	Yes	1923	Sanitary Water Board	None	Yes		Penalty, fine $100–$500
Rhode Island	Yes	1920	State Dept. of Health	None	Yes	Yes, sewage of Newport, Jamestown, and North Shoreham exempt	Penalty, fine to $500 or imprisonment to 1 year for each month
South Carolina	No						
South Dakota	Yes	1935	Commission on Water Pollution	None	Yes		
Tennessee	Yes	1945	Stream Pollution Control Board	Dept. of Public Health	Yes	Yes	Control only "excess" pollution. Penalty, fine $50–$500 for each day
Texas	Yes	1925	State Dept. of Health	State Game and Fish, Oyster Commission	Yes		Penalty, fine $100–$200 for each day
Utah	No						
Vermont	Yes	1904	Dept. of Public Health	Water Conservation Dept., 1941	Yes		
Virginia	Yes	1946	State Water Control Board	State Dept. of Public Health	Yes		Penalty, fine $50–$500 for each day
Washington	Yes	1945	State Pollution Control Commission	State Dept. of Health	Yes		Penalty, $100, or imprisonment for 1 year, or both
West Virginia	Yes	1929	State Water Commission	Health Dept. Conservation Commission	Yes	Yes, coal mining and mine drainage excluded	Penalty, fine $100 for each day
Wisconsin			Committee on Water Pollution (State Board of Health)		Yes		
Wyoming	Yes	1923	State Board of Health	Fish and Game Dept.	Yes	Yes	Pertains only to domestic supplies and damage to fish
District of Columbia	No						Police dept. empowered to prevent pollution of streams by garbage, offal, etc.

On the government level, there is the treaty between the United States and Great Britain relating to boundary waters between the United States and the Dominion of Canada. Under this treaty an International Joint Commission was set up in 1912 and has since been functioning for the regulation of pollution in the international waters lying between the United States and Canada.

Table 7-2 lists the agencies existing in the several states for control of pollution and general data relating to them.

Bibliography

1. Agencies for the Control of Pollution by Industrial Wastes, Committee No. 6, On Industrial Wastes in Relation to Water Supply, *Journal, American Water Works Association*, vol. 11, p. 628, May, 1924; and vol. 12, p. 410, December, 1924.
2. O'Connell, W. J., Jr., Cooperative Planning for Disposal of California Industrial Wastes, *Western City*, May, 1944, pp. 22–24.
3. Bloodgood, D. E., Effect of Stream Pollution Regulation and Control, *Proceedings, American Society of Civil Engineers*, vol. 74, pp. 1048–1051, September, 1948.

CHAPTER 8

DISTRICTS FOR INDUSTRIAL-WASTE TREATMENT

In order to coordinate the activities of several communities and to get concerted action for amelioration of stream pollution caused by domestic sewage and industrial wastes, it has become common in recent years to form what are known as "sanitary districts." These usually are separate organizations developed for the purpose of handling all the sanitary work for a group of communities in a given locality, usually a drainage area. They are formed by agreement among the interested communities, who turn over to a central organization the work of engineering, investigation, financing, and construction of plants for the treatment of the sewage or the industrial wastes, or both, of the communities entering into the compact.

Usually these districts are within the borders of a single state and are subject to the general laws of that state. Ordinarily, the district organization is given the right, by legislative action, to issue bonds or other obligations to cover the cost of surveys, engineering designs, and construction of the works. In order to retire these bonds and amortize the investment, the district is usually given the right to charge for its services. Sometimes a "sewer-service charge" is made against each householder or industrial plant within the jurisdiction of the district. In other cases, each individual community pays the district an annual lump sum and itself collects from house owners and industrial plants for service rendered.

A considerable number of these districts have been formed in the United States, and the indication is that many more will be formed. The outstanding example, and perhaps the best known of such districts, is the Sanitary District of Chicago which includes in its jurisdiction the city of Chicago and a number of outlying adjacent communities in Cook County, Illinois. The bonds of this district are commonly offered to the public and represent a good investment.

The district form of operation has a number of definite advantages, especially in some of the more congested sections of the country, where there are many small communities and many industrial plants. Some of these advantages are as follows:

1. A single authority is able to establish jurisdiction over the quality of the streams within its boundaries and control the pollution of those streams.

2. The construction of one or more large sewage-treatment or waste-treatment works is possible, which will cost less than a number of scattered smaller establishments.

3. The district is able to clean up pollution by taking the financial load from the smaller individual communities and getting the work under way without the usual difficulties which are encountered when a number of small communities each endeavors to handle its own wastes.

4. The district authorities are able to make a comprehensive survey of the entire area under their jurisdiction and work out a solution which will serve the best interests of the section as a whole. The result is a coordinated program which allots to each community the work it may do.

5. The state health authorities are able to deal with one organization instead of a multitude of small entities.

6. The district engineers are permitted to take advantage of the latest developments in treatment at a minimum cost to the individual units.

7. The district organization is able to engage the best possible engineering talent to undertake its large projects.

8. The treatment is concentrated at one central site, instead of at a number of small scattered plants.

9. Lower operating costs are possible, as one large modern treatment plant will cost less to operate than a number of smaller ones. The result is lessened costs per annum to the taxpayers in the group.

10. The cost of policing is reduced, as there will be one plant only to look after and maintain at efficiency, instead of a number of small ones.

11. The district is able to obtain and retain more experienced and skillful operating personnel, because the project is of sufficient size to attract the best type of supervisory personnel and the pay schedules are better.

12. The district is allowed to set up standards to which any industrial plant or other municipal entity desiring to treat its wastes in the common system must adhere so that units in the system operate on the same basis.

13. The district is able to control the waste discharges of all the industries within its jurisdiction to produce effluents that may be handled in its system or to combine wastes from several adjacent plants or those in nearby sections, which may result in lowered costs to these industries. Whereas, if an individual city were to take in the wastes from a given plant, the ratio of the wastes to the sewage of that community might be so high as to cause the industry to install complete treatment works or to pay a proportionate share of the cost of such works for the city.

In many of these districts, the organization is responsible for constructing not only the treatment works but also the intercepting and main sewers which will collect the sewage and wastes from a given community and conduct them to the central treatment point. This, in itself, will relieve the smaller communities of a large expense, as they need construct a main sewer only to the boundary of their town, where their wastes are picked up in the large trunk sewers and carried to the treatment works.

The operating costs of the district plant or plants, together with the annual fixed charges, are allocated each year, and a charge is made against the individual householder or industrial plant on the basis of their proportionate contribution of sewage or wastes. As the large concentrated district works will cost less to operate per unit of volume than a smaller plant, the total cost to the individual contributor will be less than it would be with the smaller individual plant. Any maintenance and repair costs for the large plant would also be distributed over a much greater number of population units.

It is a well-established fact that a small plant, designed to treat a small volume of sewage or wastes, will cost more per unit of volume than a single large plant which may serve many times the volume of the small one. Every plant requires a certain number of employees to operate it, and the large plant, with perhaps the same number and type of units as the small plant, does not require employees in the same proportion as a number of small plants having the same total volume capacity as the large one. The units in the central plant are larger than those of the small plant but require little more attention.

Another important advantage of the large district plant is that it is of sufficient size to warrant the use of by-products of the plant processes. The three normal by-products of a waste-treatment plant are sludge, gas, and final effluent. In a small installation, serving a few people and a small volume of flow, the amount of these by-products is so small that drying the sludge to produce a salable fertilizer ingredient is not warranted, the gas is insufficient in volume to warrant the installation of gas-driven generators to utilize the energy contained in it, and the amount of final effluent is so small that it does not usually pay to endeavor to find a use for it.

On the other hand, the amount of sludge produced in a large plant is sufficient to warrant the installation of a dewatering and drying plant which will produce a substantial annual tonnage of dried sludge which, in many cases,[1] is sold at a price which brings in a revenue to the plant. Again, the amount of gas is so great that it pays the large plant to install modern gas-engine-driven generators to utilize the fuel value of the digester gas to develop power. This power potential is usually sufficient in any plant to enable it to produce on its own property from this low-cost waste fuel sufficient power to run the several units in the plant. In some cases there is an excess of power which may be used by other municipal entities or sold to outside users. In a large plant the volume of final effluent will be sufficiently large to warrant a study of the possible use of this effluent as irrigation water or for reuse as cooling water either by the plant or by other industries in the neighborhood. The city of Baltimore receives a revenue from such use of effluent by selling several millions of gallons per day to the Bethlehem Steel Company for its cooling purposes.

The use of the digester gas for power is discussed fully elsewhere, but for large plants it is a decided economical factor, as the plant may thus produce its own power at low cost, which in many cases materially reduces the cost of plant operation. Likewise, in concentrated districts where much power is in demand for industrial purposes, this release of power by industry enables the public utility to sell power to other users at a higher rate than it would normally obtain from a municipality or a large industrial user. In the City of New York every sewage-treatment plant now built includes the necessary gas-engine generators to utilize the gas from the digesters in the plant, and this has enabled the city to manufacture at a saving a large percentage of the power it requires in the operation of these plants. In the new large sewage-treatment plant at Los Angeles, Calif., the operation is predicated on the basis that practically all the power required to operate it will be produced in the plant itself from the gas derived from the digestion of the sewage sludge.

This reuse of by-products, which in small plants are usually wasted and return no revenue, is not only a potential source of revenue for the large district plant, but is also a recognition of the modern trend of the avoidance of waste and the utilization of by-products. It is an example of efficient management and the best type of scientific engineering.

Although the majority of the districts formed in the United States and England have been organized primarily for the purpose of handling sewage, plus the industrial wastes of the locality, the author is of the opinion that in the future, with the increased public interest and action in the prevention of pollution by industrial wastes, the use of the district type of organization in heavily industrialized sections will be seriously considered.

These industrial districts would probably be corporations set up by the members, within the corporation laws of the state, and their costs would be allocated among the individuals on some satisfactory basis of volume of waste flow, character of waste, tonnage of product, or some other adaptable unit.

The industrial-group organization would be formed by representatives of the individual members, with a governing board selected annually from the separate plant managements. It would be able to employ the highest type of skilled operating personnel, and in some cases the laboratory facilities of individual members could be used for the control of the group plant. This cost could be charged to general expense and spread over the entire group cost. Thus the individual plant laboratories and chemists could perform a useful and remunerative service to the group.

The revisions of plant operation or processes to reduce the type, concentration, or volume of wastes, which are frequently necessary to eliminate industrial-waste pollution, can be handled by the group advisers more efficiently than by outside consultants, as these men would be cognizant of the plant processes and methods and could recommend or suggest changes that would achieve this purpose with the minimum of revision or interruption.

Further advantages to be gained by such industrial groups are discussed in Chap. 10.

Bibliography

1. Utilization of Sewage Sludge as Fertilizer, Federation of Sewage Works Associations, Manual of Practice No. 2, 1946.

CHAPTER 9

SAMPLING AND ANALYSIS OF WASTES

The most important factor in attacking an industrial-waste problem is a complete knowledge of the character of the waste or wastes to be treated. A cursory glance at a particular waste will not enable anyone to solve the problem satisfactorily. Naturally, by looking at a waste one can tell whether or not its color must be removed, or whether it is heavily laden with solids, and the general size and character of those solids. But other polluting factors, such as acidity, alkalinity, chemical constituents, toxic materials or elements which would affect the use of a stream for its normal purposes, cannot be determined macroscopically.

The first step then, after an industrial-waste problem has arisen, is to determine the nature and character of the wastes. This involves a knowledge of the following factors:

1. *The volume.* This should be measured in convenient units, such as gallons per minute, per hour, or per day. If the waste is discharged in batches at odd hours, the amount discharged per batch or at any one time should be determined.

2. *The periodicity of flow.* In some plants, where batch operations are the rule, the vats, kettles, or tanks which contain the waste materials, or the residues of the processes employed, are emptied within a short period of time. A vat may hold only a few hundred gallons, or it may hold several thousand gallons. It must be determined whether one vat is emptied at a time, or whether several vats containing the same or different wastes are discharged into the drains at the same time. The total volume of these discharges can be ascertained from a knowledge of the cubic content of the vessels or vats.

3. *The operating schedule of the plant.* In some plants, operations which create wastes requiring treatment function during a certain working period of the day, and all waste of this type is discharged during that period. If this is the case, the total amount of each waste and its character must be accurately measured and determined and reduced to a rate of flow. In other cases, the vats or vessels are not emptied during the normal working period of the day; but after the normal day shift has left, the clean-up crew comes along and cleans out all the vessels for the next day's shift. This clean-up process is frequently more apt to create an

industrial-waste problem than the actual wastes produced by the plant in its normal productive period. Such is frequently true of a plant handling milk, such as a dairy or a creamery. Here, it is the custom, after the day's milk has been processed, to take down and clean all the piping for the next day's operation. Often, in this operation, cleaning fluids, caustics, and other materials are used which produce a waste liquor that creates a much more serious problem in its inhibitory effect on bacterial processes than the actual milk wastes themselves. If this clean-up occurs in the plant under consideration, the volume and character of these wash-up wastes must be accurately determined.

4. *Color*. It is important to indicate the color and the density of color of a waste and, if possible, determine the cause of this color. Color is frequently one of the most common complaints against industrial wastes. While the color may actually be harmless, those who see it in a stream frequently complain of it as the most serious polluting element. It is important to note color because if correctly evaluated it may sometimes be dissipated by proper mixture with clear waste waters, or the waters of the receiving stream may be used to dilute the color to a point where it no longer offends. This can frequently be done at small expense compared with the cost of precipitation by chemicals or other means.

5. *Biochemical oxygen demand (BOD)*. This factor is important as it is considered as the criterion of the strength of a waste and of its power to damage a stream used for potable waters or fishing. The BOD of a waste indicates to a certain degree the type and extent of treatment which must be employed to reduce the oxygen-absorbing power to a point where it will not reduce the oxygen content of the stream to a dangerous point. Some wastes have a low solids content but a very high oxygen demand; others have a high solids content and a relatively low oxygen demand. A different type of treatment and perhaps an entirely different process of treatment may be required to treat these two kinds of wastes.

6. *Settleable and suspended solids*. These are important because they act as a guide to the type of treatment that may be indicated or as a lead to the possible inclusion of these wastes with the sewage of the municipality.

7. *Total solids*. These include solids in suspension and in solution and are a guide to the type of treatment to be employed.

8. *Hydrogen-ion concentration (pH)*. This is a guide to the acidity or alkalinity of the waste and is frequently an indication of whether or not it may be included with normal sewage or with other wastes or whether or not it will require neutralization. It may also lead to a study of the possibility of combining this waste with another to obtain natural neutralization or precipitation.

9. *Temperature.* This factor is important as it may indicate whether or not a given waste must be cooled before it is treated. Wastes, such as those from the manufacture of alcohol, are frequently discharged at a temperature close to the boiling point. In this state they are not only difficult to handle but are destructive or inhibitive to bacterial processes and tend to cook the materials with which they are combined. Where digestion is part of the process to be employed in the treatment, wastes with a temperature above 130°F are particularly deleterious in their effect on the operation of the digestion cycle. If such wastes are to be handled, it may be necessary to consider a cooling step before digestion. On the other hand, wastes with a temperature below 50°F will inhibit the bacterial life in a digester and will stop all action temporarily.

10. *Chemical constituents.* It is important to know the various chemical constituents of a waste in order to use proper treatment. Cyanide, chloride, sulfate, and phenol are all highly polluting, and the content of these in a waste will give the investigating chemist or engineer a basic starting point for his study.

11. *Fats and greases.* The content of fats, greases, etc., is important as these ingredients are difficult to remove and unless removed frequently cause trouble in plant units, clogging pipes, nozzles, and other small orifices. Grease in a warm liquid may not appear to be harmful, but frequently as the liquid cools the grease, fat, or soap congeals and causes nauseous mats on the surface of settling tanks and digesters and gradually forms a deposit on pipes and other surfaces which may in time cause a shutdown of the treatment plant.

12. *Silica.* If the silica is high in percentage and is in a suspended state, it may cause severe abrasive trouble in pipes and small orifices or apertures.

13. *Bacteria.* Certain classes of wastes which contain the washings from animals (skins, hides, etc.) may contain large quantities of bacteria, many of which are harmful to humans. Tannery wastes, for instance, frequently contain anthrax bacilli, which are extremely difficult to destroy by any of the usual processes. Even after digestion the spores of anthrax may be present.

14. *Organic matter.* Many wastes in which there are high percentages of organic matter, particularly if in large part volatile, may be treated by the normal processes used for sewage and can often be incorporated into the sewage flow and handled at the municipal plant.

15. *Oils and emulsions.* Oil, if in emulsion, may go entirely through a treatment works and eventually show up on the surface of a watercourse. Strenuous methods must sometimes be used to break an emulsion, but at

the same time the methods used for this may also clear up one or more of the other pollutional elements.

DETERMINING THE VOLUME

The method used to determine the volume of waste depends mainly on the size of the flow. Several general methods are used to make tests on volume:

1. Weirs.
    a. Rectangular.
    b. V-notch.
    c. Proportional.
2. Nozzles or flumes.
    a. Parshall flume.
    b. Kennison nozzle.
3. Flowmeters.
4. Measuring boxes.
5. Containing vessels or vats.
6. Buckets or pails.
7. Timing of the filling of tanks with known volume.

Weirs

The simplest method of determining volume is perhaps by the use of the well-known rectangular weir, which is merely a widened section of the channel or stream in which the waste is flowing, with a weir opening at the end. Figure 9-1 shows a normal type of rectangular weir, and Table 9-1 gives the flow volumes of such weirs. These weirs are easily made and do not require a skilled operator to compute the volume of liquid passing over them. They are reasonably accurate and satisfactory except when any liquid is involved which contains a large volume of solids which settle out in the section upstream from the weir.

The only instrument required to read a rectangular weir is a rule, or simple hook gauge, and even this is not necessary if gauge markings are made on the side of the weir aperture where the depth of flow may be measured.

Slightly more complicated to build is the V-notch weir, as the notch must be fairly accurately cut. This weir is more effective, easier to read, and more accurate in cases where the flow drops off to a low point at certain periods of the day. Figure 9-2 shows the normal form of this weir, and Table 9-2 gives the average readings of such weirs.

The proportional weir is still more complicated to construct and more accurate than the rectangular weir and is better adapted for daily recordings of the flow where the measuring device is to be installed as a permanent fixture of the plant. Where it is desired to ascertain the volume of flow merely as a basis of plant design and when the weir will not be used as a permanent fixture, the standard, easily made rectangular weir is recommended.

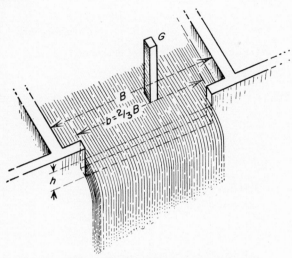

Gage or point of measurement of depth = 6 ft.
upstream from crest

Fig. 9-1. Rectangular weir.

TABLE 9-1. Flow over Rectangular Weirs—Gallons per Minute per Inch of Width (b) and Various Depths (h)

Depth of water, h, in.	Fractions of depth, in.							
	0	⅛	¼	⅜	½	⅝	¾	⅞
0	0.00	0.0748	0.374	0.673	1.047	1.421	1.95	2.394
1	2.99	3.515	4.114	4.787	5.460	6.134	6.882	7.631
2	8.453	9.20	10.098	10.921	11.819	12.676	13.614	14.587
3	15.484	16.73	17.504	18.55	19.524	20.646	21.693	22.815
4	23.937	25.059	26.181	27.378	28.400	29.697	30.969	32.166
5	33.437	34.609	35.981	37.252	38.524	39.871	41.217	42.564
6	43.910	45.331	46.753	48.174	49.521	51.017	52.438	53.934
7	55.355	56.851	58.348	59.918	61.415	62.985	64.556	66.202
8	67.698	69.269	70.84	72.486	74.131	75.777	77.423	79.069
9	80.789	82.435	83.155	85.876	87.596	89.317	91.037	92.833
10	94.552	96.349	98.144	99.939	101.735	103.605	105.400	107.270
11	109.14	111.011	112.881	114.751	116.721	118.566	120.501	122.281
12	124.326	126.271	128.29	130.235	132.181	134.200	136.220	138.165

Plan   Elevation

Measurement point = 4 x *H* upstream from weir

FIG. 9-2. V-notch weir.

TABLE 9-2. DISCHARGE OVER 90-DEG TRIANGULAR V-NOTCH WEIRS

H = head		Q = volume, gpm
Feet	Inches	
0.05	$\frac{5}{8}$	0.673
0.10	$1\frac{3}{16}$	3.815
0.15	$2\frac{3}{8}$	9.874
0.20	$2\frac{5}{8}$	21.229
0.30	$3\frac{5}{8}$	57.899
0.40	$4\frac{13}{16}$	117.593
0.50	6	204.218
0.60	$7\frac{3}{16}$	320.465
0.70	$8\frac{3}{8}$	468.579
0.80	$9\frac{5}{8}$	651.702
0.90	$10\frac{13}{16}$	872.079
1.00	12	1,131.054
1.10	$13\frac{3}{16}$	1,431.322
1.20	$14\frac{3}{8}$	1,974.678
1.30	$15\frac{5}{8}$	2,102.468
1.40	$16\frac{13}{16}$	2,596.488
1.50	18	3,078.982

Nozzles or Flumes

If permanent measuring devices are to be included in the design, the best types, especially if the wastes contain large solids or stringy material, are the Parshall flume and the Kennison nozzle.   These devices offer no obstruction to the flow of liquid, and the Parshall flume, especially, is easy to build.   For measuring flows to determine volumes for plant design, a Parshall flume of smooth wooden boards, which may be put together in a few hours, and a simple float-operated gauge will give accurate measurements of the flow, recorded on a chart for reference.   Figure 9-3 shows the general layout of a Parshall flume, and Table 9-3 gives the dimensional data for various flows of liquid.

The Kennison nozzle is a metallic spout embodying the same general principle as the Parshall flume or Venturi meter and has the advantage that it may be installed on the end of a pipe. Like the Parshall flume, it requires a gauge operating on the difference in head of water passing through the constriction of the throat to indicate the volume of liquid passing through. It may be fitted with a recording gauge.

Flowmeters

Various types of flowmeters are available, such as the Venturi meter of either the long- or short-tube type with their attendant indicating, registering, and recording gauges. These are made by a number of manufacturers. They are accurate to a high degree, but as the Venturi tube is usually of cast iron or other metal it is relatively costly to install and is best suited for a permanent installation for recording the flow during the operation of the plant.

Meters, such as the Sparling and others, using vanes or propellers revolving in the pipe line are not recommended for measuring waste flows containing large or stringy solids. Hair or textile fibers catch on these submerged devices and will sometimes cause them to break or at best will form an obstruction in the pipe or channel. They work satisfactorily on flows which contain no large solids or fibrous materials and are best suited for permanent installations.

Measuring Boxes

If the flow of wastes is very small, a fairly accurate measurement may be made by constructing a wooden box, the volume of which is known. This is placed under a pipe or channel where there is a free fall of liquid. By timing the period taken to fill the box to the overflow point, a fairly accurate idea of the volume of flow may be had. The box is cheap to construct but requires constant watching as it must be emptied as soon as it is full in order to get another measurement. Variations in rates of flow can be determined in this way, however.

Vessels or Vats

Where an industrial plant operates its processes on a batch system and the actual volume of the vessels or vats is known, a sufficiently accurate determination of the volume of waste being discharged over a period of time can be gained by counting the number of times per day, or other period, the vat or vats are dumped. While this will give a record of the discharge of the individual vat or vats, it will not give an accurate idea of the rate of flow of the accumulated wastes, if several vats are being discharged at odd times. This method also requires close personal check of the fillings and dumpings of the vats and the time periods in order to arrive at a daily volume or rate of flow.

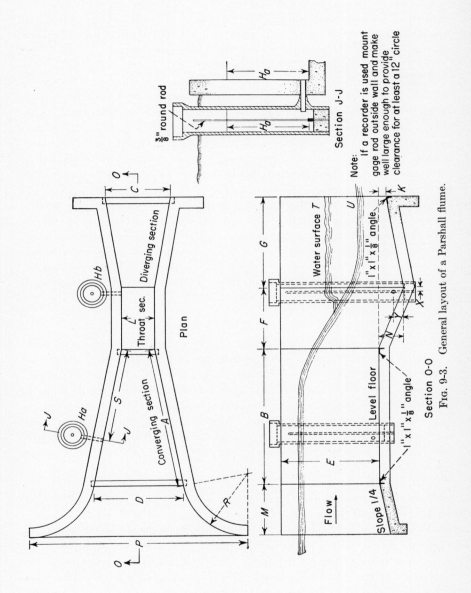

FIG. 9-3. General layout of a Parshall flume.

TABLE 9-3. DIMENSIONS AND CAPACITIES OF THE PARSHALL MEASURING FLUME FOR VARIOUS THROAT WIDTHS*
(Letters refer to dimensions, Fig. 9-3)

L, ft-in.	*A*, ft-in.	*S*, ft-in.	*B*, ft-in.	*C*, ft-in.	*D*, ft-in.	*E*, ft-in.	*F*, ft-in.	*G*, ft-in.	*K*, in.	*N*, in.	*R*, ft-in.	*M*, ft-in.	*P*, ft-in.	*X*, in.	*Y*, in.	Free-flow capacity, ft per sec	
																Min	Max
0-3	1- 6⅜	1- ¼	1- 6	0-7	0-10³⁄₁₆	2-0	0-6	1-0	1	2¼	1-4	1-0	2- 6¼	1	1½	0.03	1.9
0-6	2	1- 4⁵⁄₁₆	2- 0	0-3½	1- 3⅝	2-0	1-0	2-0	3	4½	1-4	1-0	2-11½	2	3	0.05	3.9
0-9	2-10⅝	1-11⅛	2-10	1-3	1-10⅝	2-6	1-0	1-6	3	4½	1-4	1-0	3- 6½	2	3	0.09	8.9
1-0	4- 6	3- 0	4- 4⅞	2-0	2- 9¼	3-0	2-0	3-0	3	9	1-8	1-3	4-10¾	2	3	0.11	16.1
1-6	4- 9	3- 2	4- 7⅞	2-6	3- 4⅜	3-0	2-0	3-0	3	9	1-8	1-3	5- 6	2	3	0.15	24.6
2-0	5- 0	3- 4	4-10⅞	3-0	3-11½	3-0	2-0	3-0	3	9	1-8	1-3	6- 1	2	3	0.42	33.1
3-0	5- 6	3- 8	5- 4¾	4-0	5- 1⅞	3-0	2-0	3-0	3	9	1-8	1-3	7- 3½	2	3	0.61	50.4
4-0	6- 0	4- 0	5-10⅝	5-0	6- 4¼	3-0	2-0	3-0	3	9	2-0	1-6	8-10¾	2	3	1.3	67.9
5-0	6- 6	4- 4	6- 4½	6-0	7- 6⅝	3-0	2-0	3-0	3	9	2-0	1-6	10- 1¼	2	3	1.6	85.6
6-0	7- 0	4- 8	6-10⅜	7-0	8- 9	3-0	2-0	3-0	3	9	2-0	1-6	11- 3½	2	3	2.6	103.5
7-0	7- 6	5- 0	7- 4¼	8-0	9-11⅜	3-0	2-0	3-0	3	9	2-0	1-6	12- 6	2	3	3.0	121.4
8-0	8- 0	5- 4	7-10⅛	9-0	11- 1¾	3-0	2-0	3-0	3	9	2-0	1-6	13- 8¼	2	3	3.5	139.5

* Courtesy of The Foxboro Company, Foxboro, Mass.

Buckets or Pails

Where very small volumes of wastes are encountered, they may frequently be measured sufficiently accurately by means of buckets or pails of known volume. This method is similar to the measuring-box method and so requires constant personal attention during the measuring period. It is the simplest and cheapest method of making measurements, as the utensils required are usually available and no construction work is required, but it is not recommended except for very small flows.

TAKING SAMPLES

Before any tests can be made on industrial wastes it is necessary to obtain accurate samples of the wastes. This is important, as improperly taken samples can lead to erroneous conclusions. If the waste to be treated is an uncommon one, the main characteristics of which are not generally known and where variations occur from plant to plant, the samples taken must be characteristic of that particular waste. They must be taken in a manner that brings to the investigator all the elements, which may be the cause of the pollution, in the proportions in which they are found in the actual waste that will ultimately reach the treatment plant.

Grab samples taken at odd times are merely a visual guide to the appearance and composition of the waste at that moment, but industrial wastes are much less uniform in their composition from hour to hour and day to day than is normal domestic sewage, and few assumptions can be safely made from grab samples as to the collective character of the wastes.

In many plants, particularly in textile mills, where dyeing is part of the process, the colors of the wastes change from time to time during the day, and as the coloring materials used are frequently of different chemical composition they do not all react to the same treatment. If the wastes are to be treated as they flow to the plant, it is most essential that frequent samples of the various effluents be taken, with accurate flow readings at the same time, to determine the volume and percentage concentration of one waste as compared with another of different color and composition. If the wastes are to be collected and combined in a holding tank until a uniform mixture of the entire flow of the day is obtained and then a uniform rate of flow of the combined and mixed wastes is to be treated, then it is important to obtain a representative sample of the combined flow, with rate readings.

In some industrial plants, where a variety of operations is carried out, several classes of wastes may be discharged during the working day. As some of these wastes may be more difficult to treat than others, or some may not require treatment at all, it is unwise to assume that a composite of the entire waste flow is the ultimate aim. It frequently happens that some form of minor treatment may be indicated for a particular waste, which will reduce it to a common norm that will make it possible to treat the resultant combined waste at a lower cost and with less plant than if all the wastes were to be pooled together. The chemical composition of some wastes is such that they may cause colors to set, rendering them very difficult to treat, whereas some form of treatment before their entrance in the consolidation tank would prevent this action and keep the over-all cost of treatment down.

At a large industrial plant in the East, it was found that 26 different wastes were discharged from various operations within the bounds of this one plant. Some of these wastes, those from the photographic laboratories for instance, contained silver in solution, which could be recovered much more readily from the small volume of silver-containing wastes than if these were mixed with the very large volume of other wastes. Other wastes had alkaline or acid characteristics which made them valuable as neutralizers at certain times of the day, thus eliminating the purchase of neutralizing chemicals. Had all these wastes been discharged at various periods of the day, in many instances an alkaline waste which had value as a neutralizer for an acid waste would have been discharged and passed in and through the plant before the acid waste reached it. Therefore, the neutralizing value would be lost, and when the acid waste arrived, a commercial alkali would have to be used to neutralize it.

It is of prime importance that a preliminary survey of a plant be made before any recommendations are made, that samples of the individual wastes be properly taken and kept separately, and that data be available on flow, flow periods, characteristics, etc. Samples must also be taken of the combined wastes flow in the event that subsequent investigation indicates that the most reasonable and practical plan is for the treatment of the combined wastes.

The quantity of the sample is equally important. It must be sufficient to enable the chemists or engineers to make a series of tests on it. A medicine bottle full is usually useless. At least 5 and preferably 10 gallons of each waste or combination should be available. This matter should be determined by the chemist, engineer, or laboratory engaged to make the tests. Some laboratories are content to make tests in the normal laboratory test tubes, which naturally take very little material. Others are not satisfied with such minute demonstrations but make their tests in small-scale plant units in order to be able to correlate the results of the tests into large-scale plant practice with some expectations of equal results. These tests may require several gallons or more of waste for each test.   Other laboratories have special testing methods which involve continuous runs and can be expected to produce results that can be safely used as the basis of design for a full-scale plant.   These tests naturally require a much larger volume of the waste than a test-tube or beaker determination.   However, as it is important that an investigation give a clear picture to the industrialist of the ultimate initial and operating cost of the plant, it is essential that the test work be done on a scale that will enable the investigators to state with reasonable assurance that the results obtained can be reproduced in a full-scale plant, with perhaps but a negligible variation in the end result.   These large-scale tests give a clear indication of the amount of chemicals that may be required.

If the waste is one that is discharged from a dye vat in a textile mill, or other type of vat or batch process, then a sample can be taken of the waste as the vat is dumped.   If the process and material used in the vat have not changed during the operation, a sample taken at the time of discharge will be satisfactory.   This sample must be clearly marked with the date and time taken, number of the vat or vessel from which obtained, temperature, process employed, and names of the mill and of the person who obtained the sample.   If it is one of a number of samples, it should also be given an identifying number or symbol.

If the sample to be taken is of a flow in which several wastes are combined and in which the strength and volume change during the day, then samples should be taken each hour, sometimes half-hourly, and marked and kept separate.   If the entire flow is to be retained in a holding basin and run through the treatment plant at a uniform rate at a later time, then the samples of the day's run should be placed in a large vessel and thoroughly mixed and the final sample taken at the end of a full 24 hours. Even in this case, however, it is well to take individual samples of the separate wastes as they are discharged, for it sometimes happens that, whereas combined treatment of the wastes has been the primary indication, later investigation of the individual wastes may show that the practical and most economical method will be to treat one or more of the wastes separately before combining it with others.

Samples should always be taken and kept in clean glass bottles.   It is permissible to use porcelain-lined pails in which to collect samples, provided that the porcelain lining is unbroken.   Carboys or other large glass containers in which samples are to be kept or shipped should be thoroughly cleaned, as a residue of acid or other substance left in them may cause a chemical or physical change in the waste which can easily throw an investigator off the track.

The temperature of the waste is important.   If the waste is collected and not received at the laboratory for several days, it will undoubtedly have a different temperature than when taken. As the treatment in the final plant must be based on handling the wastes as they reach the plant and as temperature has a definite effect on reactions, settling rates, etc., the investigator must be able to reproduce the actual conditions in his tests.

For instance, the wastes from the manufacture of alcohol from cane-sugar molasses are discharged from the distillery close to the boiling point. Owing to the high BOD of these wastes, the recommended treatment is digestion as the first step. As the optimum temperature for anaerobic mesophilic digestion is between 90 and 95°F, it would be fatal to the digestion process to put the raw hot wastes into the digester. Therefore, the first step in the treatment of such wastes must be a cooling step to bring the wastes down to the satisfactory temperature for digestion.

If the wastes contain solids or fibrous materials, the samples must be taken in such a way that the proper proportion of these materials can be retained in the sample; otherwise, if the sample contains only the liquid portion, it does not present the true picture to the investigator, and in the plant design some vital feature may be omitted, causing later difficulty in operation which may be expensive to correct. If solids and fibrous materials are present, the sample should be taken in a receptacle with a mouth or opening sufficiently large to catch these ingredients.

The taking of samples may require the entire time of one or more men for a period of several days. This may seem like an inordinate expense, but the final cost of a treatment plant based on the examination of proper samples compared with grab samples may be so much less that the cost of the careful sampling will be ultimately repaid many times over. In cases where the wastes are uniform in character and large-volume samples are desired, simple and relatively inexpensive automatic sampling devices may be obtained on the market which may be installed to take continuous samples and empty them into a container without the need of constant manual attention. However, the average case does not warrant this expense as, unless the plant processes change every day for a month, it will rarely be necessary to take samples over a longer period than a week. If a regularly organized firm is engaged to work out the problem, it will usually be able and willing to take care of the sampling at little extra cost and without interference with the duties of the plant personnel. In fact it is advisable to place this responsibility on the investigator, for not only does he then have full knowledge of the conditions, but as he makes the samples to suit his own needs he cannot place the blame for improper sampling elsewhere.

If samples are to be shipped to a distant laboratory by a common carrier, they should be carefully boxed and protected against damage.

Barrels or steel containers may be shipped without further crating, but bottles and other glass containers should be carefully cased and marked with a warning that they contain glass. The cases and boxes should be carefully marked with the names of the shipper and the particular plant from which they came and each case, box, or container given a distinctive mark or number, which is to be transmitted to the receiver so that he may readily identify the different samples. A full description of the contents of each sample should be sent to the investigator with all the pertinent data before the samples reach him.

If the samples are to be sent from a foreign country, it is important to note on the shipping documents that the contents of the various cans, bottles, or barrels are samples of waste products for investigation and testing purposes, are not for sale, and are of no commercial value. Important samples of industrial wastes, although valueless to anyone, have frequently been held up and even destroyed by customs officials upon reaching another country because they were not properly marked as to their origin and identity. At other times, heavy customs duties have been assessed for wastes not properly marked.

Likewise, if the wastes are subject to deterioration or are volatile and may be the cause of possible rupture or explosion of their containers if placed in hot places on shipboard, the containers or cases should be clearly marked to indicate that they must be kept in a cool place and away from fires. A few precautions of this nature will frequently prevent serious misunderstandings and expense and will eliminate the sending of additional samples. In one case in the author's experience, a waste material was sent in barrels from Canada but only the empty barrels were received. Upon investigation it was found that, because the barrels were not marked to indicate their contents, the customs men at the border had no information as to the material, and as the waste was one high in organic matter which had partially decomposed, the odor of the contents was such that the customs officials decided that whatever had been in the barrels was so far gone that it would be of no use to anyone and the simplest way (which they took) was to empty the material down the sewer.

MAKING TESTS

As stated, it is necessary to know the characteristics of each class of waste, particularly if those from a single plant vary. The tests to be made differ with each waste problem and depend upon the requirements of the case. The average tests are outlined in the earlier part of this chapter, but in some cases, if there is a possibility of the recovery of valuable products from the wastes, elaborate laboratory work may be required, which will demand the attention of a skilled chemist. Individual tests must be made on the various wastes to determine their strength and character so that a proper weighting of each waste may be made in determining a method of treatment for a possible combination. If there are several wastes from a single plant, tests should be made on properly weighted samples, gauged as to their ratio to the total flow from the plant, in order to evaluate the possibility of combined treatment.

Certain tests may be made in the field, such as observations of the color, temperature, and volume of each type of waste, the periodicity of flow, and the character of the solids in the waste. Frequently, if the wastes are of such a character that transportation to a distant point would bring changes in their physical, chemical, or biological aspects which might result in a different type of treatment, it is sometimes best to make tests of the volume of solids by simple Imhoff cone or jar tests. Most industrial plants today have some sort of laboratory with the normal equipment in which various tests may be made. Where such facilities are available, it is considered advisable to carry out certain tests on precipitation with various reagents to get a general idea of the reactions. Most plant laboratories are equipped to make suspended-solids tests, pH determinations, etc., and these are best made on the sample while it is still in its original condition to act as a guide for future detailed laboratory work. In the field also, with the knowledge of the volume of flow of each waste and the period of that flow, combinations can be made which are comparable to the actual flow and which will give information of value in later studies.

The BOD test is one which cannot be made in the average plant laboratory, and it may be necessary to make this test where there is better equipment. In some cases, if the laboratory of the investigator is at a long distance from the plant, it may be advisable to have the BOD tests made at some local laboratory equipped for that purpose. Many cities have commercial laboratories which, for a small fee, will do this sort of work. As wastes with a high organic content change in BOD as the waste ages, it is important, if the BOD is the main condition to be corrected, to have this work done as soon as possible after the sample is obtained. In cases where biological treatment is indicated, exact knowledge of the BOD is important as it has a definite bearing on the plant units to be provided for its reduction. A few days, delay in making a test on a waste with a high organic content may result in a much more expensive treatment than is really necessary. Therefore, the plant owner is well advised to spend the small sum required for immediate BOD tests.

If the wastes are to be handled in a municipal plant of the biological type and a charge is to be made for handling the wastes based on BOD or the excess of the waste BOD over the BOD of the normal sewage, it is especially important to have an exact knowledge of the waste BOD in order to determine the fair charge to be made. Frequently, municipal plants which have not been designed with the idea of handling industrial wastes may, however, still be able to do so if the wastes to be handled do not contain too high a degree of BOD. Likewise, if the BOD of the wastes is so high that studies indicate that the existing plant could not handle it, it may be necessary to consider increasing the size of the plant biological units or to compel the industrial plant to pretreat its wastes to reduce the BOD to a point where the municipal plant could handle them. All these facts indicate the importance of getting an accurate and early knowledge of the BOD of the fresh waste.

There are two tests for determining the strength of raw wastes or treated effluents. The more common one—the BOD test, just discussed —is, as its name implies, a biological determination measuring the amount of organic substances in a medium which can be oxidized by biochemical agencies under certain conditions. The other—the COD (chemical oxygen demand) test—is an oxidation of strictly chemical nature produced under rigid conditions.

Some confusion exists as to the relationship between the two methods. In effect they are complementary, but neither can be substituted for the other. To make the two tests directly comparable would require that all the constituents which could be chemically oxidized could also be biochemically oxidized and that the constituents would be equally attacked chemically or biologically. This does not occur regularly, as some substances, such as acetates and some fatty acids, are readily oxidized by microorganisms but resist chemical oxidation. Reversely, cellulose resists biological oxidation in aerobic systems. Thus the results of the two tests on such substances would not be equivalent. Numerous COD methods have been developed, and the Standard Methods Committee of the Federation of Sewage Works Associations is now evaluating them. The COD test, according to Ettinger,[11] has certain advantages over the BOD test as it can be used to obtain results quickly, whereas the normal BOD test requires 5 days. It also may serve as a preliminary index to the selection of appropriate dilutions for the BOD test. Where wastes containing toxic materials cannot be satisfactorily examined by the BOD test, it may serve as an index. Where equipment and material for a BOD test are not available, the COD test may give a reasonably accurate result. For certain chemical wastes, the COD test is perhaps the best means of measuring the amount of material being discharged.

The suspended solids in the waste are also important in considering the design of plants, but field tests for these are not as essential, as these solids do not increase with time. In some cases, suspended solids may become comminuted or broken up in transit or in their passage through pipes and bends, but the normal suspended-solids test will still register the true amount.

Table 9-4 presents a comprehensive way of sampling sewage, making analyses, and interpreting the results obtained and gives a brief description of test procedures that are equally adaptable to investigations on industrial wastes.

Industrial-plant owners can save money and time by having their own chemists or engineers keep records of flows, periods of flow, and character of wastes and also make suspended solids, BOD, pH, temperature, and other tests. These records are very valuable to an investigator, particularly if they have been kept over a period of years, as they immediately give an indication of what to look for when the tests are made and they act as a check on the calculations.

In many municipalities there are laboratories at the local water or sewage plant equipped for making all the tests mentioned, and an industrial-plant owner in a city so equipped can make arrangements to have the local plant operators or chemists do this work for them at small cost, as they can carry on the tests on wastes at the same time as they do their own routine work. As a matter of fact, in some cases, this is a good policy, as it may indicate to the municipal officials that the wastes may be handled readily in the existing plant without upsetting plant processes or operation procedures, thus leading to an economical solution of the industrial-plant problem. Such cooperation may act to soften the requirements in a pollution problem, as the city officials may be convinced that the wastes are not so bad as they were described by the complainants and can be handled at small cost. The investigator will encourage this procedure wherever possible, as it is his duty to solve each problem in the most practical and economical manner and at the least cost to the plant owner.

Laboratory tests made on proper samples of the wastes, with the exact knowledge of their composition and volume of flow, will enable the investigator to develop a method of treatment. However, he will undoubtedly have ideas and methods of his own which may color his final recommendations and may also determine the type of treatment and his plant design. He should always look toward the most economical result and should not restrict himself to one solution only but, with a knowledge of the waste and the requirements of the case, apply that method or process which will bring the desired results at a reasonable cost.

Upon completion of his work, the investigator should make a complete report to the plant owner, outlining the work done, giving analyses of the

TABLE 9-4. INTERPRETATION OF SEWAGE ANALYSES AND SEWAGE-PLANT OPERATING RECORDS*

Test	Sampling points	Reason for test	Analysis and interpretation of results	Brief procedure of test
Screenings: 1. Quantity, lb or cu ft per million gal **2. Moisture, % of solids**	As removed from screens	1. To determine time periods for intermittent operation of mechanical equipment. To determine time periods for collection by trucks. To reveal abnormal contributions to system. To complete record of solids removal by plants 2. To determine whether or not screenings have been drained sufficiently to be burned efficiently in incinerator	1. Quantity from coarse screens (½–3-in. openings) is usually 0.5–6 cu ft per million gal. Quantity from fine screens (¾–$3/32$-in. openings) is usually 5–30 cu ft per million gal. Weight per cu ft 40–60 lb. Variations from above values and the average from the plant in question may indicate large contributions from industrial, commercial, or similar sources 2. Usually between 75 and 90 % of moisture in screenings by ordinary draining for 1 day. Dewatering centrifuges and presses usually reduce moisture to 60–75 %. To feed incinerator economically, screenings should contain between 60 and 80 % moisture. BTU used per pound of screenings incinerated ranges between 1400 and 3500	1. The quantity is measured by weighing a day's collection of the material which has been allowed to drain; or the volume is measured 2. The percentage moisture is determined by weighing and drying a representative sample of about 1 lb in an oven at 103°C for 12–24 hr. The sample is weighed while still warm, and loss of weight divided by weight of dry solids multiplied by 100 is the percentage moisture
Grit: 1. Volume, lb or cu ft per million gal 2. Size and type of solids being removed (for sieve tests and volatile solids test, see Sludge)	As removed from grit chambers	1. To determine time periods for manual cleaning and to set time periods for intermittent operation of mechanical grit removers 2. To complete the records of solids removed by the plant	1. For combined sewers average quantity of grit commonly deposited is 2–3 cu ft per million gal. To allow for maximum storm demands between cleaning operations, 10–30 cu ft per million gal grit-storage space	1. Quantity is measured by weighing the amount collected in 1 day after it has been allowed to drain; or the volume is measured

Determination	Where sampled	Purpose	Remarks
			is generally provided in grit chamber channels. Grit chambers should be cleaned about every 2 weeks under normal conditions and every few days at time of successive storms. Large amounts of grit gathering in screening chambers in sanitary sewage-treatment plants may indicate broken lines, presence of illegal storm-drain connections, open manholes, etc. Modern tendency is to provide a grit chamber for treatment plants treating sanitary sewage as well as those for treating combined sanitary sewage and storm drainage
Scum or skimings, cu ft per million gal	1. Grease or skimming tanks 2. Settling tanks 3. Filters 4. Aerators, etc.	To determine efficiency of skimming tanks To determine whether additional amount of air is necessary to increase flotation of grease	Amount skimmed from tanks varies from 0.1 to 5.0 cu ft per million gal. Volume above normal may indicate industrial-, garage-, etc., waste discharge. Grease causes clogging of pipes and should be removed as early as possible in the treatment process. Grease and scum should not be put in digestion tanks because they interfere with the digestion and drying of the sludge Can be measured by allowing the collected material to stand in a tank until water and scum separate. The water is drawn from the bottom of the tank and the volume occupied by the scum measured. Care should be taken to ascertain if gases in the scum have escaped and have caused the scum to settle as sludge. Sludge settling with the water should be measured as part of the scum
Total suspended solids (includes settleable and nonsettleable solids), ppm	1. Raw sewage primary 2. Settling-tank effluent 3. Filter effluent 4. Final effluent 5. Aeration tanks	To determine reduction of suspended solids by plant as a whole in order to satisfy requirements set by state health authorities for watercourse into which effluent is finally discharged	See Table 9-5 for average values of raw sewage, and values and efficiency of removal to be expected from the various units and the plant as a whole. Higher amounts of suspended solids in raw sewage may indicate in- A Gooch crucible is prepared, ignited, and weighed. A sample of sewage or effluent of 50 to 100 ml is filtered through, and the crucible is dried for at least 2½ hr in an oven at 108°C. It is then cooled in a dessicator,

TABLE 9-4. INTERPRETATION OF SEWAGE ANALYSES AND SEWAGE-PLANT OPERATING RECORDS.*—(*Continued*)

Test	Sampling points	Reason for test	Analysis and interpretation of results	Brief procedure of test
	6. Supernatant from digestors	To determine reduction of suspended solids by each unit in the plant To determine characteristics of activated sludge or the sludge index in order to ascertain the proportion of the material which settles with difficulty	dustrial wastes or low per capita flow. Smaller amounts of suspended solids and large flows may indicate infiltration. Lower efficiencies than normally expected may indicate that units should be cleaned and mechanical equipment (tanks and filters) adjusted more often. The low efficiencies may also indicate that the recirculation ratio in high-rate trickling filters should be changed, or that the amount of return activated sludge and air supply in aeration tanks should be increased Aeration-tank samples (activated-sludge process). Limits of suspended solids in mixed liquor should be 1,200–3,000 ppm for diffused aeration plants, and 500–1,200 ppm for mechanical aeration plants. A sludge index of 100 is normally expected in diffused-air plants. The sludge index may be as high as 300 in mechanical aeration plants. "Bulking" occurs with higher sludge indices. When bulking occurs, sludge rises and flows over effluent weirs	weighed, and the parts per million of suspended solids calculated by multiplying the gain in weight in milligrams by 1,000 divided by the number of milliliters of sample taken Sludge index is the volume in milliliters occupied by 1 gram of dry suspended matter after the aerated liquor has settled for 30 min. A 1-liter sample from the outlet of the aeration tank is settled for 30 min in a 100-ml graduated cylinder and the volume occupied by the sludge is reported in milliliters. The dry suspended solids are then determined in parts per million. Computation: (Millions of settleable sludge plus parts per million of suspended solids) times 1,000

Determination	Sampling points	Purpose	Significance	Method
Total solids (includes screenings, grit, scum, suspended solids, and dissolved solids), ppm	Raw sewage	To determine characteristics and condition of the sewage. To reveal industrial wastes	The following are the average parts per million of total solids that different strengths of sewage would contain: weak, 400 ppm; medium, 700 ppm; strong, 1,200 ppm. Suspended solids are usually about half of the total solids. For industrial wastes, some dissolved solids may have to be removed before the effluent is put into a stream	Total solids are determined by drying at 103°C a sample of 50 ml in a silica dish which has previously been ignited and weighed. The dish containing the dry solids is cooled in a dessicator and weighed. The calculation is the same as that for suspended solids
Dissolved solids, ppm	1. Raw 2. Primary settling tank 3. Filter effluent 4. Final effluent	To reveal breaking down of sewage during treatment and effectiveness of treatment on the portion of organic matter which is in solution	Indicates age of sewage. The more stale the sewage is, the greater the percentage of dissolved solids. For domestic sewage, dissolved solids normally have little meaning. Dissolved solids in domestic sewage are usually approximately two-thirds of total solids. For industrial wastes, dissolved solids may have large BOD requirements, which must be satisfied	Dissolved solids are determined by subtracting the total suspended solids from the total solids
Volume of settleable solids, cc or ml per liter	1. Raw sewage 2. Final effluent	Where primary treatment is used and laboratory facilities are limited, test affords approximate measure of performance	Imhoff tanks and primary settling tanks should remove about 45-60 % of suspended solids	An Imhoff cone is filled to the liter mark with a thoroughly mixed sample; settled for 1.75 hr. The material clinging to sides is gently knocked down and settled 0.25 hr longer. The number of milliliters of settleable solids is then read on the Imhoff cone graduations
pH (hydrogen-ion concentration)	1. Raw sewage 2. Primary tank effluent 3. Final effluent 4. Sludge in settling tanks 5. Sludge	1. To reveal staleness and presence of industrial wastes in sewage (raw). To determine proper kinds of chemicals and dosage in chemical treatment plants for good coagulation and precipitation	1. pH values in raw sewage lower than the pH of the water supply indicate septic or stale sewage or presence of industrial wastes. pH values higher than that of the water supply also indicate industrial wastes	The hydrogen-ion concentration of sewage and sludge is determined by colorimetric methods (color comparison.) Color indicators for pH ranges between 5.2 and 9.6 are of greatest use. Sludge samples are diluted with

TABLE 9-4. INTERPRETATION OF SEWAGE ANALYSES AND SEWAGE-PLANT OPERATING RECORDS.*—(Continued)

Test	Sampling points	Reason for test	Analysis and interpretation of results	Brief procedure of test
		2, 3, 4. To determine pH in order to control conditions in the tanks by adding necessary chemical, so as to promote bacterial activity and prevent sludge bulking 5. To determine the condition of the sludge in the separate digestion tanks or in the digestion chamber of an Imhoff tank. To determine dosage for coagulation prior to vacuum filtration	In chemical treatment, the various coagulants give best results for specific ranges of pH. Coagulant pH ranges: aluminum sulfate (alum), 5.5–8.0; ferrous sulfate, 8.5–11.0; ferric sulfate, 5.0–11.0; ferric chloride, 5.0–11.0 For proper digestion of sludge, the pH value should be kept above 7.3. Values lower than 7.0 indicate an acid condition and should be corrected by addition of lime to digesters	nine times their volume of distilled water and allowed to settle. The supernatant is decanted and used for the determinations. Electrometric methods are used for more precise determinations
Total alkalinity ppm in terms of $CaCO_3$	1. Raw sewage primary 2. Tank effluent 3. Final effluent	To determine efficiency of chemical treatment plants	High values in raw sewage indicate industrial wastes. Domestic sewage is normally alkaline (approximately 20–40 ppm)	To a 100-ml sample of sewage 4 drops of methyl orange indicator is added, and the sample is titrated to the end point with $N/50$ sulfuric acid. The milliliters of acid used are multiplied by 10 to give parts per million of total alkalinity as calcium carbonate
Total acidity ppm in terms of $CaCO_3$	1. Raw sewage primary 2. Tank effluent 3. Final effluent	To determine efficiency of chemical treatment plants	High values in raw sewage indicate industrial wastes. Domestic sewage is normally alkaline (approximately 20–40 ppm)	10 drops of phenol-phthalein is added to a 100-ml sample of sewage, and the sample is titrated with $N/50$ sodium hydroxide until a permanent end point is reached. The calculation is the same as that for alkalinity
Sludge: 1. Moisture and total solids, % of sample of sludge	1, 2. Fresh sludge 1, 2, 3. In Imhoff tank and separ-	For control of sludge works, drying, vacuum filtration, digestion, or incineration	1. Moisture of fresh and digested sludge is usually between 85 and 99 % dependent upon the	1. 50 grams of sludge is weighed as rapidly as possible in a tarred evaporating dish and is

2. Ash and volatile matter, % of dry solids 3. Temperature of sludge in digesters	ate digestion tanks 1. Sludge bed before and after drying. Before and after vacuum filtration	process of treatment. In general the longer the sludge is digested and the greater the amount of supernatant removed, the less will be its moisture content. Vacuum filters and centrifuges will produce a sludge cake, with a moisture content between 55 and 85 % Sludge must be conditioned with chemicals prior to vacuum filtration. Doses of lime, 5–15 % of the dry solids, and doses of ferric chloride, 1–5 % of the dry solids, are generally effective When sludge is dewatered to 80 % moisture or less it may be mixed with garbage and rubbish and burned in an incinerator. High moisture content indicates ineffective concentration 2. High ash reflects grit or industrial wastes. Low reduction of volatiles during digestion indicates low efficiency of digestion 3. Best temperature for mesophilic (medium-temperature) digestion is 85–95°F and normally should be maintained in digesters. Best temperature for thermophilic (heat-loving) bacteria is 125°F	evaporated to dryness overnight in an oven at 103°C. It is then cooled in a dessicator; reweighed or evaporated on a water bath; dried at 103°C; cooled and weighed to constant weight 2. The residue from the determination of moisture is ignited in an electric muffle at 600°C (dull red heat) for 60 min and is then cooled in a dessicator and reweighed
Relative stability (putrescibility), or number of days required for decolorization	1. Filter effluent 2. Final effluent 3. Stream above 4. Stream below	To determine the percentage of oxygen available as dissolved nitrite nitrate, oxygen to the total oxygen required to satisfy the BOD	Fill a 150-ml glass-stoppered bottle with sample, avoiding aeration. Add exactly 0.4 ml of methylene blue indicator solution below the surface of the

TABLE 9-4. INTERPRETATION OF SEWAGE ANALYSES AND SEWAGE-PLANT OPERATING RECORDS.*—(Continued)

Test	Sampling points	Reason for test	Analysis and interpretation of results	Brief procedure of test
		To determine adequacy of treatment for discharge into receiving stream. This determination is being replaced by more exact tests, such as dissolved-oxygen, nitrite, nitrate, and BOD tests. For small plants with limited facilities it is useful for indicating satisfactory operation of biological oxidation processes		liquid. Incubate at 20°C with a water seal, observing the sample daily until decoloration takes place. Results are reported as follows: _Days_ _% Stability_ 1 21 3 50 5 68 7 80 10 90 12 94 14 96 16 97 18 98 20 99
Oxygen consumed (test now being largely superseded by BOD test), ppm	1. Raw sewage 2. Tank effluent 3. Final effluent	To measure plant efficiency in removing the organic matter which takes up oxygen from receiving stream. Used in conjunction with BOD test	As a result of these tests, sewage may be classified as: weak, 75 ppm; medium, 165 ppm; strong, 265 ppm. This classification influences the size of filters	A sample of sewage or effluent of 5–100 ml is poured into a 250-ml flask. Distilled water is added to bring the total volume to 100 ml. 10 ml of 1.3 sulfuric acid and 10 ml of a standardized potassium permanganate solution (1 ml = 0.1 mg of oxygen) are added. The flask is then submerged in boiling water for 30 min. 10 ml of an ammonium oxalate solution equivalent to the permanganate is added. The flask is removed from the bath and the sample is titrated with permanganate solution to a permanent-pink color. A blank

Determination	Point of sampling	Significance	Method
Dissolved oxygen (DO), ppm	1. Raw sewage 2. Filter and aerator effluent 3. Final effluent 4. Receiving stream above and below point of discharge of effluent	Presence of dissolved oxygen (DO), 1 ppm or more, in raw sewage usually indicates fresh sewage and sometimes infiltration. Stale and septic sewage contains no dissolved oxygen. Solubility of atmospheric oxygen in water in summer is about 5–7 ppm, in winter about 10–12 ppm	determination is run on distilled water. The oxygen-consumed value in parts per million is calculated by subtracting the number of milliliters of permanganate used for the blank determination from the number used in actual determination, multiplying by 1,000, and dividing by 10 times the volume of sample in milliliters

To check performance particularly of aeration tanks and filters

A 300-ml glass-stoppered bottle is filled completely with the sample. A minimum of disturbance is made, and precautions are taken to prevent the entrainment of air bubbles. 0.7 ml of concentrated sulfuric acid and 1 ml of potassium permanganate solution are added below the water surface. After the stopper is replaced, the bottle is shaken and allowed to stand for half an hour. The stopper is removed and 1 ml of ammonium oxalate solution is added, the stopper replaced, and the bottle reshaken

When the pink color disappears, the stopper again is removed and 2 ml of manganese sulfate and 3 ml of alkaline potassium iodide solution are added below the surface. The stopper is immediately replaced and the bottle thoroughly shaken. The precipitate that forms is allowed to settle; the stopper is removed and 1 ml of concentrated sulfuric

TABLE 9-4. INTERPRETATION OF SEWAGE ANALYSES AND SEWAGE-PLANT OPERATING RECORDS.*—(*Continued*)

Test	Sampling points	Reason for test	Analysis and interpretation of results	Brief procedure of test
				acid is added. Again the stopper is replaced and the bottle shaken until the precipitate is completely dissolved. Iodine is liberated in proportion to the amount of dissolved oxygen present. A 200-ml sample is withdrawn from the bottle and titrated with $0.125N$ sodium thiosulfate solution to the starch end point. The number of milliliters of sodium thiosulfate solution used is equivalent to the number of parts per million of dissolved oxygen present in the sample
Biochemical oxygen demand (BOD), parts per million	1. Raw sewage 2. Primary tank effluent 3. Filter effluent 4. Final effluent 5. Stream above 6. Stream below. 7. Digester supernatant	This is one of the basic methods of evaluation of plant efficiency and adequacy of receiving stream for the required dilution of the effluent	See Table 9-5 page 84 for average values of raw sewage and values and efficiency of removal to be expected from the various units and the plant as a whole. Higher values of BOD in raw sewage may indicate industrial waste or stale or concentrated sewage. For additional comments, see test on total suspended solids	The BOD of a sample of sewage is determined by making three dilutions of the sample with buffered distilled water saturated with dissolved oxygen and placing each dilution in a 300-ml glass-stoppered bottle which is filled to capacity. A bottle filled with the dilution water alone (blank) is included. The amount of dilution depends upon the strength of the sewage or effluent and is based on the estimated strength range. The bottles are incubated for 5 days at 20°C. On removal from the incubator, the amount of dissolved oxygen is determined for all samples. The

Determination	Object	Sample	Standard	Method
				parts per million of BOD is calculated for each dilution by subtracting the parts per million of dissolved oxygen in the dilution from that of the dilution-water blank, multiplying by 100, and dividing by the percentage dilution. Results from each dilution are averaged to give the final result
Chlorine residual, ppm	To determine whether sewage is being chlorinated sufficiently	Final effluent	15–30 min (depending on state health laws) after chlorination the chlorine residual should be 0.5 ppm	Residual chlorine is generally determined by the o-tolidine test although the starch-iodine test is sometimes used. o-Tolidine forms a yellow color with chlorine in acid solution. In making the determination 1 ml of o-tolidine is added to a 100 ml sample of sewage or effluent. After 15 min the color formed is compared with a series of standards in which the depth of color is equivalent to known amounts of chlorine
Ammonia nitrogen, ppm	To determine efficiency of filters and aeration tanks in nitrification and stabilization (changing N and NH_3 to NO_2 and NO_3)	1. Raw sewage 2. Filter or aeration-tank effluent 3. Final effluent	The following are the average parts per million of ammonia nitrogen in various strengths of raw sewage: weak, 4 ppm; medium, 12; strong, 22. High values in raw sewage indicate strong sewage or industrial wastes. Use results obtained for filter effluent and final effluent in conjunction with results of nitrate-nitrite test	100 ml of sample is placed in graduated cylinder and 1 ml of 10 % copper sulfate solution is added. The solution is mixed and 1 ml of 50 % sodium hydroxide solution is added. The solution is again mixed and precipitate is allowed to settle. A measured portion of the clear supernatant is pipetted into a Nessler tube. 2 ml of Nessler's solution is added and tube is filled to the mark with ammonia-free water. After 10 min the color formed is compared with

82 INDUSTRIAL WASTE TREATMENT

TABLE 9-4. INTERPRETATION OF SEWAGE ANALYSES AND SEWAGE-PLANT OPERATING RECORDS.*—(Continued)

Test	Sampling points	Reason for test	Analysis and interpretation of results	Brief procedure of test
Nitrates (NO_3) and nitrites, (NO_2), ppm	1. Raw sewage 2. Filter or aeration-tank effluent 3. Final effluent	To determine efficiency of filters and aeration tanks in nitrification and stabilization (changing nitrogen and NH_3 to NO_2 and NO_3)	Average NO_3 and NO_2 production from nitrogen and NH_3 by various processes is as follows: trickling filters, 2–13 ppm; sand filters, 4–12 ppm; activated sludge, 0.1–6 ppm; sedimentation or Imhoff tanks; 0 ppm; chemical treatment, 0 ppm	permanent or previously prepared standards of known ammonia-nitrogen content. From matched standard the parts per million of ammonia nitrogen in sample is calculated A 25-ml sample of effluent is placed in a small casserole, 2 ml of sodium hydroxide solution is added, and the mixture is slowly boiled down to half volume. The sample is then washed with ammonia-free water into a large pyrex test tube with a 100-ml calibration mark. The tube is filled to the mark with water and a strip of aluminum foil added. A stopper equipped with a Bunsen valve is fitted tightly into the tube. When the reaction has ceased and the liquor is clear, 50 ml is pipetted off. Aliquots of this sample are Nesslerized and compared with ammonia-nitrogen standards. From the matched standards, the parts per million of nitrogen as nitrite-nitrate is calculated

* Reprinted by permission from Elwyn E. Seelye, "Data Book for Civil Engineers," Vol. 1, Design, John Wiley & Sons, Inc., New York, 1945. These data were compiled by Seelye from original sources. BOD required (ppm) is generally less than total suspended solids (ppm).

Fresh sewage contains dissolved oxygen. BOD required contains dissolved oxygen. BOD requirement is generally higher than total suspended solids.

Stale sewage contains no dissolved oxygen. BOD requirement is generally higher than total suspended solids.

Septic sewage is undergoing putrefaction in the absence of oxygen. BOD requirement is generally equal to or slightly less than total suspended solids.

wastes, and recommending a method of treatment with appropriate sizes of plant units and estimated costs of operation so that the owner may study these suggestions, determine if they are suited to his purposes and his bank account, and later obtain prices on the structures and equipment required.   In such reports, a variety of treatment methods should be reported, especially if chemical precipitants are employed, as various combinations of chemicals produce different results.   Certain coagulants may be readily procurable in one locality and yet may be a scarce and expensive commodity in another; therefore, the plant owner should be permitted to select the method or process best suited to the local sources of supply.   Some textile and chemical plants use certain chemicals in their normal operations.   If one or more of these can be employed in the waste-treatment process, rather than others which may have to be purchased elsewhere, the owner will be assured of lower cost and uninterrupted operation of the plant, as he will usually have a supply of the needed chemicals.

The test report, in giving the results obtained with several types or combinations of precipitants and with various detention periods in settling tanks and other units, enables the engineer to evaluate these in terms of initial plant cost and operating expense.   It is frequently shown that a certain combination of precipitants will produce a good result with a relatively short period of detention, whereas a lesser amount of the same precipitant with a longer detention period in the tanks will produce the same result.   In the first case the initial plant cost would be less than for the latter, but the cost of precipitants would be greater. As the precipitants are a daily charge against the operation, the annual bill for them may amount to a considerable sum, whereas the initial cost of the tanks is an item of capital investment.   By putting in larger tanks and reducing the amount of chemical required, the over-all annual operating cost may be materially lowered.   This is fully explained in Chap. 4.

The plant owner who has engaged an investigator is entitled to all the information obtained in the study and should evaluate this carefully with his own engineers and, with his knowledge of his own processes and costs of production, determine for himself the solution which will best produce the results required by the authorities.   He should be equally frank and cooperative in giving the investigator all the data that may be required so that an intelligent and practical solution may be reached.   A reputable engineer will not divulge the plant processes which may be trade secrets of a given industrialist, and a complete knowledge of these processes may help materially in solving the problem.   Frequently, with such knowledge, an investigator may be able to indicate slight

TABLE 9-5. SEWAGE AND WASTE CHARACTERISTICS AND AVERAGE EFFICIENCIES OF PLANTS AND UNITS

Sewage or waste	Suspended solids		BOD	
	Lb per capita per day	Lb per employee per day	Lb per capita per day	Lb per employee per day
Separate sewer..................	0.17	....	0.12	
Combined sewer..................	0.33	....	0.25	
Tannery wastes..................	....	12.0	....	25.3
Chemical wastes.................	....	7.4	....	22.5
Organic wastes..................	....	2.4	....	2.9
Pickling-liquor wastes.............	....	3.8	....	3.6
Dye wastes......................	....	5.4	....	44.2
Laundry wastes..................	....	22.2	....	22.8
Distillery wastes.................	....	181.0	....	470.0
Dairy wastes....................	....	5.7	....	44.6
Miscellaneous...................	....	6.8	....	13.2

Approximate Efficiencies of Plant Units

Units	Suspended solids reduction, %	BOD reduction, %
Settling tank (2 hr).................................	45–60	30–45
Imhoff tank (2–3 hr)...............................	45–60	20–45
Trickling filter (low rate)..........................	10–30	55–75
Sedimentation tanks with slow sand filter............	90–98	85–92
Sedimentation tanks and standard low-rate trickling filter.	75–85	70–90
Sedimentation tanks with high-rate filter:		
Single-stage intermediate (clarifier and filter).........	75–85	50–60
Single-stage complete (clarifier, filter, clarifier in series).	85–90	85–90
Two-stage complete, (clarifier, filter, filter, clarifier in series).......................................	90–95	90–92
Activated-sludge process............................	85–95	80–95
Chemical precipitation..............................	65–90	45–75

changes in plant procedure which will reduce or may even eliminate certain wastes that may be difficult or costly to treat.

In making tests on industrial wastes, the procedure given in "Standard Methods for the Examination of Water and Sewage"[3] or in "Laboratory Manual for Chemical and Bacteriological Analysis of Water and Sewage"[6] is recommended.

Bibliography

1. New England Sewage Works Association, Report of Committee on Sewage Sampling, *Sewage Works Journal*, vol. 5, No. 5, pp. 826–843, September, 1933.

2. Heukelekian, H., Use of Direct Method of Oxygen Utilization in Waste Treatment Studies, *Sewage Works Journal*, vol. 19, p. 875, 1947.
3. Standard Methods for the Examination of Water and Sewage, American Public Health Association, 9th ed., 1946.
4. Analyzing Municipal and Industrial Wastes, Solvay Sales Corporation, Technical Bulletin 11.
5. Beal, G. D., and S. A. Braley, The Need for Uniformity in Methods of Analysis and Reporting Water Borne Industrial Wastes, Reprint, Bulletin of American Society for Testing Materials, June, 1949.
6. Theroux, F. R., E. F. Eldridge, and W. L. Mallman, "Laboratory Manual for Chemical and Bacteriological Analysis of Water and Sewage," 3d ed., McGraw-Hill Book Company, Inc., New York, 1943.
7. Ingols, R. S., J. C. Hildebrand, and G. M. Ridenour, Measuring the Strength of Sewages and Trade Wastes: B.O.D. or O.C.? *Water & Sewage Works*, vol. 97, p. 21, January, 1950.
8. Fischer, A. J., and G. E. Symons, The Determination of Settleable Solids by Weight, *Water Works and Sewerage*, vol. 91, p. 37, January, 1944.
9. Weil, B. H., P. E. Murray, G. W. Reid, and R. S. Ingolds, Bibliography on Water & Sewage Analysis, Special Report 28, State Engineering Experiment Station, Georgia Institute of Technology, Atlanta, Ga., 1948.
10. Mohlman, F. W., E. Hurwitz, and G. R. Garnett, Experience with Modified Methods for B.O.D., Paper, Symposium on Recent Research on Water, Sewage and Industrial Wastes, National Institute for Health, Washington, D.C., June, 23–24, 1949.
11. Ettinger, M. B., Analytical Procedures for Industrial Wastes, *Water & Sewage Works*, vol. 97, No. 7, pp. 292–294, July, 1950.
12. Moore, W. A., R. C. Kroner, and C. C. Ruchhoft, Dichromatic Reflux Method for Determination of Oxygen Demand, *Analytical Chemistry*, vol. 21, pp. 953–957, 1949.
13. Objectives for Boundary Water Quality Control, Board of Technical Advisers, International Joint Commission, U.S. Public Health Service, mimeographed, 1948.
14. Velz, C. J., Sampling for Evaluation of Stream Pollution, *Sewage & Industrial Wastes*, vol. 22, No. 5, p. 666, May, 1950.
15. Lovett, M., Some Notes on the Analysis of Sewage and Trade Effluents, Paper, Meeting North East Branch, Institute of Sewage Purification (England) Wakefield, England, Jan. 20, 1950.
16. Hauck, C. F., Sampling Industrial Wastes, *Public Works*, April, 1950, pp. 44–45.
17. Langelier, W. F., and D. H. Caldwell, Monometric Measurement of B.O.D. of Domestic and Industrial Sewage, Paper, Twentieth Annual Meeting Federation of Sewage Works Associations, San Francisco, Calif., July 21–24, 1947.
18. Kline, H. S., Samples for Industrial Waste Surveys, Paper, Fifth Industrial Waste Conference, Purdue University, Lafayette, Ind., Nov. 29–30, 1949.
19. Hatfield, W. D., Limitations, Interferences and Precautions in Analytical Determinations for Certain Toxic Wastes, Paper, Twenty-fourth Annual Conference Michigan Sewage Works Association, Traverse City, Mich., May 23–25, 1949.
20. Sample, J. A., Sampling Method for Industrial Wastes, Paper, Third Annual Meeting West Virginia Sewage & Industrial Wastes Association, Wheeling, W.Va., Sept. 20–22, 1949.
21. Lyman, R. R., Measurement of Flowing Streams, A Simple and Accurate Method of Using the Weir, Bulletin 5, Utah Engineering Experiment Station, September, 1912.

CHAPTER 10

COMBINING WASTES FROM SEVERAL PLANTS
TO REDUCE COSTS

Pollution of streams by industrial wastes is not usually caused by one plant. In the majority of cases several industries are involved. The wastes may be from industries of a like nature as sometimes happens in certain parts of the country. In certain sections of New England the entire industry of a given community may be textiles and allied crafts associated with textile production. In central and western Pennsylvania, the tanning industry is the dominant one. In Wisconsin, Michigan, and upper New York State the milk industry, with its associated industries of butter and cheese manufacture, will be exclusive in several areas. In Florida, certain parts of California, and throughout the Middle Western states the canning industry will prevail. In Pennsylvania, in and around Pittsburgh, steel mills cluster, and in North and South Carolina and Georgia textile mills will be the rule.

In sections where a particular industry prevails, much is to be said in favor of considering the waste problem as an industry problem rather than as an individual-plant problem, and general studies can be made on the wastes of several plants performing similar operations, although their actual processes may differ slightly. In a number of such cases, the industries themselves have banded together into an association and have set up research groups and laboratories and, in some instances, pilot plants in which special studies are made on the wastes peculiar to that industry.

The principal objective of these investigational groups is usually two-fold: (1) to endeavor to work out a method or methods of treatment which will satisfactorily treat the wastes of the entire industry at a moderate cost, and (2) to investigate the possibilities of recovery of valuable ingredients in the wastes, which may be reused to reduce plant operating costs. The paper industry and the distillery and fermentation-products industry offer the greatest hope of recovering or developing by-products of value from the wastes. The result not only reduces the pollution factor but at the same time returns an income to the plant which partially, at least, offsets the cost of the treatment. The chemists and engineers of these groups, being conversant with the processes used in these industries, have concentrated on the problems of their industry and, in numerous cases, have developed worth-while methods both for treatment and recovery. Each member of such an association contributes a small part of the total cost of the research work, and in this manner more and better work can be done than if an individual plant were to attempt it alone.

Another factor in this group effort is one of policy, as a strong group of this nature backed by an entire industry will gain the confidence of the authorities, who will usually willingly cooperate with them to grant the time necessary to work out the problems in an orderly manner, satisfactory both to the plant owners from the financial standpoint and to the authorities from the viewpoint of elimination of pollution. These industry groups can aid in the formulation of intelligent legislation or prevent confiscatory legislation which does not always work to the public benefit. In general, it can be said that today the industries realize that they cannot continue to pollute the streams; therefore they are willing to engage in a sincere effort, collectively, to ascertain what can be done with their wastes at a moderate cost. In this way, they not only serve the public in a worthy manner but also benefit themselves in good will and actual expense. A result of such an effort is the National Council for Stream Improvement set up by the pulp and paper industry to study the wastes of the various elements of that industry and to work out methods of treatment. At the same time, they study the recovery problem and ascertain what by-products can be economically recovered from the wastes and perhaps sold at a profit. In some instances, this research has revealed previously unknown or unexplored sources of materials for which there is a present or possible demand. This has been particularly true in the distillery industry where cattle food has been produced from the spent grains and liquors of the plants. Yeast is also a by-product of the same industry.

This group research also leads to a determination of the possibility of grouping plant wastes, not only because a single large plant to treat a considerable volume of wastes may be built and operated at lower cost than a number of smaller plants, with lessened cost to the individual plant owner, but also because wastes of different character may be used in a large group plant to react with other wastes and thus produce necessary plant operations without recourse to outside purchased reagents or precipitants.

To illustrate, a waste which is acid and would normally require lime or another alkali for neutralization may be combined with a waste of high alkalinity from another plant, which will serve as the neutralizing agent at no cost except for the pipe line to bring the two together. In other cases, wastes having a high solids content which require coagulants to precipitate them may be combined with wastes having constituents of coagulating value, and so the effect will be obtained at little cost, whereas otherwise coagulants would have to be purchased. In still other cases, wastes of small volume and high BOD from one plant may be combined with wastes from another plant having a large liquid volume and low BOD to produce a final effluent which by dilution may have a BOD within the limits of the established maxima; at least this dilution may reduce the BOD to a point where the combined wastes may be readily and economically treated by normal biological methods.

For instance, assume a waste with a volume of 100,000 gallons per day and a BOD of 1,000 ppm. This waste will contribute a total of 834 pounds of BOD per day. If the maximum BOD to meet the requirement for discharge into a stream or into a municipal sewerage system is 300 ppm, it would be necessary to treat this waste to bring the final effluent down to 300 ppm, a reduction of 70 per cent. This treatment may entail the construction of an expensive plant. On the other hand, if there is within reasonable distance a plant which has a waste volume of 1 million gallons per day with a BOD of only 200 ppm, the two wastes may be combined, with the result that the final effluent, without any further treatment, will have a BOD of slightly over 272 ppm, or sufficient to bring it within the established maximum. The only expense will be for the pipe line to bring the wastes together and the tank in which the wastes are mixed.

In many industrial areas where a variety of types of plants exist, proper study of all the wastes before any action is taken might well lead to the development of a group plant, which would be economical for each industry concerned and at the same time solve the pollution problem. In many cases a group-treatment plant, by its use of natural reactions between the wastes, would turn out an effluent which could be readily handled by the local sewerage facilities without requiring extensive alterations or additions to these works at public expense.

As it has become a recognized principle that industrial plants should pay a fair charge for the handling of their wastes in municipal sewage-treatment works, and as criteria of the conditions under which such wastes will be received are set up, the group plant, by turning out a waste effluent within the limits set by the municipality, would save considerable annual expense to the group members by making it possible to set up a standard charge on a volume basis for the wastes taken into the public system. At the present time, an industry discharging a high-concentration waste into a municipal system may be required to put in a pretreatment works at its own plant to reduce the strength of its wastes to the norm set by the municipality. With a group plant, utilizing the reactive powers of the individual wastes, this norm would be easier to achieve and would, in many cases, relieve the individual plant owner of the necessity and expense of constructing pretreatment works. The possibility of such a group plant is a good argument for industries in a given locality, faced with a general pollution cleanup, to form an industrial research group, in which each industry as a member could study its individual and collective problems and work out combinations which would achieve the desired result. The individual cost of participation in such a collective group would be small, and the ultimate individual share in the construction and operating cost of the group plant would likewise be reduced. Where such a group plant could be established, it would be operated by a staff supported by the members, and the unit cost per member would be very much less than if each manufacturer had his own small plant with the total initial and operating cost solely his responsibility. It is regrettable that this idea has not been more carefully explored in congested industrial districts where a variety of plants exist. The units of a group plant would of course be larger than those for individual installations, but it is a well-known fact that the cost of a large plant is always less on a unit basis (*i.e.*, per million gallons treated) than a small independent plant or a number of small plants having the same total capacity as the one large one. In the operation of a large plant there is also a considerable economy, as such a plant may be operated by a relatively small total staff, whereas each individual plant must have its own staff. A further saving in a group plant is in equipment and electric-current usage.

Assume a group of 10 small individual plants, of a similar character, with 5 motors in each plant, or a total of 50 motors. A large plant, unless of very unusual size, would probably have the same number of motors, or a total of 5 against the total of 50 in the individual units. Again assume that the 5 motors of each individual plant total 5 horsepower. For the 10 plants this is 50 hp. In the large plant with modern well-designed equipment, the total horsepower of the 5 motors required would probably not be over 15. This shows a clear saving of 35 horsepower. The 10 small plants, with all motors running 24 hours per day, would require a total input of 895 kilowatt-hours of current per day, or a grand total of 326,775 kilowatt-hours per year. On the other hand, the large single plant with 24-hour operation of all units would require only 96,820 kilowatt-hours per year, a clear yearly saving of 229,955 kilowatt-hours, which not only represents an item of consequence in operation cost, but also releases that much power for use by other industries. Likewise, if the wastes have an organic content which responds to modern digestion methods, sufficient digestion-tank gas would be produced to warrant the installation of a gas-engine generator set which could probably develop all the power required to run the larger plant. Each small plant would not produce sufficient gas to warrant the cost of an engine-generator installation.

In order to arrive at a proper evaluation of all the factors to be considered in combining several wastes or combining all wastes into a group plant, individual studies and tests must be made on the individual wastes, as to composition, volume of flow, periodicity of flow, characteristics of the wastes, color, BOD, acidity, alkalinity, etc., and proper combinations tried out to determine the exact nature of the reactions that would take place and to act as a guide in the design of a plant to handle the joint flow. This points to a survey of the wastes of all the plants in a given area and a thorough study of all the data collected to guide the investigators and engineers to a reasonable conclusion.

A check list for the composition of industrial wastes that was used in California[3] is given below to indicate the factors that should be taken into consideration in making a comprehensive study of industries in a given locality.

1. Volume.
    a. Daily.
    b. Hourly.
    c. If uniform daily through the year.
    d. If uniform hourly but seasonal.
    e. High hourly peak.
    f. High daily peak.
2. Chemical characteristics.
    a. Biological.
        (1) Bacteria.
        (2) BOD
        (3) Disinfecting ingredients.
        (4) Fungi.
        (5) Toxicity.
    b. Mineral.
        (1) Acidity and alkalinity.
        (2) Acid sludge.
        (3) Brine.
        (4) Coagulant ingredients.
        (5) Dissolved oxygen.
        (6) Metallic ions (iron, copper, manganese, alumina, arsenic, lead, zinc, etc.).
        (7) Nitrates.
        (8) Sulfates.

    (9) Chlorides.
   (10) Total suspended solids.
   (11) Total dissolved solids.
   (12) Organic matter.
  c. Organic.
    (1) Amines.
    (2) Catalysts—inhibitors.
    (3) Chlorine requirement.
    (4) Gelatinous matter.
    (5) Grease.
    (6) Hydrocarbons.
    (7) Pulp or fibers.
    (8) Soaps, detergents.
    (9) Starch.
3. Physical.
  a. Corrosivity.
  b. Color.
  c. Oil.
  d. Sediment—silt.
  e. Temperature.
  f. Volatile compounds.

Another form for such a survey and the composite sheet for the collected data were devised by the author after consultation with the health authorities of the city of São Paulo, Brazil, for use in making a comprehensive and complete survey of the more than 800 individual industrial plants in and around that bustling industrial city of the Southern Hemisphere. This form comprised the following data:

1. Name of plant.
2. Nature of industry.
3. Products manufactured.
4. Main materials used in manufacture.
5. Source of water supply used in the industry.
6. Volume of daily flow of wastes.
7. Period of flow.
8. Nature of residual liquors (wastes).
  a. Composition.
  b. Acid or alkaline.
  c. Temperature.
  d. Color.
  e. Odor.

  f. Toxic.

  g. Forms slime banks in stream.

9. Treatment given (if any).

  This study led to the collection of a great mass of data which has been extremely useful to the sewage authorities of São Paulo in formulating a general program of sewage and industrial-waste treatment for the city to protect the waters of the small Tiete River, which is the sole point of discharge for the sewage and wastes of the vicinity, the entire flow of which is very little in excess of the daily volume of sewage and wastes discharged into it.

Bibliography

1. Pickett, A. M., W. A. Schneider, R. Pomeroy, and A. M. Rawn, Industry Waste Disposal Studied in Los Angeles, Conférence, Southern California Section Institute of Food Technologists, Los Angeles, reviewed, *Engineering News-Record*, vol. 139, No. 2, p. 132, July 10, 1947.
2. Besselievre, E. B., and A. Anable, Liquid Wastes from Industrial Plants and Their Treatment, *Transactions, American Institute of Chemical Engineers*, vol. 27, p. 122, 1931.
3. A Report of Procedure for the Handling of Industrial Wastes, The Committee on Industrial Wastes of the California Sewage Works Association, *California Sewage Works Journal*, vol. 17, No. 1, pp. 47–84, 1945.

CHAPTER 11

THE POLLUTIONAL EFFECT OF VARIOUS WASTES

All liquids which may be classed as industrial wastes, *i.e.*, liquid effluents discharged from an industrial plant or operation, are not necessarily pollutional, nor do they all have a detrimental effect upon streams into which they are discharged. But many of them, in fact the great majority of industrial effluents, do have some pollutional character.

Cooling waters, which are classed as industrial wastes, normally have no effect upon a stream or sewage-treatment plant, except that in the latter case they may be in such volume as to overload the units of the plant which are based on flow rates. In general, unless the sewerage-system and treatment-plant facilities are so greatly in excess of the actual needed capacity that they will be able to handle this type of waste, these waters should not be discharged into sewer systems but should be discharged directly into adjacent streams or bodies of water.

However, in these times of water shortages, thought should be given to the reuse of this cooling water rather than to waste it into the streams. Usually, these waters are in considerable volume, and if water is purchased and used once only for cooling, the industry could make a considerable saving by the repeated reuse of this water. Ponds or towers to cool this water to the point where it may be reused would soon pay for themselves in cases where the water must be purchased from a municipal supply. Also, if the water is reused, the drain on the local supply is lessened and more water is available for potable and other household uses by the people of the community. In a city in which many industries use water for cooling purposes, the saving to the municipality by the reduction of consumption for this purpose would be considerable and could very well eliminate the need for the procurement of other sources of supply. As water is usually sold to industrial plants at a lower rate than that charged the householder, the total revenue to the municipality from the sale of this extra amount of water at the higher rate would be appreciable.

Many large industrial plants have their own wells, and many located adjacent to large streams frequently draw their cooling waters directly from these sources, which, of course, does not impose any burden on the local municipal supply; so there is not the same urgency upon the industry to economize in its use of water.

There is, however, another situation to be considered, namely, where large industries, such as power plants, draw a large daily volume of water from a source which is also the source of the local municipal supply. After this water has served its purpose for cooling, it may be treated in a normal type of water-treatment plant, to remove the constituents which may make it unsuitable for potable purposes, and then supplied to the populace. By this combination of usages, it is frequently possible for a municipality to eliminate the expense of the pumping plants which it would normally construct to elevate the water from the stream. The power utility would construct these pumping stations at its expense, thus relieving the municipality of the heavy pumping charge. To make this procedure attractive, the municipality could afford to recompense the utility for the water.

As stated above, however, the great proportion of the waste discharges from an industrial plant have some pollutional or contaminating character which makes it necessary to treat them before they are discharged into a stream or into a local sewerage system. Therefore, careful investigation must be made before any wastes are accepted into a sewerage system or are permitted to be discharged into a local stream.

As pointed out earlier, the extent to which wastes must be treated depends upon several factors. These are, briefly, as follows:

1. The size and use of the receiving stream.
2. The volume of wastes as compared with the minimum flow in the stream.
3. The proximity of the nearest downstream municipality which uses the same stream or body of water as a source of potable water.
4. The condition of the receiving stream.
5. The classification of the stream, if stream classification is in force in the particular state.
6. The characteristics of the wastes and their possible effect on the use of the stream.
   a. For potable-water supplies.
   b. For recreation.
   c. For navigation.
   d. By other downstream industries.
7. The effects of the wastes on structures in and near the stream.
8. The possible effect on the local sewerage system, including the sewage-treatment works, both as to the capacity of these to handle the volume of flow and the possible effect on the units and processes employed in the sewage works.

Let us discuss these various factors.

It is readily seen that, if the receiving stream is one of small volume at maximum flow and reduced volume at minimum flow, the discharge into it of a large volume of wastes which produces a low ratio of dilution or of wastes which ccntain elements that will deplete the oxygen in the water or cause sludge banks will effect the stream for its ultimate use as a source of potable water for a downstream municipality. It is true that, with modern advances in water-purification methods, the water of almost any stream may be so treated as to render it usable again, but such treatment imposes a heavy burden of expense upon the community, out of proportion to that which would be necessary if the stream were not so grossly polluted. In practically every state of the union, and in many foreign countries, it is now recognized that the responsibility of every manufacturer or industrial-plant owner is to so treat any wastes discharged into a stream that they will not deteriorate the quality of that stream to an extent that will render it unduly costly or difficult for downstream users to enjoy it. Many authorities have established limits or maxima for the constituents of industrial wastes before they may be discharged into public streams or into local sewerage systems.

Noteworthy in this advance is the authority[21] governing the district adjacent to and including Pittsburgh, Pa., which has established the maximum limits for the constituents of industrial wastes suitable for discharge into the public sewerage systems of the district. These limits, given in Table 11-1, are so designed that the wastes will not upset the

TABLE 11-1. MAXIMUM LIMITS FOR CONSTITUENTS OF INDUSTRIAL WASTES FOR DISCHARGE INTO PUBLIC SEWERAGE SYSTEMS*

	Primary treatment		Secondary treatment
	No digestion	With digestion	
pH index..................	5.0	6.5	6.5
Total iron, ppm.............	5.0	5.0	5.0
Copper, ppm................	3.0	1.0	1.0
Chromium, ppm.............	5.0	5.0	3.0
Cyanide, ppm...............	2.0	2.0	2.0

Oils:	
Mineral.................	Should be excluded by ordinance
Soluble.................	Remove to maximum practical extent before discharge
Combustibles.............	Should be excluded by ordinance
Free mineral acids..........	To be neutralized at their source
Acetylene-generator sludge..	Should be excluded by ordinance
Pickling-liquor wastes.......	Should be excluded by ordinance

* Established by the authority that governs the district adjacent to and including Pittsburgh, Pa.

operation of the sewage-treatment works that are proposed for the municipalities of this district.

To indicate that this trend for regulation is not confined to the United States, we can cite the code established in Argentina by the Obras Sanitarias de la Nacion (Sanitary Works of the Nation),[22] which is a governmental body having general jurisdiction over the water supply, sewage, and general sanitation of the great majority of the cities and towns of that nation. This organization, in order to protect its water supplies and sewage-treatment works against indiscriminate discharges by the rapidly multiplying industrial plants of the country, has set up the following rules, entitled "Physical, Chemical and Microbiological Conditions to Which Sewage and Industrial Waste Discharges Shall Be Adjusted":

Art. 2. For factories or industrial establishments which produce liquid residues, it is not permitted to discharge into neighboring streams wastes which do not meet the following requirements:
1. There shall be presented to the general government a report in writing showing the type of industry, the class of wastes, their detailed composition, and all other data relative to the material.
2. The National Department of Hygiene will expedite its report in each case in accordance with the following requirements:
There shall not be discharged into the rivers factory and industrial wastes that contain per liter
   a. 5 to 10 ppm solids in suspension.
   b. 3 ppm organic or ammoniacal nitrogen.
   c. Liquids which require more than 2 ppm permanganate of potassium to oxidize all the organic components.
   d. 2 ppm hydrosulfuric acid or soluble sulfur.
   e. 5 ppm hydrosulfuric acid or hydrochloric acid or a free alkali.
   f. 0.05 ppm chlorine or free sulfurous acid.
   g. 0.01 ppm combined arsenic.
   h. 10.0 ppm sulfate of zinc or iron.
   i. 30.0 ppm alum or potassic iron.
   j. 200 ppm chloride or calcium or magnesium.
   k. 500 ppm sodium chloride.
   l. 0.05 ppm products of distillation of fossil coal.
   m. For small streams, hot water above 68°F.
Art. 3. In all doubtful cases beyond the interpretation of the present law, the national department of hygiene shall decide the point.

By a decree of Jan. 23, 1948, the following additional specific regulations were established:

A. Discharge into sewer mains.
   1. Temperature. Not over 104°F. Tolerance, +6.8°F.
   2. pH. Between 7.0 and 10.0. Tolerance on minimum limit, −0.5; on maximum limit, +0.5.

3. Settleable solids (10 minutes). Not admitted if of high specific gravity (sand, silica, etc.).

   In other cases, up to 5 cubic centimeters. Tolerance, 20 per cent.

4. Settleable solids (in 2 hours). The nature, aspect, and volume shall be taken into account. If compact, not over 250 cubic centimeters. If not compact, any quantity. Tolerance, 20 per cent.

5. Greasy substances, tar, resin, etc. (substances soluble in cold ethyl alcohol), not over 100 ppm. Tolerance, 20 per cent.

Not admitted into sewers—wastes containing

   a. Toxic or malodorous gases or substances capable of producing odors.

   b. Substances which may produce inflammable or explosive gases.

   c. Residues of wool, hair, oakum, rags, or coarse bodies capable of producing obstructions or incrustations.

   d. Substances which by their products of decomposition or combination may produce obstructions.

   e. Residues resulting from the purification of wastes (sludges).

   f. Substances which by their nature or quantity cause difficulty or interfere with the purification processes in a treatment plant, or with the process of autopurification in the receiving stream.

White water.

   Not admitted into the sewers.

B. Discharge into storm drains and their branches.

   In exceptional cases and only when the storm drain is the only possible means of discharge for the industrial wastes, the discharge may be authorized when the liquid is adjusted to the following requirements:

1. Temperature. Not over 104°F. Tolerance, 6.8°F.

2. pH. Between 7.0 and 9.0. Tolerance for minimum limit, −0.5; for maximum limit, +0.5.

3. Settleable solids (10 minutes). The residual liquid shall not contain settleable solids in 10 minutes.

4. Settleable solids (in 2 hours). Shall not be admitted in quantity when over 30 cubic centimeters per liter. Tolerance, 20 per cent.

5. BOD. Not over 50 ppm. Tolerance, 10 per cent.

6. Total oxygen consumed. Not over 30 ppm. Tolerance, 10 per cent.

7. Residual chlorine. Those liquids which by their origin would produce contamination shall be chlorinated before discharge in a manner which, within 20 minutes after the operation, shall show in the water a minimum concentration of 0.5 ppm residual chlorine.

Industrial wastes which contain the following shall not be admitted into storm drains:

(Same as 1 to 5 of Section *A*, plus)

Colored liquids or those with offensive odors.

C. Discharge direct into watercourses.

   Industrial wastes resulting from industry may be discharged directly into watercourses of an already polluted nature, or on previous authorization from the National Executive Power, only if the wastes discharged conform to the following characteristics:

1. Temperature. Not over 122°F. Tolerance, 6.8°F.
2. pH. Between 5.5 and 8.5. Tolerance for minimum limit, −0.5; for maximum limit, +0.5.
3. Settleable solids (in 10 minutes). No effluent shall contain more than 5 cubic centimeters per liter. Tolerance, 20 per cent.
4. Settleable solids (in 2 hours). No effluent shall contain more than 150 cubic centimeters per liter. Tolerance, 20 per cent.
5. Total oxygen consumed. Not over 30 ppm. Tolerance, 10 per cent.
6. BOD. Not over 50 ppm. Tolerance, 10 per cent.

Industrial effluents which contain the following ingredients shall not be discharged into watercourses:
(Same as *A* and *B*)

Similar regulations to control the composition of wastes entering sewerage systems and public waters have been instituted by other authorities. The authorities of Peabody and Salem, Mass., a district given heavily to the leather and glue industries, require that all wastes must be treated to a point where the suspended solids in the final effluent do not exceed a maximum of 300 ppm.

As the control of industrial-waste pollution is extended and strengthened, it is probable that all state and other agencies controlling streams and municipal sewerage systems will adopt regulations along similar lines; so it will be well for any industrial-plant owner to investigate this phase before proceeding with any work. It will, in many cases, be more economical for an industry to reduce its wastes to the required standard at their source, if by that means they can then be discharged into municipal systems, than to install complete treatment works of its own. The criterion in this will be the ability of the local municipal system to carry the added load, without extensive additions or improvements to the works which will entail the expenditure of capital funds, and the local policy toward the encouragement of industry, as shown by the municipality being willing to bear some of the burden of expense.

In some cases, where large streams exist, and the volume of industrial waste is small compared with the normal stream flow, and where the usage of the stream will permit discharge of raw wastes, the dilution ratio may be such as to permit the discharge of wastes which do not discolor the water, cause deposits, or obstruct the normal flow of the stream. This is a matter for determination by the authorities concerned. In certain cases, as in Pennsylvania, the streams of the state have been classified as to their future use, their past usage, and their present condition. Where streams have been classified as "polluted" and "not suitable for use as potable sources" and the extent of industrial activity seems to indicate a continued use of those streams as depositories for industrial wastes, certain wastes may be discharged into them with little or no treatment. In other cases, where an industry is located close to a stream which is classified against the discharge of polluting wastes and there is, not far distant, a stream of the classification "polluted and suitable for discharge of wastes," it may pay the industry to investigate the possibility of piping the wastes to the second stream rather than build a waste-treatment plant to produce an effluent suitable for discharge into the first stream.

Wastes with heavy organic loads are detrimental to streams in which fish life is encouraged, as the decomposing organic matter depletes the oxygen of the stream to such an extent that fish life is inhibited. Heavy organic loads also form deposits which not only give rise to obnoxious odors, but may in time cause obstructions, which in flood periods may cause the stream to overflow at points above the obstruction, causing damage to land and residences.

Wastes with a high color content are obnoxious in many streams, particularly those used for recreation or as potable-water sources. In these cases if the wastes contain little else but color, it is usually sufficient to reduce the color by treatment to a point where dilution with the water of the stream will cause it to be unnoticeable. In certain cases, this may be accomplished by reducing the color in the plant to a definite degree and then piping some of the receiving stream water to a mixing chamber to combine with the waste effluent so that the final mixture entering the stream has little or no visible color.

Wastes with a high acid content should be neutralized before discharge into a stream which is the source of potable water as the acid content will affect the treatment processes of downstream municipalities using the stream. Also, if tannic acid is present in the wastes and the stream contains an appreciable amount of iron, a reaction causing a black discoloration of the water will take place as the result of the formation of tannate of iron.

Wastes which are discharged into streams used for recreation, for bathing or boating, etc., should be treated so as not to produce obnoxious odor in the water, or deposit floating solids which would interfere with bathing, or have in them any acids or other chemical elements which will cause irritation to the skin, eyes, ears, nose, or throat of the bathers, or cause discoloration of the water.

Discolored water is not necessarily harmful, but the average person does not realize this and is very prone to mistrust a water which is not clear when he uses it for bathing purposes. A crystal-clear water may be dangerous if it contains bacteria or disease organisms, whereas a colored water may be entirely safe. But the aesthetic sense of the bather is offended by the discoloration and is reassured by clarity.

Wastes which contain high percentages of solid matters, whether these matters are of an organic nature or are entirely inert, may cause severe interference with navigation in small rivers. By being deposited in the stream or in the backwater in docks, the sediment gradually accumulates and reduces the available draught for vessels. In many streams, this deposit entails continuous dredging of the channels and docks, which is a continuing expense for the authorities. An example of this condition occurred in the Schuylkill and Susquehanna rivers in Pennsylvania, which traverse the coal regions. The waste waters from the numerous coal washeries carried off a considerable amount of fine coal which eventually settled in the river bed. In some sections of these rivers, this bed of fine coal was 3 to 6 feet deep, and numerous small operators made their living dredging the streams for the reclamation of this fine coal, much of which was sold to local power companies for use in their steam plants. As this bed of fine material moved slowly and continuously down the rivers, an operator could stay in one spot for a considerable length of time. In recent years, the authorities of Pennsylvania have made strenuous efforts to stop this discharge of waste, and many of the coal companies have installed plants to remove the fine material from their wastes before discharge into the stream. The effect of this cleanup upon the two rivers has been very impressive.

Wastes which contain acids or which have a high organic content subject to decomposition may cause damage to structures along the stream. The acids will attack iron and steel and concrete piers and structures, as well as wooden piles and other structures actually located in the water. Boat bottoms will suffer from this contact and will require seasonal painting and attention. In the Passaic River in New Jersey, before the cleanup program of the Passaic Valley Sewerage Commission was initiated, the gases formed by decomposition of organic matter discharged into the river from the many textile mills destroyed the paint on buildings adjacent to the stream.

Another cause of trouble from indiscriminate pollution by industrial wastes is the effect upon the processes of downstream industries by the wastes discharged from industries above. In some cases numerous industries of various types utilize the waters of a certain stream in their process work. If an upstream industry discharges a waste which contains chemicals or other elements which affect the product or process of the downstream user, this user may have just cause in the common law of the inherent rights of a riparian owner against the upstream polluter. In all cases it is advisable for the engineer or investigator to survey the industries downstream that use the stream and to devise a method of treatment which will render the discharge of the mill he is investigating free of any elements which will be likely to affect the processes of the downstream users. A little foresight in this regard and perhaps a slightly greater expense for the upstream mill owner, or the use of a different method of treatment, may save the upstream owner considerable later cost and trouble in defending suits for damages that might be brought against him by downstream users who could show good evidence of damage due to elements in the wastes from the upper plant. An example of such a case occurred in New Jersey and is discussed in Chap. 2.

Wastes taken into sewerage systems have a variety of deleterious effects and must be carefully studied. Wastes with a high fat or grease content cause deposits on the sewer pipes which reduce their size and cut down their capacity. Acid wastes may seriously affect concrete pipes and structures of the system. Wastes with high solids loads cause deposits which, on decomposing, may cause dangerous accumulations of toxic or explosive gases or obstructions which will reduce the capacity of the sewers and may cause backing up of sewage into the house systems of residences.

Wastes taken into municipal sewage-treatment plants usually require some degree of treatment, which varies according to the size, capacity, and type of plant available. Acid wastes are detrimental to the structures of these plants, and where biological processes are employed, they act as inhibitors to the natural action. They interfere with the bacterial action in filter beds and with the digestion of the sludge. Wastes with various chemical constituents also interfere with the biological processes. Wastes with high solids content cause difficulty in the solids-handling sections of plants by producing heavy scum accumulations and abnormal sludge volumes. If these solids are of an inert nature, they will cause unnecessary and troublesome deposits in sedimentation tanks, digestion units, etc., thus reducing the available volume of these units for their designed purpose, the handling and digestion of organic matter. Wastes with high percentages of organic matter will usually not cause any difficulty in the sedimentation section of a sewage-treatment plant but may make it necessary to provide additional sludge-digestion capacity and to enlarge the sludge-drying and handling facilities. If the sewage-treatment plant has not been designed to handle these additional heavy loads, the reception of such wastes may cause difficulties in the digestion tanks, entailing extensive and tricky control measures or the provision of greater capacity. These high organic wastes may cause an increase in the gas production in the digestion phase of several times that of the normal sewage for which the plant was designed, thus requiring revision and additions to the gas-control and handling elements.

If a sewage-treatment plant is to be designed with the idea that it will be called upon to handle a considerable volume of industrial wastes, the method of treatment employed should be carefully selected. Certain of the recognized methods of sewage treatment are more susceptible to upset from industrial-waste flows than others, and certain methods are more able to handle shock loads of industrial wastes with high BOD than others.

As the item of most concern in rendering an industrial waste suitable for discharge into a stream is its avidity for oxygen, most of the processes recognized as practical are based upon the reduction of the BOD to a point where the stream or the sewage-treatment plant will not be seriously affected. In the design of plants to handle industrial wastes as well as sewage, the accepted method of design study is to reduce the industrial wastes, from the standpoint of BOD, to a strength equivalent to a number of units of the normal sewage population. Normal domestic sewage in the United States has a BOD of 200 and 250 ppm, which corresponds on a population basis to approximately 0.17 to 0.20 pound of BOD per capita per day. In other countries where the volume of water used per capita per day is much less than that used in the United States, averaging as low as 25 to 60 gallons per capita per day, the average BOD per capita may range from 0.24 to 0.29 pound per capita per day.

Practically all industrial wastes have a higher BOD concentration than normal domestic sewage. The BODs of many industrial wastes are given in Tables 11-2, 11-3, 11-5, 11-6, and 11-7. To reduce the BOD of a waste to the equivalent of normal sewage on a population basis, which facilitates the design of plant units provided for the reduction of BOD and of the units provided for sludge digestion and handling, it is common practice to reduce the waste BOD to a "population equivalent."

A convenient formula for accomplishing this is

$$PE = \frac{F \times B \times 8.34}{X}$$

where PE = population equivalent of the waste in question
F = flow (total) or volume of wastes per day in millions of gallons or fraction thereof
B = BOD of the waste in question, expressed in parts per million
8.34 = weight in pounds of 1 ppm
X = unit of normal sewage strength in pounds of BOD per capita, such as 0.17 or 0.20 used

For example, let us assume an industrial waste with the following characteristics:

F = 100,000 gallons per day, or 0.1 million gallons per day
B = 5,000 ppm
X = 0.17 pound per capita per day

Then the formula becomes

$$PE = \frac{0.1 \times 5,000 \times 8.34}{0.17} \quad \text{or} \quad \frac{4,170}{0.17} = 24,529 \text{ persons}$$

Therefore, 100,000 gallons of the waste is equal to the normal sewage strength contributed by 24,529 persons, and the units of a plant to reduce the BOD must be designed on that basis, although the actual population of the municipality in which the industry is located may be only several thousand people.

In some cases, as shown in Table 11-2, it is common to assume units of flow for units of work done in industrial plants, and to calculate the BOD on the basis of the unit. Therefore, for a plant of a given type, say a slaughterhouse where the unit basis is per animal killed, the potential total strength of the wastes of another similar establishment may be figured by multiplying the number of animals killed per day by the unit of BOD per animal unit to obtain an idea of the total BOD produced by the wastes.

In cases where the volume of sewage treated per day is much in excess of the volume of industrial wastes, the sewage and waste may be combined and this combined discharge spread over the entire day so that the average per hour load of BOD would be lessened. Thus, assume a sewage-treatment plant designed to treat 5.0 million gallons of normal sewage per day and to handle 100,000 gallons of industrial wastes per day with a BOD of 5,000 ppm. Assume the normal sewage to have a BOD of 300 ppm; use the norm of 0.17 pound of BOD per capita per day for the sewage.

The basis of design then, for units of the plant handling the BOD, would be

$$PE = \frac{[(5.0 \times 300) + (0.1 \times 5,000)] \times 8.34}{0.17}$$

or

$$\frac{1,500 + 500 = 2,000 \times 8.34}{0.17}$$

or

$$\frac{16,680}{0.17} = 98,117 \text{ persons}$$

In this case, the design for normal sewage alone, using the same factors as above, would have been

$$PE = \frac{5.0 \times 300 \times 8.34}{0.17}$$

TABLE 11-2. POPULATION EQUIVALENTS OF VARIOUS INDUSTRIAL WASTES

Type of waste	Unit	Liquid volume of waste, gal per unit	BOD (5 days) Lb per unit	BOD (5 days) Ppm	Suspended solids Lb per unit	Suspended solids Ppm	Grease, lb per unit	Population equivalent per unit
Air-conditioning wash*	100 cu ft water	750	0.85	......	0.60	......	0.19	8
Cannery:								
Apricots (peeled) (lye)	1 ton	2,511.5	7.90	......	......	......	......	76
Apricots (no lye)	1 ton	2,511.5	4.16	......	5.41	......	......	40
Asparagus (no trim)	1 ton	6,337.5	3.9	......	1.6	......	......	38
Asparagus (trim macerated)	1 ton	7,650.0	73.0	......	76.0	......	4.4	700
Asparagus†	Case of No. 2 cans	70.0	100.0	......	30.0	......	......	0.35
Apricots†	Case of No. 2 cans	80.0	1,020.0	......	......	......	......	4.1
Cherries (dyed)†	1 ton	3,037.5	17.2	......	4.5	......	......	165
Beets†	Case of No. 2 cans	37.0	2,600.0	......	1,530.0	......	......	4.8
Beets, red‡	......	......	......	7,000	......	......	......	......
Corn†	......	......	......	625	......	......	......	......
Corn (cream style)†	Case of No. 2 cans	25.0	620.0	......	300.0	......	......	0.75
Corn (whole kernel)†	Case of No. 2 cans	25.0	2,000.0	......	1,250.0	......	......	2.5
Corn products*	1 ton corn	12,000.0	19.5	......	30.0	......	......	186.0
Figs*	1 ton	1,327.5	2.44	......	0.98	......	......	23.0
Beans:								
Green†	Case of No. 2 cans	......	......	159	......	......	......	......
Green†	Case of No. 2 cans	35.0	200.0	......	60.0	......	......	0.35
Lima†	Case of No. 2 cans	......	......	189	......	......	......	......
Lima†	Case of No. 2 cans	250.0	190.0	......	420.0	......	......	2.4
Grapefruit sections†	Case of No. 2 cans	56.0	1,850.0	......	270.0	......	......	4.8
Olives*	1 ton	5,925.5	222.0	1,490	4.34	......	9.1	2,130.0
Peas‡	......	......	......	......	......	......	......	......
Peas†	Case of No. 2 cans	25.0	1,700.0	......	400	......	......	2.1
Peas (shelled)*	100 cu ft waste	750.0	8.75	......	54.0	......	......	84.0
Peaches (macerated)*	1 ton	......	60.0	......	13.0	......	......	580.0
Peaches*	1 ton	2,610.0	29.2	......	15.0	......	......	280.0
Peaches and pears* (with trim)	1 ton	1,417.5	15.2	......	......	......	......	145.0
Peaches and pears† (with trim)	Case of No. 2 cans	65.0	1,340.0	......	......	......	......	4.4
Peach waste*	1 ton fruit	2,685.0	56.8	......	13.4	......	......	550.0

Item	Basis						
Peaches and pears:*							
Strained waste	1 ton fruit	2,115.0	43.8		13.4		420.0
After 10-mesh screen	1 ton fruit	2,115.0	35.0		11.1		340.0
Pears (macerated)*	1 ton fruit		60.0		54.0		580.0
Pear waste:							
With trim*	1 ton fruit	1,312.5	52.4		72.9		500.0
After ⅛-in. screen	1 ton fruit	1,312.5	24.7		13.1		240.0
Pork and beans†	Case of No. 2 cans	35.0	925.0		225.0		1.6
Pumpkin†	Case of No. 2½ cans	25.0	6,400.0	10,800	1,850.0		8.0
Squash†				848			
Tomatoes‡							
Tomatoes, solid pack* (waste cycloned)	1 ton tomatoes	227.25	8.42		2.88		82.0
Tomato catchup:							
Through 40-mesh screen*	1 ton tomatoes	1,402.5	7.70		2.96		74.0
No skin or pulp		450.0	25.0		27.9		240.0
Tomatoes*	1 ton tomatoes	3,607.5	29.7		8.1		290.0
Tomatoes† (whole)	Case of No. 2 cans	7.5	4,000.0		250.0		3.5
Tomato products†	Case of No. 2 cans	70.0	1,000.0		2,000.0		3.5
Spinach†	Case of No. 2 cans	160.0	615.0			0.8	4.9
Spinach (no trim)*	1 ton	4,950.0	22.2		18.9		210.0
Spinach (macerated)*	1 ton		70.0		114.0		670.0
Spinach*	1 ton	8,100.0	49.4		6.1		470.0
Sauerkraut†	Case of No. 2 cans	3.0	6,300.0		630.0		1.0
Succotash†	Case of No. 2 cans	125.0	525.0		250.0	1.0	33.0
Sweet potatoes*	1 ton	3,525.0	8.7		178.0		84.0
Milk products:							
General creamery*	1,000 gal milk	11,000.0	101.0		50.0	9.7	970.0
General dairy†	100 lb milk intake	340.0	570.0				10.0
General creamery†	1,000 gal milk	1,470.0	107.0			13.3	960.0
Milk processing*	1,000 gal milk	928.0	318.0				3,030.0
Receiving station†	100 lb milk intake	175.0	500.0	600			4.0
Receiving station‡			500.0				
Receiving stations§	1,000 lb raw milk	180.0					4.0
Bottling†	100 lb milk intake	250.0		500			6.0
Bottling‡			480.0				
Bottling§	1,000 lb raw milk	250.0	480.0				6.0
Dry milk†	100 lb milk intake	150.0					3.6
Dry milk§	1,000 lb raw milk	150.0					6.0
General dairy§	1,000 lb raw milk	340.0	570.0		540.0		10.0

TABLE 11-2. POPULATION EQUIVALENTS OF VARIOUS INDUSTRIAL WASTES.—(Continued)

Type of waste	Unit	Liquid volume of waste, gal per unit	BOD (5 days) Lb per unit	BOD (5 days) Ppm	Suspended solids Lb per unit	Suspended solids Ppm	Grease, lb per unit	Population equivalent per unit
Condensery§	1,000 lb raw milk	150	1,300	....	750	....	....	7
Condensery†	1,000 lb raw milk	150	1,300	....	....	....	....	10
Condensery‡	....	....	....	800	....	....	....	....
Dry milk‡	....	....	....	800	....	....	....	....
Whole milk‡	....	....	....	102,500	....	....	....	....
Skim milk‡	....	....	....	73,000	....	....	....	....
Whey‡	....	....	....	32,000	....	....	....	....
Buttermilk‡	....	....	....	64,000	....	....	....	....
Creamery‡	....	....	....	1,000	....	....	....	....
Cheese factory‡	1,000 lb milk intake	....	....	....	....	....	....	16.1
Receiving station‡	1,000 lb milk intake	....	....	....	....	....	....	2.8
Bottling‡	1,000 lb milk intake	....	....	....	....	....	....	4.7
Cheese†	100 lb milk intake	200	1,000	....	....	....	....	10.0
Creamery†	100 lb milk intake	110	1,250	....	....	....	....	7.0
Dried fruit:*								
Prune tendering (continuous flow)	1 ton prunes	187.5	3.1	....	1.6	....	0.3	30.0
Prune tenderizing	1 ton prunes	30.0	2.0	....	0.33	....	....	19.0
Beet sugar:†								
Flume water	....	....	....	200	....	....	....	....
Lime cake	....	....	....	1,420	....	....	....	....
Steffens waste	....	....	....	54,000	....	....	....	....
Fermentation industry:								
Brewery	1 barrel beer	204.0	1.24	....	0.62	....	0.022	12.0
Brewery	1 barrel beer	152.25	0.42	....	0.08	....	....	4.0
Brewery	1 barrel beer	321.0	3.1	....	1.7	....	....	30.0
Brewery	1 barrel beer	1,035.0	4.5	....	2.2	....	....	43.0
Brewery§	1 barrel beer	470.0	....	1,200	....	....	....	19.0
Beer slop‡	....	....	....	11,500	....	....	....	....
Yeast*	100 cu ft waste	750.0	33.7	....	Trace	....	....	320.0

Waste	Basis					
Yeast*	100 cu ft waste	750.0	15.4	......	Trace	150.0
Yeast*	100 cu ft waste	750.0	43.86	......	......	410–480
Spirit vinegar*	100 cu ft waste	750.0	106.0	......	18.2	1,020
Spirit vinegar*	100 cu ft waste	750.0	68.5	......	15.3	659
Spirit vinegar*	100 cu ft waste	750.0	137.0	......	......	1,300
Distilling grain:§						
Combined (washed)	1,000 bu grain	600,000	230.0	230	360	3,500
Thin slop	1,000 bu grain	......	......	34,000	......	55,600
Tailings	1,000 bu grain	......	......	740	......	50
Condensate		......	......	1,200	......	1,500
Distilling molasses§	100 gal 100 proof alcohol	8,400	......	33,000	3,270	12,000
Distillation:†						
Butyl alcohol		......	......	10,800	......	......
Ethyl alcohol and acetone						
Alcohol from crude molasses (England)‡		......	......	15,000–16,000	......	......
Malthouse wastes‡ England:						
First steep water		......	......	960	......	......
Second steep water		......	......	920	......	......
Third steep water		......	......	185	......	......
Fourth steep water		......	......	254	......	......
Germinator drum		......	......	50	......	......
Distillery wastes‡		......	......	15,000–16,000	......	......
Winery (California)†‡		......	......	3,500	......	......
Still liquors (South Australia)‡		......	......	16,000	......	......
Coke wastes§	100 tons coal, coked	360,000	......	85	115,000	......
Coal washery§	1,000 tons coal	......	......	15	......	1,500
Oil:						
Oil field§	100 bbl crude oil	18,000	......	20	50	60
Oil refinery§	100 bbl crude oil	77,000	......	......	......	15
Coke,† by-product plant	Per ton coal	3,600	85	......	......	11
Soft drink bottling†	Per 100 cases bottled	1,500	150	......	......	......
Laundry†	100 lb dry wash	350–500	1,000–1,500	400–600	1.28	20.25
Wash water*	100 cu ft waste	750	1.45	1.72	1.66	14.0
Wash water*	100 cu ft waste	750	2.24	1.94	1.72	21.0
Wash water*	100 cu ft waste	......	6.03	2.12	......	58.0
Wash water*	100 lb clothes	169.5	0.51	0.44	0.38	5.0
Wash water*	100 lb clothes	103.5	0.53	0.29	0.24	8.0

TABLE 11-2. POPULATION EQUIVALENTS OF VARIOUS INDUSTRIAL WASTES.—(Continued)

Type of waste	Unit	Liquid volume of waste, gal per unit	BOD (5 days) Lb per unit	BOD (5 days) Ppm	Suspended solids Lb per unit	Suspended solids Ppm	Grease, lb per unit	Population equivalent per unit
Pigment manufacture*	1 ton product	4,560	9.85	......	0.49	......	......	950
Potato products,* potato chips	100 cu ft waste	750	8.41	......	14.0	......	1.5	80
Roofing paper:*								
Rag and paper felt	1 ton product	23,775	18.2	......	25.7	......	1.98	176
Rag and paper felt	1 ton product	126	3.14	......	49.2	......	2.81	30
Paperboard	1 ton product	36,075	18.2	......	144.0	......	8.89	175
Grain products,* wheat cereal	1 bu wheat	6.6	0.77	......	1.92	......	0.0016	7.0
Horse bleeding*	1 horse	1.05	......	......	......	......	......	9.0
Slaughterhouse:*								
Meat packing:								
Cattle slaughter	1 animal	285	1.85	......	1.30	......	0.51	18.0
Hog slaughter	1 animal	65.4	0.42	......	0.55	......	0.09	4.0
Sheep slaughter	1 animal	54.9	0.28	......	0.19	......	0.04	3.0
General packing house	1 animal	603.75	5.38	......	3.37	......	......	51.0
General slaughterhouse	1 animal	360.0	7.72	......	3.21	......	......	74.0
Pork packing	1 animal	226.5	4.20	......	2.61	......	......	40.0
Hog killing	1 animal	143.25	0.42	......	0.98	......	......	4.0
Cattle slaughter	1 animal	396.75	3.79	......	3.11	......	......	36.0
Lard and sausage	1 animal	44.25	1.51	......	0.89	......	......	15.0
Pork packing	1–190-lb hog	124.75	3.04	......	2.91	......	0.13	29.0
Pork packing	1 animal	562.5	3.14	......	......	......	......	30.0
1,563 hogs / 797 cattle / 34 sheep	1 animal	1,470.0	7.2	......	4.88	......	1.8	69.0
10,262 hogs / 1,652 cattle / 2,295 sheep	1 animal	647.5	3.88	......	3.29	......	1.09	37.0
240 cattle / 520 hogs / 560 sheep / 240 calves	1 animal	90.0	0.67	......	0.41	......	0.13	6.0

Item	Basis							
Small packing house	1 equivalent hog	982.5	1.01	....	3.25	....	1.2	10
Large packing house	1 equivalent hog	720.0	3.30	....	2.80	....	0.92	31
Rendering (meat)	1 ton meat scrap	490.5	23.9	....	27.1	....	16.4	230
Rendering (meat)	1 employee day	425.25	6.65	....	1.15	....	....	63
Rendering (sardines)	1 ton fish	51.75	14.5	....	6.0	....	0.9	140
Meat packing houses§	100 hog units	550.0	....	....	....	....	....	25.0
Meat packing houses§	100 hog units	550	....	900	....	650	....	14.0
Slaughterhouse	100 hog units	160	....	2,200	....	930	....	6.0
Stockyards	1 acre	25,000	....	65	....	175	....	180.0
Meat Packing†:								
Packing	1 hog unit	550	....	900	....	....	....	24.0
Slaughterhouse	1 hog unit	150	....	2,200	....	....	....	17.0
Stockyards	Per acre	25,000	....	65	....	....	....	80.0
Poultry dressing†:§	Per 1,000 lb live weight	2,200	....	....	....	....	....	300.0
Pulp and paper:§								
Paper mill (no bleach)	1 ton paper	39,000	24	19	....	452	....	26.0
Paper mill (bleach)	1 ton paper	47,000	121	....	....	....	....	40.0
Pasteboard	1 ton paper	14,000	965	....	156.0	....	....	197.0
Strawboard	1 ton paper	26,000	300	....	660.0	....	....	1,254.0
Deinking	1 ton paper	83,000	....	....	790.0	....	....	1,250.0
Paper pulp:								
Groundwood	1 ton dry pulp	5,000	645	....	....	....	....	16.0
Soda	1 ton dry pulp	85,000	110	....	1,720.00	....	....	460.0
Sulfate (kraft)	1 ton dry pulp	64,000	123	....	....	....	....	390.0
Sulfite	1 ton dry pulp	60,000	443	....	....	....	....	1,330.0
Pulp and paper:‡								Per ton day
Paper mill average	Lb waste per ton product	3.7	....	....	....	....	....	22.2
Sulfite pulp and paper	Lb waste per ton product	154.0	....	....	....	....	....	834.0
Groundwood pulp and paper	Lb waste per ton product	2.5	....	....	....	....	....	15.7
Kraft pulp and paper	Lb waste per ton product	119.0	....	....	....	....	....	717.0
Rag pulp and paper	Lb waste per ton product	46.0	....	....	....	....	....	276.0
Board mills	Lb waste per ton product	11.1	....	....	....	....	....	66.6
Sulfite pulp	Lb waste per ton product	185.0	....	....	....	....	....	1,108.0
Groundwood pulp	Lb waste per ton product	7.8	....	....	....	....	....	46.8

TABLE 11-2. POPULATION EQUIVALENTS OF VARIOUS INDUSTRIAL WASTES.—(Continued)

Type of waste	Unit	Liquid volume of waste, gal per unit	BOD (5 days) Lb per unit	BOD (5 days) Ppm	Suspended solids Lb per unit	Suspended solids Ppm	Grease, lb per unit	Population equivalent per unit
Paper mills:†								
Miscellaneous (no bleach)	Per ton pulp	36,000	19.0	......	......	......	......	36.0
Miscellaneous (with bleach)	Per ton pulp	47,000	24.0	......	......	......	......	56.0
Paperboard	Per ton pulp	14,000	121.0	......	......	......	......	84.0
Strawboard	Per ton pulp	26,000	695.0	......	......	......	......	900.0
Tannery:								
Vegetable†	Per raw hide	800	1,200.0	......	......	......	......	48.0
Chrome†	Per raw hide	......	......	......	......	......	......	24.0
Hide tanning*	1 cattle hide	260.25	1.52	......	4.65	......	0.43	15.0
Hide tanning*	1 cattle hide	416.25	2.15	......	4.85	......	......	20.0
Hide tanning*	1 cattle hide	270.0	3.18	......	......	......	......	30.0
Calfskin tanning	1 skin	75.0	0.80	......	......	......	......	9.0
Sheepskin tanning	1 doz skins	48.38	0.33	......	......	......	......	3.0
Harness tanning	1 hide	384.0	4.50	......	......	......	......	43.0
Vegetable (Michigan)‡	......	......	......	600	......	......	......	......
Textile:§								
Cotton:								
Sizing	1,000 lb goods processed	60.0	......	820	......	......	......	2.0
Desizing	1,000 lb goods processed	1,100.0	......	1,750	......	......	......	96.0
Kiering	1,000 lb goods processed	1,700.0	......	1,240	......	......	......	108.0
Bleaching	1,000 lb goods processed	1,200.0	......	300	......	......	......	17.0
Scouring	1,000 lb goods processed	3,400.0	......	72	......	......	......	12.0
Mercerizing	1,000 lb goods processed	30,000.0	......	55	......	......	......	83.0
Dyeing:								
Basic	1,000 lb goods processed	18,000.0	......	100	......	......	......	90.0
Direct	1,000 lb goods processed	6,400.0	......	220	......	......	......	71.0
Vat	1,000 lb goods processed	19,000.0	......	140	......	......	......	130.0
Sulfur	1,000 lb goods processed	5,400.0	......	1,300	......	......	......	360.0
Developed	1,000 lb goods processed	14,400.0	......	170	......	......	......	120.0
Naphthol	1,000 lb goods processed	4,800.0	......	250	......	......	......	59.0
Aniline black	1,000 lb goods processed	15,600.0	......	55	......	......	......	41.0

Item	Unit						
Print works	1,000 lb goods processed	4,500.0	.....	95	.....	.....	15.0
Finishing works	1,000 lb goods processed	6.0	.....	1,250	.....	.....	0.4
Rayon:§							
Copper-ammonia process	1,000 lb product	160.0	.....	4.4	.....	19.0	35.0
Viscose	1,000 lb product	140	.....	110.0	.....	9.6	800
Hosiery	1,000 lb product	9,000	.....	330.0	.....	.....	150
Silk	1,000 lb product	13,700	.....	1,720.0	.....	.....	1,180
Wools:§							
Dyeing and scouring (no wool grease)	1,000 lb product	70,000	.....	114.0	.....	.....	400
Dyeing and scouring (100 % wool grease)	1,000 lb product	240,000	.....	125.0	.....	.....	1,500
Textile:*							
Wool pulling	100 lb wool	3,570.0	35.1	.....	22.5	0.87	340
Cotton-yard dyeing	100 cu ft waste	750.0	14.0	.....	0.15	0.62	135
Wool scouring‡		.....	.....	1,200	.....	.....	.....
Wool scouring†	Per 100 lb wool processed	126.0	9,300	.....	7,300	.....	.....
Soap manufacture:*							
Combined waste	100 cu ft waste	750.0	4.38	.....	4.75	2.21	42.0
Combined waste	1 employee day	1,102.5	2.74	.....	77.2	.....	26.0
Vegetable oils,* acidulating waste	1 ton oil	385.5	1.03	.....	0.47	0.24	10.0
Vitamins and biologicals,* vitamin B	100 lb product	264.0	155.0	.....	.....	.....	1,500.0
Domestic sewage, residential no known industrial waste*	Per person per day	27.97	0.104	.....	0.109	0.19	1.0

* R. E. Ramseier, The Evaluation of Industrial Wastes in the East Bay, *California Sewage Works Journal*, vol. 14, No. 1, pp. 26–37, 1942.

† Public Works, October, 1949, pp. 41–43.

‡ H. J. N. Hodgson, Sewage and Trade Waste Treatment, Report to Government of South Australia, Adelaide, Australia, August, 1938.

§ E. B. Besselievre, Industrial Wastes Section, Dorr Company Technical Manual, 1947.

or

$$\frac{12,510}{0.17} = 73,588 \text{ persons}$$

Thus, it will be seen that the 100,000 gallons of industrial waste per day is equivalent to 24,529 persons, whereas the 5 million gallons of sewage, at the normal American daily volume of 100 gallons per capita per day, would represent only 50,000 persons. In other words, one-fiftieth of the liquid volume has the same strength as the large volume of sewage and is equal to practically one-half the total number of persons in the city.

TABLE 11-3. ANALYTICAL DATA ON TANNERY WASTES*

Waste	Discharge, gal per day	Specific gravity	pH	Total solids, ppm	Nitrogen, ppm	Hide substances, ppm	BOD, ppm	Oxygen consumed, ppm
Soaks..............	9,000	1.004	7.45	8,352	88.6	496	600	900
Limes..............	3,300	1.002	11.5	36,488	28.6	160	1,700	1,750
Lime wash..........	4,000	1.004	8.1	8,944	225.0	1,257	535	900
Unhairing and defleshing...........	3,860	1.000	10.5	3,860	166.0	929	3,000	1,050
Deliming and bating.	600	1.001	6.7	5,644	325.0	1,818	1,650	900
Tanning............	18,000	1.013	5.4	33,496	.....	.....	13,600	22,000
Soda pool..........	21,000	1.015	9.3	21,244	43.0	204	3,750	15,900
First rinse.........	.....	1.005	7.9	12,820	.....	.....	2,750	9,125
Acid pool..........	1,800	1.015	1.8	13,460	25.7	155	2,000	5,425

* H. B. Riffenburg and W. W. Allison, Treatment of Tannery Wastes with Flue Gas and Lime, *Industrial & Engineering Chemistry*, vol. 33, p. 801, June, 1941.

The case cited here is not an uncommon one, but in many cases the wastes of an industrial center are so great in volume and BOD that, when reduced to a population equivalent, the resultant total BOD requires a plant out of all proportion to the size that would be required by the normal population of the city for its sewage alone. Although a waste with a strength of 3,000 ppm BOD is above the average, cases are extant, such as in wastes from breweries, whisky distilleries, and distilleries for production of alcohol from sugar-cane molasses, where the BOD of the wastes is as high as 17,500 ppm. In several cases in the author's experience, it has been 30,000 ppm. It can readily be seen that, if wastes of such strength exist in large volume, the load imposed upon a biological type of plant would be tremendous, and if the municipality were to be called upon to build that plant at public expense, it would place an exorbitant burden on the taxpayers of the community. In such cases, it is extremely important that measures be taken to have the producers of such high-

TABLE 11-4. ESTIMATION OF WATER USAGE BY 20 SELECTED INDUSTRIES

Industry	No. of establishments	Production	Estimated water consumption	
			Gal per unit	Million gal (year 1947)
Steel (finished)..........	419	61,857,241 tons	65,000	4,020,721
Oil refining.............	437	1,887,890,000 bbl	770	1,453,675
Gasoline.................	.....	791,325,000 bbl	357	791,325
Wood pulp:				
Sulfate................	.....	5,356,710 tons	64,000	342,829
Sulfite................	.....	2,795,960 tons	60,000	167,758
Soda..................	.....	491,580 tons	85,000	41,784
Groundwood...........	.....	2,049,814 tons	5,000	10,249
Total wood-pulp establishments......	226			
Paper...................	.....	10,646,833 tons	39,000	415,226
Paperboard.............	.....	9,186,810 tons	15,000	137,802
Total paper establishments............	665			
Coke....................	167	79,146,000 tons	3,600	284,373
Beer....................	440	88,027,000 bbl	470	41,373
Whisky.................	226	246,443,000 gal	80	21,155
Milk, cream, and butter..	.....	72,440,000,000 lb	0.11–0.25	14,286
Canning* and preserving†	2,265	391,546,000 cases	7.5–250	8,520
Manufactured ice‡.......	3,423	36,100,000 tons	243.85	8,802
Soft drinks.............	5,618	927,700,000 cases	2.5	6,250
Woolens and worsted fabrics...............	495	464,563,000 lb	70	3,252
Wool scouring...........	74	210,172,000 lb	1.26	2,648
Tanning.................	561	238,731,000 lb	8	1,910
Soap....................	249	4,138,001,000 lb	0.25	1,034
Meat packing (hogs).....	2,153	51,678,047 hogs	11	568
Cane sugar§............	25	358,000 tons	1,000	358
Rayon (all types)........	38	746,900,000 lb	0.16	119

* Estimate of water consumption includes water used in processing 14 fruits and vegetables for which consumption factors are available. This accounts for only 177,321,000 cases. Total water used by this group is probably two or three times the volume given.

† Excluding fish.

‡ Includes filling cans and pulling cores.

§ Includes refining only.

TABLE 11-5.   ANALYSES OF INDUSTRIAL WASTES HANDLED AT SEWAGE-TREATMENT PLANT, BOROUGH OF SLOUGH, ENGLAND*
(April, 1948, to March, 1949)

Type of waste	No. of samples	pH	Oxygen absorbed, N/80 KMnO₄ lab., ppm		Chloride ions, ppm	Nitrogen, ppm				Acidity or alkalinity, CaCO₃	Suspended solids, ppm	BOD (5 days at 18.3°C)	Remarks
						Ammonical		Oxidized					
			3 min	4 hr		NH₃	NH₂	NO₂	NO₃				
Acid wastes	30	5.9	9.4	33.5	147	0.8	0.9	0.17	1.7	653	224	51	Chromium, iron, HF, copper
Plating waste	44	5.4	2.7	11.8	143	7.7	3.9	1.12	18.2	44	219	2	Cyanides, nickel, zinc
Lead paint	29	6.9	177	209.3	451	3.3	0.5	0.8	94.6	5,402	340	422	Total lead as PbO: 4577
Synthetics, chemicals	35	7.8	185.3	613.3	492	26.1	8.0	0.06	Nil	2,782	431	1,643	Solvents, paints, oils, Cr
Fats, soaps, cosmetics	26	7.8	18.8	51.1	317	18.9	2.3	Nil	Nil	319	379	2,670	Solvents, soaps, grease
Foods and confections	39	6.7	43.5	1,900	176	6.7	6.8	Nil	Nil	289	407	3,802	Sugars, starches, etc.
Gas liquor	10	8.0	6,890	10,554	5,049	6,061	222	Nil	Nil	2,420	144		Sulfides, CNS, phenols, etc.
Starch and glue products	4	7.3	58	310.8	138	0.3	1.7	Nil	Nil	344	496	2,060	Free starch
Wallpaper manufacture	9	6.8	5.8	52.9	101	0.7	1.6	Nil	Nil	258	1,877	325	Copper, zinc, nickel, chromium, starch
Rubber and latex	11	7.2	104.7	323.6	97	485.3	13.2	Nil	Nil	927	1,033	443	Coagulated rubber
Dyeing, bleaching textiles	9	6.1	35.0	136.4	532	3.4	2.9	Nil	Nil	18	57	148	Free chlorine, sulfides
Anodizing	3	6.9	0.4	3.9	96	0.4	0.3	0.03	Nil	200	Nil	7	
Surface waters	26	7.9	7.1	20.2	111	6.2	3.6	Nil	Nil	397	2,440	96	Fats, oils, bitumens, chemicals
Others	17												Seaweed, sludges, etc.

* Sewage & Industrial Wastes, vol. 22, No. 2, p. 257, February, 1950.

TABLE 11-6. CALCULATED COMPOSITE OF ALL CANNERY WASTES AND ESTIMATED POPULATION EQUIVALENT OF EACH WASTE ON THE BASIS OF ITS BOD BASED UPON THE PACKING CAMPAIGNS OF 1935-1937

(City of Sacramento, California)

Product	Plant*	Raw tons received per season Avg	Max	Tons waste to sewer per season Avg	Max	Avg start and finish date	No. of operating days per season Avg	Max	Raw tons received per day Avg	Max	Adopted value of pop. equiv. per ton	Population equiv. of individual cannery wastes Avg	Max	Total gals water used per year	Gal water used per day	Gal water per ton of waste
Olives.........	A	625	.....	None		12/17-2/3	20	..	31	.....	?	?	?			
Spinach........	A	3,500	6,160	1,760	3,092	3/20-4/20	24	34	146	257	30	4,380	7,710	15,791,855	657,994	8,972
	B	4,166	4,228	2,267	2,457	4/7-4/30	19	20	219	244	30	6,570	7,320	18,796,819†	989,306†	8,291†
Total.........		7,666	10,388	4,027	5,549			34	365	501	30	10,950	15,030			
Asparagus......	A	5,900	6,785	3,180	3,654	4/17-6/15	60	76	98	109	230	22,540	25,070	55,951,184	932,520	17,594
	C	11,040	12,046	4,170	4,580	4/10-6/20	70	72	158	175	230	36,340	40,250	104,695,072†	1,495,643†	25,107†
Total.........		16,940	18,831	7,350	8,234			76	256	284	230	58,880	65,320			
Apricots......	A	1,650	.....	?	?	6/23-7/16	18	..	92	...	200	18,400	18,400			
Peaches........	A‡	800	.....	95	.....	8/12-8/29	20	..	40	...	200	8,000	8,000	2,164,248	108,212	22,781
	A§	8,700	11,919	259	355	7/21-9/20	41	46	212	372	200	42,400	74,400	26,812,206	653,956	103,522
	B	4,946	6,172	515	630	8/1-9/12	21	22	235	280	200	47,000	56,000	15,242,891†	725,852†	29,598†
	C	9,765	9,878	990	1,000	8/1-9/12	39	41	250	261	200	50,000	52,200	30,094,387†	771,651†	30,398†
Total.........		24,211	28,769	1,859	1,980			46	737	923	200	147,400	190,600			
Figs..........	A	890	.....	?	?	8/27-10/10	29	..	31	...	30	930	930	31,325,245	522,087	49,099
Tomatoes......	A	12,000	16,320	638	870	8/30-11/6	60	68	200	302	200	40,000	60,400			
	B	38,300	50,000	11,300	15,000	9/1-10/30	69	87	555	575	200	111,000	115,000	99,979,738†	1,448,982†	8,848†
Total.........		50,300	66,320	11,938	15,870			87	755	877	200	151,000	175,400			
Pumpkins......	A	4,800	5,328	37	41	10/24-11/25	24	31	200	233	?	?	?	13,742,957	572,623	371,431

* Plants are designated as A, B, and C.
† Calculated on basis of tonnage of raw product received, using "water to product" ratio of plant A, which was measured.
‡ Yellow freestone peaches.
§ Yellow cling peaches.

strength wastes reduce them to a normal sewage strength before discharging them into a public sewerage system.

TABLE 11-7.   CHARACTERISTICS OF STRAWBOARD WASTES*

Waste	No. of samples	Total solids, ppm	Total solids volatile		Suspended solids	Volatile		BOD (5 days at 20°C), ppm
			Ppm	%	Ppm	Ppm	%	
Total wastes	5	3,835	2,611	68	1,707	1,230	72	847
Machine water	5	2,729	1,963	72	931	748	80	314†
Primary beater	2	17,847	12,353	69	5,190	3,470	68	
Secondary beater	3	7,095	4,932	69	2,951	2,183	74	1,665‡
Washer-breaker beater	1§	15,900	11,320	71	7,460	4,910	66	

* D. E. Bloodgood and G. Erganian, Characteristics of Strawboard Wastes, *Sewage Works Journal*, vol. 19, No. 6, pp. 1021–1031, November, 1947.

† Average of two tests.

‡ Result of one test.

§ Result of tests by James Hargleroad.

Bibliography

1. Jenne, L. L., Industrial Pollution of the Schuylkill River, *Industrial & Engineering Chemistry*, vol. 22, pp. 577–583, 1930.
2. Calvert, C. K., and E. H. Parks, Population Equivalent of Certain Industrial Wastes, *Sewage Works Journal*, vol. 6, No. 3, p. 597, November, 1934.
3. Breedham, C. C., Effects of Trade Effluents on Sewage Purification, Institute of Sewage Purification (England), July 6, 1933.
4. Coblentz, M. H., The Industrial Waste Problem in Sanitation, *Sewage Works Journal*, vol. 5, No. 3, pp. 523–531, May, 1933.
5. Waste Water: Industry Problem, *Business Week*, No. 966, Mar. 6, 1948.
6. Deason, H. J., Sources, Character and Effects of Pollution in Water Supplies, *Sewage Works Engineering and Municipal Sanitation*, vol. 17, No. 10, pp. 538–539, October, 1946.
7. Parker, L. T., Pollution Causes Damage, *Sewage Works Engineering and Municipal Sanitation*, vol. 17, No. 9, pp. 463–464, September, 1946.
8. Siebert, C. L., A Digest—Kind, Character, Pollution Effect and Control of Certain Industrial Wastes, Pennsylvania State Department of Health, Bureau of Engineering, 1934.
9. Besselievre, E. B., The Disposal and Utilization of Industrial Wastes, Report 546, Alexander Hamilton Institute, New York, December, 1931.
10. Beaumont, H. M., Effects of Industrial Wastes, Paper, Twenty-third Annual Meeting Pennsylvania Sewage and Industrial Wastes Association, State College, Pennsylvania, Aug. 24–26, 1949.
11. Ellis, M. M., Industrial Wastes and Fish Life, Paper, First Industrial Waste Utilization Conference, Purdue University, Lafayette, Ind., Nov. 29–30, 1944.

Abstracted, *Sewage Works Journal*, vol. 18, No. 4, p. 764, July, 1945; *Water Works & Sewerage*, vol. 92, No. 5, pp. 171–174, May, 1945.

12. Hauck, C. F., Influence of Wastes on the Treatment and Use of Water, *Chemical Engineering Progress*, vol. 43, p. 9, 1947.
13. Adams, C. D., Control of Taste and Odor from Industrial Waste, *Journal, American Water Works Association*, vol. 38, p. 702, 1946.
14. Patrick, Ruth, Pollution Effects on Stream Biology, Paper, Twenty-third Annual Meeting Pennsylvania Sewage and Industrial Wastes Association, State College, Pennsylvania, Aug. 24–26, 1949.
15. Eldridge, E. F., Studies of Biochemical Oxygen Demand of Trade Wastes, *Engineering News-Record*, vol. 105, No. 1, p. 12, 1930.
16. Fisher, L. M., Effects of Industrial Wastes and Sewage on Shellfish and Fin Fish, *Civil Engineering (ASCE)*, vol. 8, No. 7, pp. 454–456, July, 1938.
17. Heukelekian, H., Method for Studying the Toxicity of Industrial Wastes, *Water & Sewage Works*, vol. 95, p. 449, 1948.
18. Industrial Wastes Often Dangerous, *The American City*, vol. 60, No. 5, p. 11, May, 1945.
19. Anderson, B. G., The Toxicity Thresholds of Various Substances Found in Industrial Wastes, *Sewage Works Journal*, vol. 16, No. 6, p. 1181, November, 1944.
20. Hazen, R., Effects of Industrial Waste, Paper, Third Joint Meeting New York State Sewage Works Association and New England Sewage Works Association, Albany, N.Y., May 26–27, 1947.
21. Industrial Waste Limits, *The American City*, vol. 65, No. 1, p. 15, January, 1950.
22. Trelles, R. A., Condiciones Fisicas, Quimicas y Microbiologicas a Que Deben Ajustarse las Descargas de Liquidos Residuales, Cloacales, etc. Sobre El Problema de la Contaminacion de Las Cursos de Agua en El Pais (Argentina), *Revista de Obras Sanitarias de la Nacion*, Ano XII, No. 127, pp. 9–29, July, 1948.

CHAPTER 12

METHODS OF WASTE TREATMENT

In general, the methods that have been developed for the treatment of municipal sewage and, in some cases, for the treatment of municipal water are adaptable to the treatment of industrial wastes. Owing, however, to the composition and characteristics of industrial wastes, it may be necessary to rearrange the units and to have an unbalance in the size of one unit or another as compared with normal sewage-treatment practice. Nevertheless many of the same factors and principles prevail.

Whether an industrial waste is treated separately, on the site of the industry in question, or is discharged into the public sewerage system and treated with the city sewage, data show that the same general methods may be used.

In general, three methods of treatment are adaptable to industrial-waste treatment. These are

1. Physical.
2. Biological.
3. Chemical.

In many cases all three may be required, in others one or two methods may be combined into a practical and economical plant to achieve the desired result.

PHYSICAL MEANS

We have learned, through experience, that nature provides for the disposition of all material, reducing it through processes of her own to the basic elements. However, efficient as nature is in accomplishing this reduction, she is sometimes slower in the execution and completion of these processes than we, in our impatience and modern call for speed, can await, and it becomes necessary to assist her with our modern mechanized methods. By providing an environment suitable for more rapid action and by mechanized means of handling and disposing of the end products of natural actions and reactions, we have found it possible to reduce the size and cost of treatment plants and, at the same time, remove some of the visual and nasal nuisances that have been the accompaniment of unassisted natural forces.

Many wastes, such as those from slaughterhouses and plants for the preparation of meat products, tanneries, vegetable and fruit canneries, textile mills, paper mills, and other industrial processes which contain fibers or scraps of material, contain a lot of solids of little further use, little recovery value, which can be the cause of much trouble in the treatment works if they are not removed from the wastes at an early stage.

Other wastes, and perhaps some of those mentioned above, contain inert solids, such as dirt, grit, and other inorganic extraneous matter, which become part of the waste flow in one manner or another. In a treatment system, these elements tend to clog pipes and apertures, cause abrasion and wear, and pile up masses of heavy matter which must be removed at a cost.

A third class of material, organic matter, is contained in high percentages in many wastes. This is the material with which we are basically concerned. It causes the pollution we are called upon to eliminate or the visual and nasal nuisances which have been the cause of the complaint. It is, usually, the oxygen-depleting substance which renders our streams the open sewers that some of them have become and has been the cause of the current legislation and concerted action which is being taken against the continuance of pollution from industrial sources.

As there are these three classes of material in many wastes, it is convenient to visualize the problem of treatment as a problem in classification. In order to handle and treat each of these constituents effectively in the way best suited to it, with the least interference with the processes intended for the reduction of the other elements, we must develop a type of plant for a given waste which will also include the proper method for separating these various ingredients and treating them as individual components.

In the separation by physical means, the following methods are now recognized:

1. Interference, by screening.
2. Flotation.
3. Gravitation.

Interference

Large objects, stringy substances, fibers, and extraneous objects which have no proper place in a waste flow but get into it in strange ways may be readily and cheaply removed by mechanical screens, either of the revolving type or the bar or vibrating type. If this material is not subject to fracture or breakage upon impact with an obstruction, much of it may be easily removed from the waste flow by placing in the channel a set of bars sloping upward at an angle of about 30 degrees, with spaces between the bars varying from $\frac{1}{2}$ to 2 or 3 inches as the case requires. The large objects, often of a nature which does not readily decompose or cause any trouble other than unsightliness, upon reaching this bar obstruction, are held back by it, and the flow containing the organic matter and other smaller solids passes on through to the following treatment units. As this mass collects upon the bars it tends to cause a dam, which will raise the level of the liquid on the upstream side of the bars above that of the downstream level. If this mass is allowed to collect for any appreciable length of time, it may cause a serious backing up of the flow or flooding. Therefore, to remove this accumulation, the screen bars must be raked frequently, either by hand or by mechanical means. This action is entirely physical and requires little time in its execution.

The inert material, such as grit, dirt, sand, and bits of inorganic matter, which has passed the screen will, if the velocity of the flow of waste is reduced, gradually settle to the bottom of a channel or tank. Experiments and actual plant operation have shown that the reduction of the velocity of flow to about 1 foot per second will permit the settlement of these objects; yet this velocity is such that it will maintain in suspension the organic solids which are to be handled in the final plant. This velocity drop may be accomplished in several ways. One conventional method is to provide an enlargement of the flow channel by widening it to the point where the velocity will reach the desired point. The heavier solids, entering this widened section, immediately begin a trajectorial course downward and, if the channel is of the proper length, will reach the bottom before the exit is reached. As the solids follow a relatively straight downward trend, if the channel is very deep the distance traveled will be much greater than if the channel is shallow and the distance between the flow line and the bottom is short. As these solids are not carried in one particular layer or stratum of the liquid, to retain all these solids the length of the channel must be based upon the assumption that the solids are traveling on the surface of the liquid. Thus, those which are traveling in that level will be caught before they reach the exit, and naturally all those which are being carried in lower strata will settle to the bottom in a shorter distance.

These channels, commonly called "grit chambers," are based on the assumption that the flow of liquids will always have a velocity of 1 foot per second. However, as the volume of flow varies during the day owing to plant operational schedules, the velocity frequently drops below 1 foot per second. When this occurs not only the inert inorganic solids but also some of the lighter solids, which would not settle when the velocity is retained at 1 foot per second, will settle in the grit chamber. When this happens, the collected grit will contain some of the organic matter which is subject to decomposition and the production of odors.

In some cases, notably that of Syracuse, N.Y., elaborate electrical control methods have been resorted to, with multiple channels and float-controlled gates at the entrance and exits of each channel, in an attempt to maintain this critical velocity of 1 foot per second. In view of the detailed design which must be applied to these conventional channels to maintain this critical velocity, numerous engineers and engineering organizations have developed units which will overcome this deficiency (Fig. 12-1).

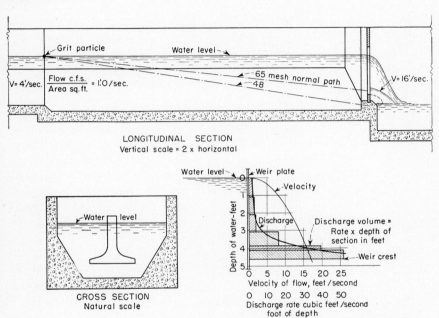

Grit chamber with proportional weir for controlling depth of flow in main channel. Curves show velocity of flow and discharge rate through orifice at various water depths.

FIG. 12-1. Recent chamber design employing proportional weir. Even though the design maintains a velocity of 1 foot per second satisfactorily, applying the settling path of 48- and 65-mesh grit reveals a lack of sufficient settling area for retention of 65-mesh grit and finer. How much 48-mesh grit will be retained is problematical. (*Courtesy of Engineering News-Record.*)

In the conventional grit channel, it was common practice to provide for a periodic shutdown of the channel to permit it to be cleaned of the accumulated material. This required duplicate channels in the plant in order not to stop the flow during the cleaning of one channel. These channels were cleaned either by men with shovels or by grab buckets which dug out the accumulated mass. As the grit, in the conventional type of channel, is usually mixed with decomposing or decomposable organic matter, the job of cleaning was unfit for human activity and unpleasant for the neighborhood. The accumulated material, with its high percentage of organic matter demanding prompt disposal, was usually buried. This method required large areas of ground available as burial grounds, which could have been put to better purpose. The shutdown and physical removal of the material were also items of considerable expense. Likewise, there was additional expense in the initial plant for the extra channels.

The trend has been to devise grit chambers, basically designed to handle flows at a velocity of 1 foot per second, in which it is recognized that this velocity is not constant. These units, now universally used in the majority of plants, have been developed by several companies and are based on the principle that the settled material, whether it is clean grit or grit mixed with organic matter, will be removed continuously by mechanical collectors and will be washed, so that the organic matter is returned to the flow of liquid for treatment in the units provided for that purpose. By this means two points are achieved: the need for duplicate channels, except in very large plants, is removed, and the continuous removal of the accumulated deposit eliminates the need for shutting down the unit. Perhaps the most important factor is that an undiminished sedimentation volume in the unit is maintained. In the older types of manually cleaned channels, as the deposit accumulated, reducing the space available for sedimentation, the velocity of flow through the unit was gradually increased. The result was that, if the deposit was allowed to remain for a long period, the velocity through the unit would be such that not only would it become ineffective in permitting transported solids to settle, but actually, because of the high velocity, the rapid flow would pick up solids previously deposited and carry them out. The entire function of the unit was thus nullified.

Because the settled material is continuously collected and removed, without manual attention, the channel is maintained at a volumetric efficiency which assures its continued proper function as a grit remover. But most important of all, at times of low velocity, when organic matter also settles, the constant removal and washing of the organic matter back into the flow produce a clean, relatively organic-free grit which does not require burial. In many cases, this grit may be used as fill in low areas around the plant, which are then available for other purposes. In several cases, it has been used for making walks and paths around the plant.

Perhaps the greatest benefit of this mechanically cleaned type of grit chamber is that its design requires much less detail. While the basic principle is to design it on the basis of a maximum velocity of 1 foot per second, it is, nevertheless, recognized that at times this velocity will be lowered and organic matter will settle out. However, as the deposit is continuously removed and the washing elements of the units separate the organic matter from the grit and return it to the flow, it is not a matter of importance that the critical velocity be maintained. The results of the use of these units for grit removal are lowered first cost of plant, lowered operating costs for removal of grit, and lowered costs of grit disposal.

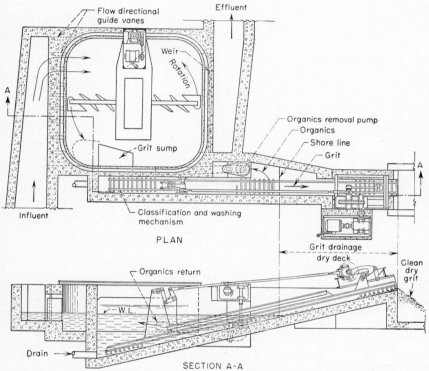

FIG. 12-2. The Dorr Detritor. (*Courtesy of Engineering News-Record.*)

Whereas the older form of grit chamber required periodical shutdowns for cleaning, these modern units frequently run for periods of years without shutdown, except for an occasional painting of the mechanism.

The size of grit or particles which must be removed is a matter for study. In sewage-treatment work, investigators have concluded that the grit which is most apt to cause trouble is 65 mesh, or 0.20 millimeter, in size, and coarser. Complete removal of practically all (95 per cent) grit of 65-mesh and over is the aim of most designers today. However, in some cases, it may be necessary to design for the removal of grit 100 mesh

and even finer. The basic theory in the design of the modern grit
remover, particularly of the type known as the Detritor (Fig. 12-2), is
that specific gravity and particle size have the most bearing on the settling
rate. Richards developed the theory years ago that of two particles
having different specific gravity, the one having the higher will fall faster,
and that of two particles of the same specific gravity, the larger will

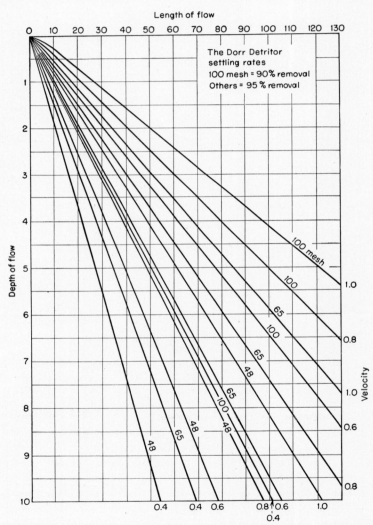

Fig. 12-3. Paths of settling of particles of representative sizes of sewage grit in
characteristic grit-chamber velocities. (*Courtesy of Engineering News-Record.*)

settle more rapidly.   Shape also has a bearing on the settling rate.   Of
three particles which have just passed the same screen, a round grain will
settle more rapidly than a long narrow grain, and the latter will settle
more rapidly than a flat grain.   Figure 12-3 gives the paths of settling

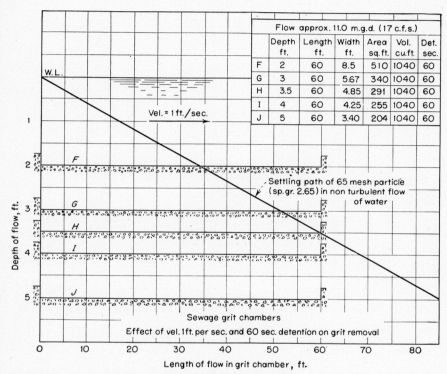

Fig. 12-4.   Sewage grit chambers.   Effect of velocity of 1 foot per second and
60-second detention on grit removal.   Observing the path of 65-mesh grit through
chambers having a common length but various combinations of width and depth to
secure a common detention of 60 seconds at a velocity of 1 foot per second in all five
designs.   The high importance of surface area in contrast with cross-sectional area
or velocity is thus revealed.

of grit particles of various sizes at velocities commonly found in grit
chambers.

Experience over the years has definitely demonstrated to the satisfaction of most observers that area is of greater importance in removing grit
or any particle which settles than depth of liquid or length of channel or
tank.   Figure 12-4 shows the path of settlement of 65-mesh particles in
chambers of the same length but with various depths and widths to obtain
a velocity of 1 foot per second.   Figure 12-5 illustrates the significance of

area in comparison with other dimensions, when the factors in common for the different lengths and widths of tanks are surface area and 1 foot per second velocity. With these facts established, it may be said as a general rule that the capacity of a grit chamber is in direct proportion to the area, regardless of the relation of width, depth, and velocity.

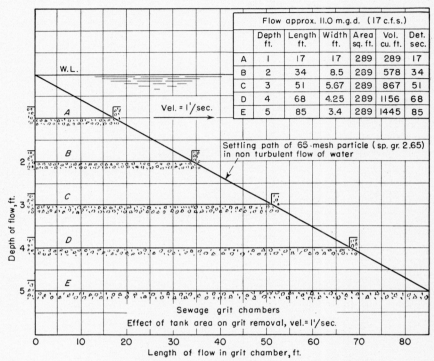

	Flow approx. 11.0 m.g.d. (17 c.f.s.)					
	Depth ft.	Length ft.	Width ft.	Area sq. ft.	Vol. cu. ft.	Det. sec.
A	1	17	17	289	289	17
B	2	34	8.5	289	578	34
C	3	51	5.67	289	867	51
D	4	68	4.25	289	1156	68
E	5	85	3.4	289	1445	85

FIG. 12-5. Sewage grit chambers. Effect of tank area on grit removal. The factors in common for the five chambers are surface area and the 1 foot per second velocity of flow. Taken with Fig. 12-4, this graphical study also reveals the high significance of surface area in contrast with other dimensions. (*Courtesy of Engineering News-Record.*)

Assuming that the best design, from an economic and construction standpoint, is a square tank, the formula given in Table 12-1 may be used

TABLE 12-1

Mesh of Grit to Be Removed	Overflow Rate, Gal per Sq Ft per Day
35	73,000
48	51,000
65	38,000
100	25,000

for figuring the size of the grit chamber required to remove grit of a certain size from a given volume of flow.[33]

As an example, let us assume a flow of 1,000,000 gallons from which it is desired to remove practically all grit of 65 mesh or over. The proper size chamber would be 1,000,000/38,000 = 26.31, or a square tank having an area of 26.31 square feet.

Flotation

Many industrial wastes contain large percentages of fine solids, fats or greases, or fibrous material. These solids frequently are indigestible, do not decompose, or inhibit further plant processes and interfere with plant operation. Grease and fatty materials, when in contact with the colder liquids of the waste and in their passage through pipe lines, tend to congeal, thus forming coatings in the pipes which may eventually clog them entirely or cause trouble in distributing devices on filters, etc. The small, fibrous material forms mats on the surface of settling tanks, causing unsightliness and interference with operation, and forms surface mats and scums in digestion tanks which interfere with the function of the unit and prohibit the emission of the gas formed in them.

Several methods exist for removing this type of material from wastes. One form embodies the blowing of air through the mass to give buoyancy to the lighter solids, causing them to rise to the surface, where they may be skimmed off. Another more modern form utilizes a vacuum to bring these light solids to the surface of a tank. In this unit the waste is first put through a short period of aeration for the purpose of forming minute air bubbles which tend to surround the small light particles and impart more buoyancy to them. The waste then enters a closed tank in which a vacuum equal to 9 inches of mercury is maintained. The combination of the air-buoyed particles, with their tendency to rise to the surface, coupled with the pull of the vacuum causes the solids to accelerate their upward trend and accumulate quickly on the surface of the liquid, where they are continuously collected and removed by mechanical scum removers. These solids are then passed out through a separate discharge pipe and may be sent directly to digesters or other units best suited for their disposal without passing through the units of the plant.

This unit, because of the combination of aeration and vacuum, may be operated at rates very much higher than are normally employed for gravitational and unassisted sedimentation and flotation. In a normal settling tank equipped with sludge-collection and scum-removal devices, it is common practice to provide for a flow rate of 800 and 1,000 gallons per square foot of tank surface. In the vacuum type of unit, known as a Vacuator, the rates are seldom less than 5,000 gallons per square foot of

tank area and, depending upon the type of material to be removed and
its rate of rise, they have been installed with rates as high as 10,000 gallons per square foot per day.   In recorded installations, this unit has
been shown to remove, at these rates, material equal in amount to the
larger sedimentation tanks designed for the much lower rates common to
them.   Thus it can be seen that, in a plant containing a high percentage

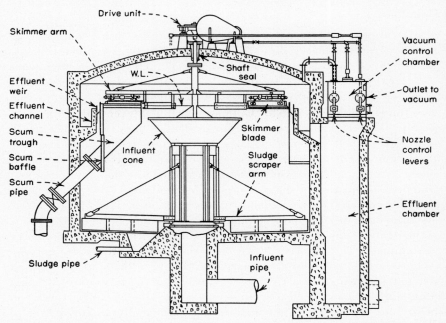

FIG. 12-6.   Vacuator of the "constant-level" type.   The cylindrical tank with a
dome-shaped cover is under a constant vacuum of about 9 inches of mercury.   Sewage
enters a central draft tube from which it is distributed by means of a flared-top
section.   Floating solids, buoyed up by fine air bubbles, are skimmed from the liquid
surface and carried to a trough.   Settled solids are removed from the bottom with a
scraper mechanism.   (*Courtesy of Engineering News-Record.*)

of fine light solids, units of this type will be materially smaller in size and
cheaper in cost than conventional sedimentation units.   They are particularly effective with wastes containing oil and with cannery and other
wastes containing voluminous light solids.   The type of unit known as
the Vacuator is shown in Fig. 12-6.

Gravitation

The third method of physical separation of materials from liquids is
that of gravitational sedimentation.   The use of sedimentation, or

settling, tanks is one of the oldest methods of removing solids from flowing liquid by natural means. The principle of these tanks is that their dimensions are such that the velocity of flow through them is reduced to the point where all the settleable solids carried by the flow will settle. The older form of settling tank, first conceived on this principle, was actually merely a widening of the carrying channel to the point where the solids in suspension would begin their downward path, and these widened channels were of sufficient length so that those solids following a straight line downward would eventually reach the bottom of the tank or a point below the influence of upward travel of the outgoing liquid and would remain in the tank. The velocities in such tanks at times fell as low as ¼ foot per second. The solids lighter than liquid, which tend to float, would rise to the surface and form a scum or mat.

These tanks were at first large rectangular basins to which flow was admitted and in which the deposited solids were permitted to accumulate until there was a sufficient amount to warrant shutting down the unit for cleaning. Owing to infrequent removal, the bottom sludge and top scum sometimes accumulated to the extent that they almost met in the middle, and the velocity of flow through the remaining small space became so great that it actually picked up solids instead of dropping them, with the consequent deterioration of the effluent. Because of the necessity of periodic shutdowns for cleaning, it was advisable to have a battery of these tanks.

The inadequacy of such tanks with the resultant lack of uniformity of clarification was the main cause of the modern development of the mechanically cleaned unit. As long as the velocity in the unmechanized tanks remained at a point low enough to permit solids to settle, the effluent would be of a more or less satisfactory character, from the standpoint of the removal of solids. However, as the tank filled up, the volumetric efficiency was reduced and the velocity through it gradually increased so that a graph of results showed a gradual reduction of the percentage of removal. When this reached a danger point, the tank was shut down, emptied, and the accumulated sludge cleaned out.

There are two schools of thought as to the proper shape of the modern mechanically cleaned sedimentation tank. One faction favors the rectangular tank, in which the length is several times the width; the other favors the circular or the square tank, either fed at the center with an overflow weir around the periphery of the tank, or fed at one side and overflowing at the opposite side. In the rectangular type, the flow is admitted at one end and travels the length of the tank and over a weir at the opposite end. As the cross-sectional area of the tank is the same for its entire length, the velocity of flow through it is constant, and solids

TABLE 12-2. AVERAGE RESULTS FOR VARIOUS CANNERY WASTES RECEIVED AT PALO ALTO*

Period	Character of waste	Type of samples†	Flow, mgd	Overflow rate, gal per day per sq ft	Suspended solids			Settleable solids			BOD		
					Influent, ppm	Effluent, ppm	Reduction, %	Influent, ppm	Effluent, ppm	Reduction, %	Influent, ppm	Effluent, ppm	Reduction, %
July 1–23	Domestic	24-hr	2.06	2,140	249	128	48.6	....	....	....	202	166	18.9
		8-hr	2.58	2,690	296	138	53.4	....	....	....	221	182	17.6
July 26–Aug. 6	Domestic and 1 mgd apricot	24-hr	2.94	3,060	266	145	45.5	174	68	60.9	305	264	13.4
		8-hr	3.57	3,700	325	168	48.3	215	82	61.9	295	248	15.9
Aug. 9–13 and Aug. 30–Sept. 10	Domestic, peach, and pear	24-hr	2.68	2,790	300	186	38.0	170	78	54.1	610	571	6.4
		8-hr	3.14	3,270	365	217	40.5	225	108	51.9	606	588	3.0
Sept. 13–17	Domestic, peach, pear, and tomato	24-hr	3.14	3,270	303	178	41.2	198	85	57.1	792	722	8.8
		8-hr	3.58	3,730	292	166	43.1	193	84	56.5	748	692	7.5
Sept. 20–24‡	Domestic, peach, and recirculation	24-hr	5.38	5,600	299	226	24.4	....	....	....	448	429	4.2
		8-hr	5.91	6,150	322	207	32.6	....	....	....	405	380	6.1
Sept. 27–Oct. 12	Domestic and tomato	24-hr	2.97	3,090	301	214	28.9	....	....	....	416	383	7.9
		8-hr	3.57	3,710	360	234	35.0	....	....	....	434	403	7.0
Over-all average§		24-hr	2.75	2,860	285	169	40.7	181	77	57.5	467	422	9.6
		8-hr	3.29	3,410	328	185	43.6	211	91	57.0	461	423	8.4

* R. P. Logan, Scum Removal by Vacuator at Palo Alto, *Sewage Works Journal*, vol. 21, No. 5, pp. 799–806, September, 1949.
† 24-hr composites and 8-hr daytime composites.
‡ All filter effluent recirculated through Vacuator to increase overflow rate; discontinued because of extreme pump surges.
§ Results for recirculation period (Sept. 20–24) omitted.

tend to settle in a straight downward path to the bottom. Because the line is straight, the solids in a shallow tank will reach the bottom in a shorter horizontal distance than in a deep tank, so that the chance of floating solids entering the zone of upward currents at the exit end is less.

The second theory is that a circular or square tank fed at the center with the flow going radially outward to an effluent weir around the periphery

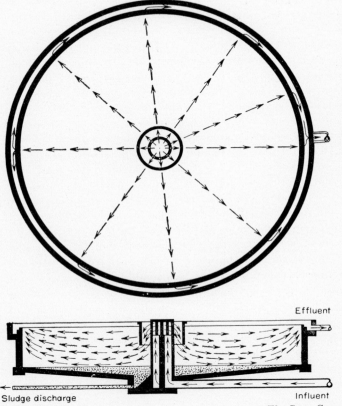

Sludge discharge

Effluent

Influent

Fig. 12-7.   Radial-flow sedimentation tank.   *(Courtesy of The Dorr Company.)*

of the tank achieves a better result from the standpoint of removal of solids. This point has been demonstrated in tests made on both types of tanks. The theory in this latter type of tank is that as the velocity of flow is highest at the point of entrance to the tank and gradually decreases toward the outlet weir, the solids released at the entrance immediately start to settle, not in a straight downward line, but in a parabolic line sloping more and more steeply downward as the solids progress outward from the center. Thus the solids reach the bottom of the tank closer to the central point of removal, in the form of a conical pile, and are out of the zone of upward current influence long before the discharge side of the tank is reached (Fig. 12-7).   The following example will illustrate these theories.

Assume a flow requiring a tank with an area of 10,000 square feet.   A rectangular tank to produce that area would be, say, 50 feet wide and 200 feet long.   The solids entering would take a straight downward path, as the velocity is the same throughout the entire length of the tank.   To achieve the same area, a circular tank would be 113 feet in diameter, and as the velocity of flow is highest at the center and reduces constantly as the flow progresses toward the periphery, the line of fall of the solids would be parabolic with the outward end constantly pulling in toward the center of the tank.   The line of travel of solids in the tank can never be more than the radius of the tank, or 56.5 feet.   An important point in the difference between the two types of tank is in the practical length of the overflow weir.   In a rectangular tank the total weir length, without resorting to unusual expedients, can be equal only to the width of the tank, or in this case 50 feet.   On the other hand, the total weir length of the circular tank of the size mentioned is equal to the entire perimeter of the tank, or in this case 355 feet.   As the weir length determines the depth and velocity of flow which passes over it, it can readily be seen that, with a weir which is 7.1 times as long in one tank as in the other, the depth of water passing over the weir will be materially less, the velocity lower, and the chance of carrying solids over lessened.

In certain cases, efforts have been made to increase the weir length in rectangular tanks by putting auxiliary effluent channels inside the tank, running effluent channels part way up the side walls of the tank, running effluent channels outwardly from the effluent end of the tank parallel with the walls, and also providing channels with weirs on both sides.   These do increase the total length of weir, the velocity over any given section is lower than with the single weir at the discharge end, and the depth of water is consequently less, but increasing the weir length in this manner does not affect the velocity through the body of the tank, which is the important factor influencing the settling rate and path of the solids. Also, the extension of the weirs back into the tank shortens the flow line and increases the tendency for solids to be carried over before they have fallen out of the zone of upward trending currents.

In certain cases, because of soil conditions, the restrictions of the available site for the plant, or personal preferences, it may be necessary to use the rectangular type of tank, but from a construction standpoint the circular tank has definite advantages in labor and material (Fig. 12-8). The circular form is recognized as the most practical and economical form

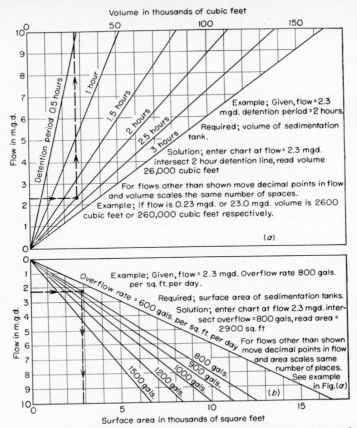

Figure (a):

Volume in thousands of cubic feet

Flow in m.g.d.

Detention period 0.5 hours, 1 hour, 1.5 hours, 2 hours, 2.5 hours, 3 hours

Example; Given, flow = 2.3 mgd. detention period = 2 hours.

Required; volume of sedimentation tank.

Solution; enter chart at flow = 2.3 mgd. intersect 2 hour detention line, read volume 26,000 cubic feet

For flows other than shown move decimal points in flow and volume scales the same number of spaces.

Example; if flow is 0.23 mgd. or 23.0 mgd. volume is 2600 cubic feet or 260,000 cubic feet respectively.

(a)

Figure (b):

Flow in m.g.d.

Overflow rate = 600 gals. per sq. ft. per day

Example; Given, flow = 2.3 mgd. Overflow rate 800 gals. per sq. ft. per day.

Required; surface area of sedimentation tanks.

Solution; enter chart at flow 2.3 mgd. intersect overflow = 800 gals, read area = 2900 sq. ft

For flows other than shown move decimal points in flow and area scales same number of places.

See example in Fig.(a)

800 gals. 900 gals. 1000 gals. 1200 gals. 1500 gals.

(b)

Surface area in thousands of square feet

FIG. 12-8. Sedimentation tanks. (*a*) Required volumes of sedimentation tanks. (*b*) Required areas of sedimentation tanks. (*Reprinted by permission from Elwyn E. Seelye, "Data Book for Civil Engineers," Vol. 1, Design, John Wiley & Sons, Inc., New York, 1945.*)

FIG. 12-9. Grouping of four circular center-siphon-feed clarifiers with central control house. Coney Island Sewage Treatment Plant, City of New York. (*Courtesy of The Dorr Company.*)

133

of structure.   This form is self-sustaining, and the walls of tanks may be thinner, requiring less form work than the walls of a long straight-sided tank.   Furthermore, if the tanks are equipped with mechanical sludge-collection and removal devices, the final installed cost of all but the smallest sizes of the circular types is ordinarily less than for rectangular tanks of equal area or cubic content.   Sometimes, however, if a rectangular tank can be coupled with other units, with walls common to both, construction economies may be established, but the same effect can be had by constructing a square tank with center feed to get the advantage of the long overflow weir line in a simple manner.   In large plants, the circular tanks may be grouped in sections of four tanks and the entire control piping for influents and effluents to all the tanks in the group contained in one structure in the center of the group, as shown in Fig. 12-9, thus not only simplifying the pipe lines and centralizing the control features, but also eliminating the necessity of building a control house outside the tank area.   In this type of grouping, the walls of the four tanks, where they converge at the center point, may be made to form the walls of the control structure.

In studying the design of any plant, full consideration should be given to both types of construction, and the one selected which, in consideration of the ground conditions prevailing at the site, the adjacency of other plant units, etc., will result in the lowest over-all construction cost.   This cost must include not only the cost of the mechanical equipment involved but also the entire construction cost of the tank, which in turn includes the total amount of concrete, excavation, form work, piping, reinforcing metal, and all other items required to make a complete job.   Frequently, the sludge-collection mechanism for a certain type of tank may be less costly than the mechanism for another type, but owing to the type of tank construction, the final over-all cost may be greater.   By proper estimating this can usually be determined quite accurately before the mechanism is selected.

BIOLOGICAL TREATMENT

Biological treatment is a secondary method—secondary in the sense that there are certain primary operations which are performed in practically every case.   In cases where the treatment must be carried to a higher degree, additional plant units must be constructed to carry out this secondary phase.   Actually the secondary treatment may be the most important phase in the reduction of the polluting elements in the wastes.

As the separation of solids suspended in liquids involves a problem in classification, the various elements of a treatment plant should be classified as:

1. Preliminary.
2. Primary.
3. Secondary.

Figure 12-10 illustrates the units and their functions, involved in each phase. In some plants, one phase only may be needed, in others all three may be required, depending upon the nature of the waste and the degree of treatment which must be provided.

There are two general forms of secondary treatment: biological, in which bacterial action is depended upon to reduce the oxygen-consuming

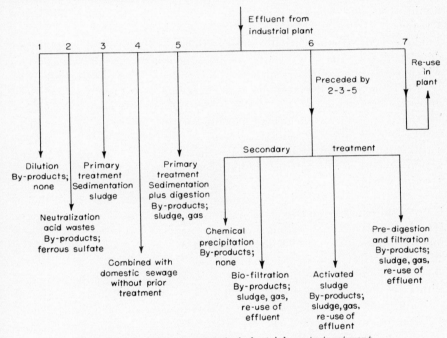

FIG. 12-10. The essentials in industrial-waste treatment.

elements and stabilize the organic matters; and chemical, in which chemical compounds are added to the wastes to neutralize acids or alkalies or to cause solids in fine suspension or in a colloidal form to coalesce and settle, thus removing the polluting elements.

Trickling Filters

Biological treatment may be accomplished in two ways. One is by the use of trickling or sprinkling filters, the other the activated-sludge method. The trickling filter is, in principle, a bed of broken stone, large gravel, broken bricks, or other irregular material, placed in a concrete or other tank or piled up. The waste to be treated is applied to this bed by means of a dosing tank, which accumulates a certain volume of waste and then discharges it to the bed. Upon reaching the surface of the bed, the waste trickles down through the interstices between the particles of the filter medium. After a short time, usually 4 to 6 weeks after the bed has been put into operation, the stones in the bed begin to accumulate a greenish-black coating of slime composed of aerobic bacteria which feed on the organic matter in the waste and consume it. As the organic matter, which is the oxygen-depleting element, decomposes, the "bacteria beds" (as they are also sometimes called) reduce the BOD of the liquid to a point where the final effluent is suitable for discharge into a stream.

These beds are of various forms. In one of the early conceptions developed in England in the later years of the nineteenth century, sewage, which sometimes settled and sometimes did not, was periodically distributed over these beds by means of revolving distributors with several arms through which the sewage flowed, the units being caused to revolve by the jet action of the liquid flowing out of orifices. Another early form was a rectangular bed to which the sewage was applied by means of a traveling distributor which spanned the bed and was propelled by the action of sewage falling from a slight elevation onto a wheel similar to a water wheel.

In the United States, trickling filters came into use early, but owing to the cold climates and freezing weather in certain sections of the country, the revolving or traveling type was not considered practical. Therefore, a form was evolved which consisted of a pipe-distribution system laid, below frost line, in the bed with risers capped with spray nozzles emerging at regular intervals. These nozzles were usually provided with a circular orifice enclosing a circular spreader, which naturally made a circular spray pattern. This system was relatively effective, but equal distribution over the bed surface was difficult to obtain. Either the sprays were overlapped in order to get complete coverage of the bed area, which caused overdosing of the area within the overlap, or if the sprays were spaced so that the perimeters of the spray patterns just touched each other, unwetted areas were left between the circles. In the winter, in very cold areas, ice piled up in these sections. This type of spray required the use of considerable head to obtain a spray which would reach out 12 feet or more. Filters using this type of distribution required a head of 6 feet or more above the stone for proper distribution.

In order to overcome this difficulty, when the 30 acres of trickling filters was built at Back River by the city of Baltimore, Md., a study was made to develop a nozzle which would make a square spray and which could be located so that the edges of the sprays would meet and not over-lap, resulting in a more uniform distribution and no unwetted areas. Such a nozzle was developed, but the machine job was very difficult as the curves of transition from a round spindle to a square head were so involved that each nozzle had to be hand-machined. This process proved to be so expensive that although some 1,200 of these nozzles were installed and they worked efficiently, to the writer's knowledge they were never used elsewhere.

While the trickling filter was used in small plants in the United States, it was not considered a practical unit for large cities because of the area required and the cost of the filter beds. With the original type of trickling filter, now referred to as the "conventional" or "slow-rate" filter, the beds were efficient as reducers of BOD only up to a rate of about 2 million gallons per acre per day. This meant that for a city with a flow of 1 million gallons of sewage per day the filter bed would be a half acre in area, a city with a flow of 25 million gallons per day would require an area of about 12.5 acres, and a city the size of New York with a flow of close to 1 billion gallons per day would require about 500 acres for the filter beds alone.

However, the effectiveness of the trickling filter and the simplicity of its operation were so well appreciated that engineers continued to study it and endeavored to find ways to increase its capacity. Little headway was made in this until about 1936, when an American engineer, Harry N. Jenks, developed what he termed the Biofiltration process. The idea in this process was that the aerobic bacteria had not exhausted their capacity to destroy organic matter in the waste during its one passage through the filter; therefore, if the sewage were to be passed through the filter several times (instead of but once as was the practice in the low-rate unit) and come in contact with these bacteria on each passage, the trickling filter would have a much higher capacity for reducing the BOD than had been suspected. Experimental work proved the point and also showed conclusively that the bulk of the work done by a trickling filter was accomplished in the upper 3 or 4 feet of the filter medium and the lower layers did so little extra work that their cost was not justified. Formerly, in the low-rate filter, it had been common practice to make the stone beds at least 6 feet and frequently 8 to 10 feet deep.

Jenks, in his experimental work showed that, instead of dosing a trickling filter at a maximum rate of about 2 million gallons per acre per day, he could step up this rate as high as 25 million gallons or more per acre per day, or more than ten times the former rate. The higher rate, of course, included the recirculated sewage, but at the same time if this were but equal to the original volume of sewage, or a ratio of 1 to 1, the sewage itself would be applied to the bed at the rate of 12.5 million gallons per acre per day, or over six times the rate permitted on the low-rate units. This meant that for a city with 1 million gallons of sewage per day, using a recirculation ratio of 1 to 1, the total area of filters required would be only about one-thirteenth of an acre instead of half an acre. Or assuming that 100,000 gallons of waste per day is to be treated and that this is applied at the low rate of 15 million gallons per acre per day,

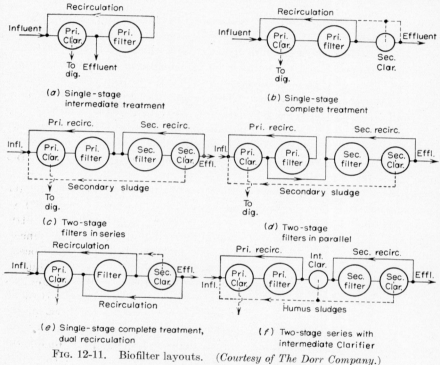

FIG. 12-11.   Biofilter layouts.   *(Courtesy of The Dorr Company.)*

the resultant filter would be only 27 feet in diameter as against the one needed for the older method of 74 feet in diameter. Therefore, a trickling filter of this type was adaptable to cities larger than had before been considered possible. Coupled with the reduction in depth of stone from 6 feet or more to 3 feet, the reduction in cost of the filter beds was very appreciable.

True, this type of operation requires pumping facilities to recirculate the filter effluent back to the primary settling tank, but as this is a low-head operation, the cost is not a large item and is easily offset by the tremendous saving in construction cost. These filters are normally equipped with revolving distributors with ball-bearing bases, which are

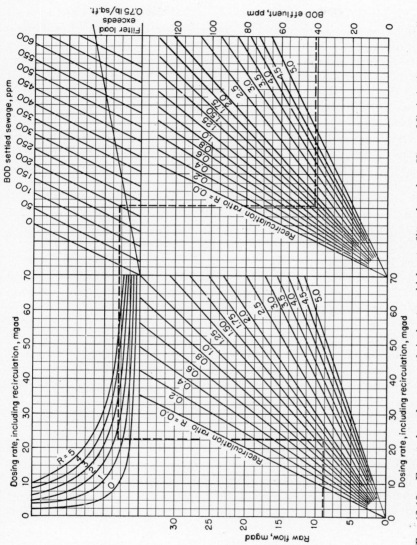

Fig. 12-12. Expected performance of single-stage high-rate filters based on Upper Mississippi group policy. *(Courtesy of The Dorr Company.)*

so made that very little head is required to operate them. It has been found that they may be operated with heads of 2 to 3 feet. This fact in itself materially reduces the operating cost, as previously the low-rate filter required 6 to 8 feet of head to operate it, and if the sewage required pumping to the dosing chamber, this extra head ran into considerable expense for power.

These filters have now come into use for cities with flows of sewage as great as 25 to 30 million gallons per day, as the area required is not out of line with other methods. The use of this type of plant has become so general in the United States and other countries that today there are over 400 plants operating on this principle, with consistently low initial costs and reduced operating charges. Several variations of the same idea have been developed, in which a part of the treated effluent is recycled at certain periods to maintain a constant flow through the plant. In the Biofiltration system, the volume of recirculation is usually constant at all times, and the total volume of flow through the plant varies according to the volume of raw sewage entering it. Special revolving distributor units have been developed to compensate automatically for the variations in flow without the necessity of manual adjustments.

The flow diagrams in Fig. 12-11 illustrate the three general forms of plant layout for the Biofiltration system. Figure 12-12 gives general data on design and the expected performance of single-stage high-rate filters with various rates of recirculation, etc.

The "high-rate" filter, as it is now properly called, is especially adapted to the treatment of industrial wastes with high BOD, as it is a form which can stand shock loads to a greater degree than any other method of treatment, without danger of upsetting the operation of the plant. These shock loads are more common in industrial-waste flows than in normal sewage, as accidents happen in industrial plants which may require the discharge of a waste of unusual strength at an unusual time. In plants in which the trickling-filter method is employed, the filters will usually be able to adjust themselves to this extra load. The high-rate filter is especially adaptable to the treatment of tannery, milk-products, fermentation, cannery, and slaughterhouse wastes. As these wastes are usually low in volume compared with the sewage flow of a municipality, the plants are relatively low in cost and of moderate size and may usually be constructed on the area available within the plant grounds.

A form of the high-rate-filter plant which has recently been developed is particularly adaptable to those cases of industrial-waste treatment where use of the trickling filter is indicated. This plant consists of a primary settling tank in which there is a partition dividing the tank into two equal parts, so that it may function both as the primary and sec-

ondary settling tank.   The trickling filter is also a double unit, built in
a circular form, with the central portion acting as the first stage in a two-
stage system and the outer annular ring of filter material acting as the
second stage.   The filter is fed by one revolving distributor with four
arms, two of which distribute effluent onto the central portion of the bed,
while the other two distribute sewage to the outer annular ring.   A still
further development of this idea is to use as the primary and secondary
settling unit a well-known combined settling and digestion unit.   With
this unit and the dual filter, the entire treatment plant consists of two

FIG. 12-13.   Packing-house waste-treatment plant.   Reitz Meat Products Company.
(*Courtesy of The Dorr Company.*)

small circular units only.   Figure 12-13 illustrates a plant of this latter
type in which packing-house wastes are treated.

The basic idea has been to develop the effectiveness of the trickling
filter, with its manifest advantages, in order to reduce plant-construction
and operating costs.   This, of course, appeals strongly to the industrial-
plant owner, whose desire is usually to build and operate a plant at the
lowest possible cost consistent with the procurement of the required
results.

For wastes which are very high in BOD and yet contain a low percentage of solids in suspension, the trickling filter is an effective unit.
But as large areas would be required to accomplish the desired result
with filters alone, a newer method has been proposed and adopted.   Here,
the BOD is reduced to a high degree in a digestion unit and a trickling
filter of the high-rate type is used to reduce the BOD remaining in the

effluent from the digester to the final degree required. This method
has been particularly adaptable to wastes from the fermentation industries, distilleries producing alcohol from sugar-cane molasses, etc. The
raw wastes are introduced into a digestion tank which has a capacity

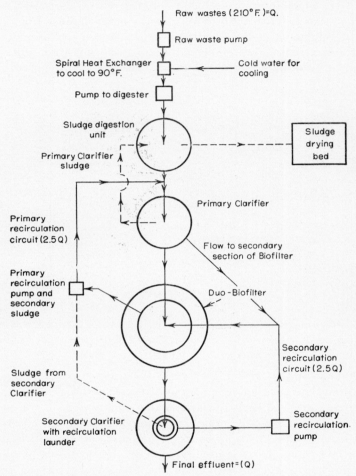

FIG. 12-14. Diagram of proposed plant for treatment of wastes from manufacture
of alcohol from sugar-cane molasses.

equal to 6 to 9 days of the total flow. The reduction of BOD accomplished in these tanks by the anaerobic digestion process is very high,
ranging between 70 and 80 per cent. Figure 12-14 illustrates a layout
for the treatment of the wastes from the production of alcohol from
sugar-cane molasses.

As an example of this method of treatment, let us assume a waste of 50,000 gallons per day volume, with a BOD of 5,000 ppm, to be reduced to a final effluent containing 100 ppm BOD. The digestion unit required on a 6-day basis would have a capacity of 300,000 gallons, or 40,000 cubic feet, which can be obtained in a tank 20 feet deep by 51 feet in diameter. Assuming a reduction of 80 per cent of the BOD in the digestion phase, the overflow from this unit will have a BOD of 1,000 ppm. This effluent, when applied to a trickling filter of the high-rate type at a loading rate of 5 pounds of BOD per cubic yard of filter bed, with a recirculation ratio of 6 to 1, would entail a filter bed with a volume of 1,668 cubic yards of medium, and at 3 feet depth this bed would have an area of 16,012 square feet, or 143 feet diameter.

TABLE 12-3. RECOMMENDED RECIRCULATION RATIOS FOR WASTES OF VARIOUS STRENGTH

BOD (raw or applied wastes), ppm	Single stage		Two-stage complete treatment (each stage)
	Intermediate treatment	Complete treatment*	
Up to 150	1.0	0.75	0.5
150–300	2.0	1.5	1.0
300–450	3.0	2.25	1.5
450–600	4.0	3.0	2.0
600–750	5.0	3.75	2.5
750–900	6.0	4.5	3.0

* Where the dual recirculation system is used, one-half of the above ratio is used in each stage of recirculation. The above recirculation ratios are based on securing maximum over-all performance for each type of plant. Lesser recirculation ratios may be used but with a proportional decrease in over-all performance.

Rather than considering the volume as the criterion, the high-rate filter is ordinarily designed on its ability to reduce BOD. The loading rates vary according to the strength of the sewage or waste, as it has been found that a filter will handle a greater load of BOD in pounds per cubic yard with a waste with a high BOD than one with a lower demand, and the recirculation ratio is stepped up as the applied BOD increases. Tables 12-3 and 12-4 show the normal loadings used for various strength wastes and the corresponding recirculation ratios recommended for the unit known as the Biofilter.

The primary advantages of the high-rate filter are (1) its smaller space requirements, (2) its ability to turn out a high-grade effluent at high rates of flow, (3) its ability to vary the degree of BOD reduction by altering the ratio of recirculation, (4) its low operating cost as compared with other methods of treatment which produce an equal high-grade effluent, (5) its ability to handle short-period shock loads, and (6) its general freedom from septic action and odors caused by long detention periods at low flow or during the night.   It is especially suitable for industrial-waste-

TABLE 12-4.   RECOMMENDED FILTER LOADINGS FOR BOD ON BIOFILTERS, 3 FT DEEP

BOD (Raw or Applied Wastes) Ppm	BOD Loadings Lb per Cu Yd per Day
100– 150	1.5
150– 300	1.85
300– 400	2.5
450– 600	3.0
600–1,000	5.0

TABLE 12-5.   CENTRIFUGAL PUMPS FOR RECIRCULATION IN BIOFILTER SYSTEMS (Vertical Type of Pumps)

Gal per min (to be pumped)	Head, ft (to be pumped against)	Size of motor required, hp
50	12	¾
100	12	1.0
150	12	1.50
200	12	1.50
250	12	2.0
300	12	3.0
400	12	3.0
500	12	3.0
600	12	5.0
800	12	5.0
1,042	12	7.5
1,250	12	7.5
1,389	12	7.5
1,736	12	10.0
2,083	12	15.0
2,430	12	15.0
2,777	12	15.0
3,472	12	20.0
4,166	12	25.0
4,861	12	30.0
5,555	12	30.0

treatment projects because of its low initial and operating costs and the reduction of manual or skilled attention to the minimum.

Perhaps the one disadvantage of the high-rate filter is the cost of the recirculation of filter and final tank effluent back into the system.   As explained earlier, the head required is very low, and an efficient centrifugal type of pump is normally used, requiring very little power.   Table 12-5 shows the power required for pumping various flows against a head of 12 feet, which is the average head required in a well-designed Biofilter plant. Actually, if the cost of this power for pumping is capitalized, it will show a saving over the initial cost of a conventional (low-rate) trickling-filter plant, with its very much larger and deeper filters, dosing tanks, and other accessories.

The Biofilter system, based on the Jenks ideas, has certain advantages in operation over some of the other high-rate types. Because the recirculation flow may be split equally between the primary and secondary settling tanks, these units may be of the same size, making it possible to design a more uniform plant and use the same forms for the walls of both tanks, thus introducing another saving in construction cost. Furthermore, no intricate control mechanism is required for the recirculation pumps, as they run continuously at a given rate regardless of the volume of sewage entering the plant. At times of low waste flow which result in long detention periods in the settling tanks, which might permit septic action to begin with its consequent obnoxious odors and scum formation if the waste contains putrescible organic matter, the recirculated effluent going steadily back to the primary settling tank dilutes the incoming low flow to such an extent that the detention period in the settling tank is not materially lengthened, and the waste passes on to the filter within a relatively short period and before it can create a nuisance. Also in this system where the waste flow is consistently lower than the plant is designed for and therefore is prone to become septic, the recirculation ratio may be increased, thus maintaining the detention period in the settling tank at a safe margin.

Activated-sludge Process

The other method of treatment which comes under the heading of biological or biochemical treatment is known as the "activated-sludge process." In this process, a mixture of sewage or wastes and activated sludge is agitated and aerated. The activated sludge is a sludge floc produced in the raw, but it is usually settled sewage or waste produced by the growth of zoogleal bacteria and other organisms in the presence of dissolved oxygen. This sludge or floc is accumulated in proper concentration by constantly returning a percentage of the final settling-tank sludge to the inlet end of the aeration tanks. The activated sludge is separated from the mixed liquid and a portion returned to the sewage flow to maintain active bacterial life. The balance of the settled sludge is discharged from the settling tank and digested or dewatered without digestion.

This process was developed because of a need for a method of treating large volumes of sewage which the trickling filter or the older methods could not handle. It has the ability to produce a high degree of treatment in a smaller area than any other method, but it has the disadvantages of requiring skilled plant operators and of not being capable of quickly absorbing shock loads. The plant designed for this process is not abnormal in first cost, as the units are moderate in size, but furnishing the oxygen required to stabilize the organic matter and agitating the liquid to prevent sedimentation of solids during the oxidation phase entails the use of large blowers or compressors which establish a high power demand, thus making for high operating costs.

The aeration tanks, the oxidizing units in the plant, may be designed for normal sewage and wastes to produce a high-grade effluent at rates equal to about 16 to 20 million gallons per acre per day, in comparison to a rate of about 2 million gallons per acre per day for the low-rate trickling filter and perhaps a maximum rate of 12 to 15 million gallons per acre per day for the more modern, effective high-rate trickling filter. But the power and general operating costs of an activated-sludge plant will usually be double those of a high-rate trickling-filter plant. In a large plant, this is a big item in the charges against the waste-treatment operation. Capitalized over a term of years these costs may be such that it would be more economical to consider another type of plant whose initial construction cost might be slightly more, but whose annual operating charges would be less.

However, where the available area is small, as happens frequently in industrial plants, the activated-sludge process has merit in that it requires a relatively small area. Several manufacturers have devised "package plants" utilizing the activated-sludge method, which are suitable for many cases of industrial-waste flows. The ultimate cost of treatment by various methods must be carefully studied, however, before deciding on any one method. A daily operating charge of $10 per day seems a small item to apply to the cost of production, but this is $3,650 per year, which is equal to the interest at 5 per cent on a principal sum of $73,000. Much additional plant could be built for less than that sum.

It may be said that the test of any unit or method of treatment is in the cost per unit of work done by that method or unit. A simple unit which costs little may reduce the suspended solids or the BOD by a very small percentage, whereas another unit may be able to obtain much greater reductions of the same elements. The second unit may cost more to install, but the cost per unit of work done may be cheaper. For example, a fine-screen unit whose installation cost may be $10,000 actually removes about 10 per cent of the suspended solids and practically none of the BOD. The cost of this unit per unit of work done is $1,000. Against this, a sedimentation tank of modern mechanized type may cost $20,000 to build but will normally remove at least 50 per cent of the suspended solids and reduce the BOD an appreciable degree. The cost of this unit per unit of work done is then only $400 and, although costing more to build, is actually the cheapest for the plant owner because unsatisfactory results with the fine-screen unit may force him to add to his plant. If in the beginning he had built the more expensive unit, the result would have been so satisfactory that he would not be required to add to his plant. This point should always be given careful consideration in considering units or methods.

The activated-sludge method requires that a large volume of air be continually supplied, the amount depending upon the initial strength of the waste and the degree of treatment required. This requirement entails the installation of large air-blowing or compressing units. It is common practice, when a high degree of treatment is required, to provide 1 to 1.5 cubic feet of air per gallon of waste treated. Thus, in a plant handling a flow of 100,000 gallons per day, the air required will be between 100,000 and 150,000 cubic feet. Such compressors and blowers require considerable power to operate them, and this is usually the major item of cost in an activated-sludge plant. The horsepower required in an average plant will range in the neighborhood of 30 horsepower per million gallons treated.

It is a well-known fact that the great bulk of the air used in an activated-sludge plant is not required for the oxidation of the organic matter, but is used to maintain the solids in the waste in suspension so that they are not permitted to settle to the bottom of the aeration tanks. To reduce this necessity for using air as an agitation unit, various units have been developed, such as mechanical agitators, driven by motors, with either a small amount of air added to furnish the needed oxygen or with various types of tubes and inspiration ducts to bring in the oxygen from the atmosphere. These devices do reduce the actual horsepower required as long as the units are small, but because they rotate at a relatively high speed, the horsepower demand rises sharply as the size of the tanks increases. For this reason, it is usual to restrict the size of tanks to about 20 feet square at the maximum; for a very large volume of flow this means the installation of a large number of individual units with its multiplication of horsepower. These mechanical aerator units are considered suitable only for the smaller plants, and in cases where the volume of industrial wastes is small they may well be adapted.

A further attempt to reduce the compressed-air demand was made by Dr. Karl Imhoff of Germany. He developed a revolving paddle-wheel assembly on a horizontal axis, to maintain sufficient agitation to keep the solids in suspension. Only a small amount of compressed air, a fraction of a cubic foot per gallon of sewage, was added to provide the oxygen required. This system did reduce the total power requirements per unit of flow treated to about half that of the normal air-diffusion system, and a number of plants using the system were installed in the United States. However, mechanical difficulties and replacement of parts were expensive and often required shutdown of the plant, causing defective treatment and possible litigation.

The most effective system for maintaining a plant in operation while making minor repairs to the air-diffusion system is that known as the "Swing diffuser," in which the diffusion tubes are suspended in short sections from independent air lines and provided with a swing joint at the top of the tank. If anything goes wrong with a single diffuser unit or the tubes become clogged or broken, this unit can be shut off, raised up, and repaired at leisure without disturbing the flow through the tank or interfering with the operation of any of the other units.

CHEMICAL PRECIPITATION

This method of treatment is particularly applicable to certain classes of wastes which contain color or finely divided solids which do not respond readily to normal gravitational sedimentation within a reasonable period. It is used also to neutralize acid or alkaline wastes and to crack grease and oil emulsions.

In the coagulation and precipitation of fine solids, chemicals are effective in causing more rapid sedimentation; therefore, smaller plant units can be used. However, as the chemical coagulants or reagents used are a daily charge against the plant operation, it is always essential that the cost of treatment be capitalized and balanced against the cost of larger plant units which would produce an equivalent result without resort to chemicals. Chemical precipitation usually produces a voluminous sludge which frequently does not dry rapidly, thus causing undue cost in this phase, so that it may be necessary to employ artificial methods of drying or dewatering the sludge. In some cases where finely divided solids are present which do not settle unaided within a reasonable time, i.e., 4 to 6 hours, the sedimentation tanks required would be so large that chemical precipitation may be warranted. This is an economic problem for the study of the investigator.

Further, if the wastes treated are later to be discharged into public sewerage systems which have biological-type treatment plants or, if the secondary treatment indicated for the waste itself is of the biological type, care must be exercised in the type of coagulants or precipitants used in order not to inhibit or destroy the bacterial action in the plant units.

This is particularly true if the secondary phase is of the trickling-filter or activated-sludge type. In these methods, a high chemical dosage may entirely destroy the bacterial life on which the success of these processes depends. Also, if the sludge is to be digested, certain chemicals in large amounts may tend to inhibit or prevent the anaerobic bacterial action which takes place in the digestion phase.

In investigating chemical precipitation, it may be found that a relatively small amount of certain chemical compounds will produce a satisfactory result. Here again, the economic factor comes into the picture, as the effective chemical may be one which is not commonly found in quantities in the local market and may be very costly in bulk. Frequently, test-tube demonstrations on a waste will indicate that certain chemicals will cause the solids to precipitate or the color to dissipate, but when calculated on a scale to handle a large volume of wastes, the total daily cost may be found to be out of reason. It has been found by most investigators that the common chemicals, such as lime, aluminum sulfate, sodium silicate, ferrous and ferric salts, are usually effective if chemical precipitation is indicated. The quantities of these chemical coagulants may be several times that required by some less common coagulant or proprietary precipitant, but the over-all cost, the important item for the plant owner, may still be lower with the use of the more common chemicals. Those mentioned are low in cost and are usually to be had in the quantities required for waste treatment in practically any locality.

Not only does the use of the common chemicals reduce the daily cost of treatment, but it also introduces other economies in plant construction and operation. Once an industrial plant has been built and put into operation, it must not shut down. Frequently, heavy penalties are exacted against an industrial plant if the waste-treatment plant is out of service. If the plant is one predicated on chemical usage, then sufficient chemical must always be kept on hand to assure continued operation of the plant. If the chemical recommended is one which must be purchased from one supplier and brought from a distance, then large quantities must be stored to avoid exhaustion of the supply. Sufficient storage space must be available to maintain this stock in a usable condition, and possibly the construction of special bins or other precautions will be required to prevent dampness, exposure to the air, or loss in other ways. The more common chemicals can usually be obtained from numerous sources, probably local or nearby. Thus such a large stock need not be kept on hand at the plant.

Another item of importance in planning the use of chemicals for waste treatment is their handling and application to the wastes. As the feeding is important to the success of the method, the chemical compound must be fed continuously and at varying rates according to the strength and volume of waste being treated at any given time. Chemicals which must be fed as solutions are much more difficult to handle than those which may be fed dry. The liquid chemicals are frequently corrosive, and small apertures in feeding devices tend to become corroded and clogged, causing interference and lack of uniformity in the supply and requiring frequent shutdown of the feeding units for cleaning or repair. If the chemicals are corrosive, special piping and metals must be used in plant units with which they come in contact to ensure continued operation and to prevent continuous repair and replacement of parts. The use of these special metals may add materially to the first cost of the units and so offset any seeming advantage in first cost because of the lesser amount of chemical required. It is necessary that a manufacturer of equipment, when asked to quote prices for an industrial-waste-treatment plant, be given all the information available as to the type of chemical compounds to be used so that he may decide whether or not his equipment will need special metals or other protection against chemical action, corrosion, or destruction of parts.

The common chemicals, lime, alum, and the ferrous salts, can be handled in the dry form by any one of several automatic feeders which feed the powdered material according to the needs of the case and maintain an accurate rate of feed. These chemicals do not require the use of special metals, such as stainless steel, copper, or other expensive materials and the chemicals themselves may be stored in sacks or barrels or in large storage hoppers arranged so that they feed down automatically to the feeders with little or no manual attention. As will be seen in Chap. 14 any feeder for dry lime must be provided with an agitator to prevent caking at the exit from the hopper. These dry feeders are reliable and relatively low in cost. They are normally provided with graduated scales which permit the operator to set the discharge rate according to the needs of the case, in pounds of chemical per hour or per unit of flow or whatever other factor he may select.

Chemicals which come in liquid form or which must be made into solutions before being used are much more difficult to handle. They usually come in barrels or relatively small glass containers which must be handled frequently to allow the concentrated liquid to discharge into a dilution tank, and they must be fed by an entirely different type of feeding device.

Chemical precipitation was used to a large extent in the early years of industrial-waste treatment in treating wastes from tanneries, slaughterhouses, canneries, textile mills, etc.; but now with advanced knowledge of the availability and possibilities of the biological methods, many of the wastes formerly treated chemically can be handled by the newer methods.

However, in certain cases, where wastes are highly acid or alkaline, it is still considered advisable to neutralize them chemically before other treatment to cause the precipitation which normally takes place when neutralization is employed.

In one organization accustomed to carrying out complete studies on industrial wastes of all kinds, it is common practice for the chemists to try out some 25 chemical compounds and coagulants, such as those listed in Table 14-1, in order to determine which is the most economical, all things being considered, for that particular waste. In practically every case, it has been found that, while some of the coagulants would produce a satisfactory result with the usage of a small amount, the use of larger amounts of the more common chemicals would produce the same result at less actual cost. The mere poundage of chemical is not the important item; it is the over-all cost of treatment that counts.

In some cases, it may be found that only a certain coagulant or chemical will produce a desired result and that the use of reasonable amounts of the common chemicals will not produce that same result. In such a case, there will be no alternative except to use the indicated coagulant, but if the daily costs for the coagulant are excessive, then other means of disposal should be explored, such as combining the wastes with others to obtain natural reactions or paying the charge that the adjacent municipality may assess for handling the wastes in its sewage-treatment works.

In some cases, the knowledge of a heavy daily cost for treatment would cause the plant owner to consider carefully before he built a plant operating on such a basis. In such a case it would be in order for him to study his plant processes and endeavor to rearrange his operations or change his production methods in some way that would eliminate the ingredient in his wastes causing the expensive treatment. This has been shown in plants manufacturing paper from wood pulp produced by the sulfite process. The cost of reducing the sulfide has been so great that orders to reduce pollution by such wastes have resulted in serious and extended research by the organization set up by the pulp and paper interests to study the possibility of reducing the wastes by distillation or evaporation or, more recently, of turning them into profitable or at least salable compounds, rather than to attempt to treat them merely as a waste problem.

The basic difference between the biological methods and the chemical-precipitation method is that, while both reduce the organic solids and the BOD, they do it by different means. The biological processes actually destroy the organic matter and stabilize it so that it has no further power to absorb oxygen and, consequently, cannot increase the oxygen depletion. In the chemical-precipitation process the operation is primarily a mechanical one in which the coagulants used cause the organic solids to precipitate and the finer solids to coalesce into precipitable entities which can be removed from the waste. Once they are removed, the oxygen demand is reduced. The solids are not destroyed in the process but are temporarily sterilized, thus forming a voluminous sludge which itself then becomes a disposal problem. The chemical-precipitation process produces more sludge to be handled, either by digestion or other methods, than the biological methods. The biological sludge is susceptible to rapid anaerobic digestion, whereas the chemical precipitate, being more voluminous, requires more digestion volume and a longer digestion period. If the chemical dosage is of an amount or of a type which naturally inhibits or delays the digestion process, it may not be practical to consider the use of chemicals for sludge handling. Lime used in large quantities will act as an inhibitor of digestion, as will ferrous sulfate when applied at rates of over 50 ppm (417.0 pounds per million gallons of waste). These factors are extremely important if the waste sludge is to be treated alone and, of more importance, if the sludge is to be combined with sludge from a biological-treatment plant for the municipal sewage.

OTHER METHODS OF TREATMENT

Mechanical Filters

The trickling filter is not included under this heading as it was discussed under Biological Treatment. We are here concerned with mechanical filters which are used in industrial-waste treatment.

The Magnetite Filter is offered for sale as a mechanical strainer in which a bed of magnetite sand is used as the filter medium. The mechanism required to operate this filter is quite complicated. It consists of a rotating or traveling unit which travels above the surface of the filter bed and contains a magnetic field of large area which is alternately energized and deenergized at regular intervals by electrical means. When the magnetic field is energized, it picks up a small amount of the surface magnetite sand in the filter, lifts it, and subjects it to a washing action for the purpose of freeing the adhering matter separated from the liquid; it then is deenergized and drops the sand back into the bed. This progressive lifting and cleaning is said to maintain the filter in a clean, operative condition at all times. The filter itself is simply a mechanical strainer, removing solids only because of their inability to pass through the bed of sand. This filter has been used as a final step, after sedimentation, to remove fine solids which have not settled out in the previous unit.

The Streamline Filter is another mechanical unit suitable for very small flows. It consists of a column of special impervious paper disks packed tightly into a cylinder. The material to be filtered is forced into the central hole in the stack of disks, under considerable pressure. The only outlet from the filter is another opening set near the outer edge of the disks. The liquid in passing from the inlet opening to the discharge opening must pass between the disks, and any solids in suspension, colloids, etc., are strained out and form a deposit on the disks. This filter has no effect on any material which is neither a solid nor an emulsion. Because of its high initial cost and the forcing of the liquid through it under high pressure, it is not a practical unit for large-volume flows. It will remove dirt from an oil waste or color from a waste if the color is in a

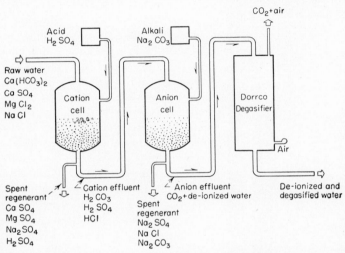

FIG. 12-15. Qualitative flow sheet for complete deionization. (*Courtesy of The Dorr Company.*)

colloidal state. It is said to be able to remove about one-third of the salt from sea water. The upkeep and attendance are high, as the disks clog up quickly and must be removed and another pack installed, requiring interruption of the operation at frequent intervals.

Another and more modern type of unit which is, in effect, a filter, is the "deionization unit." This unit consists of a cell or cylinder filled with synthetic resin which has the ability to remove acids and alkalies and other ions from liquids by converting them into other substances. These units are relatively high in first cost, and the cost of operation depends upon the character of the material being treated. The synthetic resin grains have the capacity to handle a certain amount of the acid or other ion for which they are intended, usually based on grains per gallon of the removable element. When the resins have reached the limit of their capacity to exchange their basic valency for the ion to be removed, their effectiveness ceases and they are said to be exhausted. It is then necessary to regenerate the active element of the resin by passing acid or salt through it, which restores its original power and enables it to proceed through another cycle. This operation necessitates a shutdown, which may require several hours, so that, if continuous operation

is required, it is advisable to have a duplicate set of cells available. The amount of regenerant depends upon the strength of the original raw liquid and the amount of the ion that is to be removed. These units are effective in removing sulfates, chlorides, metallic ingredients, etc., from liquids and in reducing the hardness of water and other liquids. Water passed through such a unit is equivalent to single-distilled water, and the cost is much below that for distillation. These units are able to eliminate the chlorides in water and other liquids to a point where brackish waters may be made potable and useful for pharmaceuticals and for canning and other industries which require a water similar to that produced by single distillation. Without further treatment, the deionized water is not suitable for use in ampoules containing serums, etc., for injection as the water still contains some pathogens (Fig. 12-15).

FIG. 12-16. Laboratory-type L-4 deionization unit, complete as shown. Capacity: 17 gallons per hour of deionized water. (*Courtesy of The Dorr Company.*)

The possible uses of the deionization process in the treatment of industrial wastes have not been fully explored. It is possible that, as the capacities of the synthetic resins are increased, thus permitting longer runs between regenerations, this process may come into considerable use for the treatment of small-volume high-strength wastes. The installations required are small and may usually be placed within the plant itself, thus giving them considerable appeal for industrial plants which are restricted in area or are located in city districts where an outdoor plant might not be considered practical. A complete analysis of any waste is required for the study of the application of the deionization or demineralization process, but with such an analysis and a statement of what is required to be removed or reduced, the manufacturers of such equipment can usually quickly determine the feasibility of the process and can estimate the probable cost of the initial installation and the cost of operation. The one requirement is that any liquid admitted to the cells must be pretreated to the extent that the total solids content must not be over 10 ppm, as the resin beds are not supposed to be used as mechanical filters. Figures 12-16 and 12-17 illustrate, respectively, the

FIG. 12-17. Commercial-type deionization unit. (*Courtesy of The Dorr Company.*)

laboratory unit and one size of the commercial units manufactured for this purpose.

Vacuum Filters

These units are not ordinarily used in the treatment of liquids but are designed primarily to handle the sludges resulting from some previous treatment. There are several newer types, called "precoat" filters, which may be found to have an application in removing fine solids from wastes. As the operation of vacuum filters is entirely physical, they will not remove color nor affect the BOD of wastes except to a minor degree.

The vacuum filter, in its most common form, is a round drum, covered with fine-mesh cloth or wire. The drum, provided with a vacuum inside, revolves slowly in a tub containing the material to be filtered. As the drum passes through the tub, it picks up, owing to the vacuum, a film of the wet material to be filtered, and as it revolves slowly upward the vacuum gradually pulls the occluded water from the material on the face of the filter medium. At a certain point on the downward path of the drum, the vacuum is cut off, and a blast of air provided from the inside of the drum loosens the cake which has formed and which, aided by a scraper, then falls off onto a belt conveyer or into a receptacle for final disposal. These filters will reduce the moisture in a semiliquid material from 95 per cent to about 70 to 75 per cent in one revolution of the drum, making the cake easily handled by mechanical means.

In the precoat type of vacuum filter, a blanket of the material to be dewatered or of some other inert material is permitted to form on the drum. This then acts as a filter through which the liquid is drawn, leaving the fine solids on the surface. At each discharge revolution, a very thin layer of the top surface of the blanket is removed by a scraper. The filter continues to be effective until the entire precoat layer has been cut away.

This type of filter may prove useful in reducing the solids in wastes, particularly if there is a possibility of recovering these solids for reuse. The solids retained on the filter are low in moisture and can be handled easily, but for recovery a washing operation would be required to remove the small amount of precoat material removed with them. The rates of application on a vacuum filter are high, so that even for a considerable volume they do not require a large space. The filter drums are usually covered with a woolen, cotton, or nylon cloth or with a fine wire mesh. In time, these mediums become clogged and wear, and replacement is required. The replacement is an item of expense, requiring the shutdown of the filter and several hours of labor plus the cost of the new cloth or medium. The life of these mediums varies with the type of material filtered, its effect on the fibers of the cloth, and the effectiveness of its removal from the cloth. In general practice, with careful operation, these mediums will continue to give good service for 400 to 800 hours. Medium replacement and the time required to accomplish it must be considered an operating expense against this type of unit. The initial cost of the equipment is relatively high, but the space occupied is very much less than that required with any other method of dewatering sludges, and these items must be carefully evaluated when considering this method as compared with others.

In an endeavor to eliminate the replacement of filter cloths, a new type of vacuum filter has been developed with a medium entirely composed of coil springs in the form of long cords which are wrapped around the drum. Two of these lines of springs lie on the face of the drum itself, and a third line of springs lies in the depression between the two lower lines. The idea in this construction is that the cake forms on the surface of the spring wires, and as they pass over a roller guide on the discharge side, the springs flex and open so that the cake is released. These filters have been on the market only a short time so that little data are available as to the actual success of the operation over long periods or the cost of operation. Each line of springs has a center filler or core of hard plastic material, the object of which is to prevent solids from entering the spring and clogging it. The cost of replacement of the spring medium is very high, and the initial cost of the filter unit is also much higher than for other vacuum filters of the conventional type. When data are available as to the life of the spring medium, accurate cost estimates may then be set up to determine whether the saving in cloth replacement will justify the higher initial cost. The changing of mediums on the conventional type of filter is frequently a nuisance for the operators and is the primary reason for the development of this spring type. However, if its initial cost and the eventual replacement of spring medium are higher than the cost of a normal filter and replacement of cloths over an equivalent term, its installation may be questionable.

In order to discharge the cake more effectively from the filter cloth, a type of filter was produced some years ago which used the normal type of cloth medium but in which a series of cords or strings was placed over the cloth which tended to lift the cake from the cloth at the discharge point and so assure its complete separation. This unit, however, did not eliminate the occasional replacement of the filter medium.

The vacuum filter is a very effective means of reducing the moisture in sludges, which form a homogeneous cake on the filter surface. In some cases, it is necessary to add a conditioner to the sludge, such as aluminum sulfate, lime, or ferric chloride, to cause it to coalesce into a homogeneous mass which will permit the vacuum to pull the occluded water from it without producing cracks in the sludge film. Although the required amounts of conditioner may vary with different sludges, the average amount required will be 6 to 8 per cent by weight of the dry solids in the sludge. The most advantageous amount of conditioner for a given sludge must, however, be determined on each job by actual trial. Certain sludges may also be conditioned with aluminum sulfate or lime.

Vacuum filters are extensively used to dewater domestic and municipal sewage sludge, especially in those cases where the sludge is to be further dried by means of heat for final use or disposal.

Digestion of Solids

The solids removed from industrial wastes can, in many cases, be handled in a manner similar to municipal sewage sludge. If the solids are of an organic nature, which will normally decompose, the digestion process is suitable. This process is adaptable to sludges from cannery, slaughterhouse, tannery, fermentation-products, dairy and creamery, and numerous other wastes. The process may be used in its normal place as a means of disposing of the wet sludge removed from the sedimentation basins, provided that it has not been chemically treated to such a degree as to inhibit or destroy the bacterial action required to reduce it to its basic ingredients.

It has been found that wastes which are high in hydrocarbons, such as those from canneries, dehydration plants, yeast factories, malt sirups, and distilleries (both for the manufacture of alcoholic liquors from grain and also the manufacture of alcohol from cane-sugar molasses, breweries, etc.), may be effectively treated by digestion as the first step in the treatment process. This is particularly effective on wastes in which the dissolved and colloidal solids constitute one of the major elements of pollution and the wastes have a high BOD.

This process consists in passing the entire volume of waste flow into digestion tanks, rather than the sludge, which is the normal procedure. The digester thus becomes the first unit in the plant, receiving the entire flow of raw wastes. The overflow from this unit, roughly equal to the volume put into it daily, and which in normal operation is known as "supernatant liquor," then passes to sedimentation units and possibly, depending upon the need for further treatment, may go to trickling filters or to activated-sludge units. The sludge from the sedimentation units is recirculated back to the digestion units, and at intervals digested sludge is discharged to the sludge-drying system.

Relatively high percentages of BOD reduction are obtainable with this method at moderate initial and operating costs as compared with other methods. Test data on various wastes treated by this method have shown 5-day BOD reductions of 60 to 80 per cent, with digester detention periods of 4 to 10 days.

One of the advantages of this method is said to be that the material which has undergone predigestion will have a pH stabilized close to the neutral point (7.0); therefore the resultant effluent is not so susceptible to septic action in the following units as wastes which have been treated by more conventional methods.

If the wastes are suitable for final treatment on trickling filters, particularly of the high-capacity type, predigestion will deliver an effluent which can be readily handled on filters of relatively small diameter. Other advantages of this method are that the capital cost for the plant is less than for a conventional plant, and operating costs are usually comparable to those for normal aerobic treatment. As the wastes when predigested produce a considerable volume of gas which has a definite fuel value, this gas can be used to generate power or to generate heat or steam for use in the industry. Frequently, savings due to this use may offset a considerable part of the total cost of operation of the treatment units.

As the predigestion tanks have a volume equal to several days, total flow, they act as balancing tanks to take care of the variations in hourly flow from the main plant and thus tend to deliver an effluent of more uniform character and strength, which reflects an economy in the secondary-treatment units as they can be designed on the basis of an average effluent condition rather than for some extraordinary peak flow or condition.

Table 12-6 contains operating data from representative plants, showing the results of predigestion on various wastes.

TABLE 12-6. RESULTS OF PREDIGESTION ON VARIOUS INDUSTRIAL WASTES

Type of waste	BOD, ppm		BOD reduction, %	Digestion time, days
	Raw wastes	Digester effluent		
Yeast and malt sirup..............	5,150	1,150	77.5	10
Beer slop........................	11,500	2,500	78	9.6

It would seem at first glance that to put all the wastes from an industrial plant into digestion tanks would require tanks of inordinately large size. However, on actual calculation, this is not borne out in the average case. Let us assume, for example, that an industrial plant has a daily volume of 100,000 gallons of high BOD wastes, and it is decided that a predigestion period of 8 days will be suitable. The total flow for 8 days is 800,000 gallons, or 106,666 cubic feet. Based on two-stage digestion, which is normally recommended for this system, two tanks each with a volume of 53,333 cubic feet would be necessary. With a depth of 25 feet, each tank would have an area of only 2,133 square feet, which can be had in a tank 52 feet in diameter.

To illustrate how this method works out in practice, let us consider the yeast and malt-sirup waste shown in Table 12-6. We will first study treatment on a high-rate filter type of plant with the normal procedure—sedimentation, filtration, sedimentation, and sludge digestion. The initial BOD is given as 5,150 ppm. Assume a detention period of 3 hours for the raw waste in the primary sedimentation unit to remove as much as possible of the settleable solids.   Based on data collected from a number of sewage-treatment plants, it is safe to assume that the primary settling step will reduce the BOD 30 to 40 per cent.   However, as in this case we have a much higher proportion of colloidal and dissolved solids than is normal in municipal sewage, which will not settle in 3 hours, this percentage of BOD reduction will not be obtained.   We will assume that the BOD is reduced only 10 per cent in the primary tank, which leaves a total of 4,635 ppm for the aerobic filters to handle.   From operating data on high BOD wastes, we feel safe in assuming that the load of 4,635 ppm can be applied to the filters at a rate of 5 pounds per cubic yard of filter. In the 4,635 ppm, there is a total of 38,655 pounds of BOD.   At 5 pounds per cubic yard, a filter containing 7,731 cubic yards of material would be required.   Using the standard depth of 3 feet of filter material for the high-rate filter, the total area of filter required would be 69,579 square feet, or a unit nearly 300 feet in diameter.

On the other hand, using the predigestion method and starting with the same BOD of 5,150 ppm, Table 12-6 shows that this is reduced to 1,150 ppm by the initial step.   Now there is only 9,691 pounds of BOD to be dealt with by the filter, and using the same rate of 5 pounds per cubic yard loading, we find that we need a filter with a volume of only 1,940 cubic yards and an area of 17,460 square feet, or a unit only 150 feet in diameter, which is within actual operating unit limits.

The method described makes it possible to treat high BOD wastes economically and practically and is worthy of serious consideration for strong industrial wastes of that character.

Sludge Drying

The end product of any waste-treatment operation will be a volume of wet sludge.   This will vary in amount, moisture content, and consistency for different wastes but always presents a problem in final handling and disposal which enters into both the initial and operating costs of the treatment works.

If the sludge is mainly of an organic character amenable to normal digestion procedure, then the resultant digested sludge may equal only about one-half the original sludge volume and if thoroughly digested will be inoffensive.   However, this sludge will usually be a semifluid mass, with a moisture content running from 92 to as high as 96 per cent.   The great problem in sludge handling is to reduce the moisture to a point where the sludge is relatively dry (10 per cent being the accepted upper limit) and can be readily handled for final disposal.

The normal methods of sludge drying are as follows:

1. Lagooning.
2. Open-bed drying.
3. Covered-bed drying.
4. Heat drying.
    a. Drum driers.
    b. Flash driers.
5. Incineration.

In a few cases, the wet sludge may be discharged into the sea or delivered wet to the final disposal grounds, but these cases are so rare and are so likely to become less possible in the future that they are not worthy of serious consideration here. In some cases, an industrial plant may be so located that its sludge may be economically pumped to a nearby municipal sewage-treatment plant which has the means and capacity for handling this sludge. This means of disposal may be very economical. If the digested sludge is of the same general character as normal sewage sludge, it may then be handled in the same manner and by the same methods as that sludge.

Lagooning is sometimes resorted to, but this requires the use of a large area of land and may give rise to odors which permeate the neighborhood and cause complaint. Nor is it a sightly means of disposal. If the sludge is one from a chemical-precipitation process, lagooning is a messy operation as the sludge dries very slowly, if at all, and in a short time the area covered by the lagoons is denuded of all trees and shrubbery with which the sludge comes in contact. However, where there is ample land in the vicinity of the plant, which is not suitable for other purposes, the sludge may be lagooned and will serve to fill up low areas.

Open-bed drying on sludge beds prepared in the normal manner used for municipal sewage sludge, with underdrains and a free sand-drying medium, is suitable for most sludges. The rate of drying depends upon the climatic conditions in the area, and bed space should be provided on a basis that will permit clean bed area always being available for new sludge so that it need not be put on top of drying sludge. If the climate is arid and sunny, the sludge put on the bed in an initial depth of 9 inches to 1 foot will probably dry and crack in about 7 days and will then be in a condition to be shoveled from the bed. If the area is humid or subject to much rain, the drying time will be lengthened accordingly.

It is customary, and required by practically all the boards of health of the several states, that an area of 1 square foot of open drying bed be provided per person served by the plant. As industrial-waste treatment is not usually based upon a per capita basis, it will be necessary to calculate the volume of sludge to be handled. The volume of sludge to be expected from an industrial-waste-treatment plant can be calculated only on the basis of the volume of the solids removed from the waste, the reduction in those solids obtained by digestion, and the moisture content of the wet digested sludge as applied to the drying beds. If it is assumed that a given waste has a raw suspended-solid content of 600 ppm and that 90 per cent of this is removed in the process, 540 ppm or approximately 1,440 cubic feet of wet sludge (95 per cent moisture) will result from 1 million gallons of waste. If this sludge has a volatile organic content of about 65 to 70 per cent, we can figure that the resultant sludge to be dried will be about one-half of the original amount of 1,440 cubic feet, or roughly 720 cubic feet of wet sludge per million gallons of waste. This volume will vary considerably, owing to the organic content of the sludge, its moisture, the completeness of digestion, and the general effectiveness of the treatment plant.

Open drying beds should not be composed of one large area, to be completely covered with a mass of wet sludge, but the total drying area should be divided into numerous small sections, preferably six to eight, so that small amounts of sludge may be drawn frequently from the digesters and put to dry. In this manner, not all the available bed area will be full of sludge, and there will usually be at least one bed free for reserve or in case of an emergency requiring the discharge of sludge. The sludge is usually applied to the bed at a depth of 6 to 12 inches; in normal drying weather with no rain, it should dry down to approximately one-third of that depth in a week to 10 days, when the surface will appear full of cracks. The dried sludge may be removed from the bed by spades. Furthermore, one bed of large area interferes with digester operation, as in order to fill the large bed a very large amount of sludge must be drawn from the digester. This drawdown may reduce the sludge volume in the digester unit to such an extent that there will not be sufficient seed sludge left in it to maintain rapid digestion. If the digester is one provided with a gasometer cover, the excessive drawdown may bring the sludge level below the rim of the cover and permit gas to escape. If the gas is being used as fuel, an excessive drawdown of sludge may reduce the volume in the gasometer to such an extent that it may interfere with the operation of the units requiring fuel.

Digested sludge need not be drawn every day; it may be drawn periodically when it is estimated that sufficient digested sludge has accumulated to fill one section of the drying bed. The plant operator will learn to recognize digested sludge by opening the sludge-discharge valve occasionally and observing the appearance, odor, and color of the sludge. Normal digested sludge will be quite granular in appearance, grayish black in color, and will have a slight tarry or rich earth odor, not at all unpleasant.

In areas where much rain occurs or where there is freezing weather for a period of months at a time and the drying is interfered with, or where aesthetic considerations require that the sludge must be kept out of sight, the drying beds may be covered by a glass structure similar to a greenhouse. If this is done, and the sludge is kept dry, it is usual to require only half the area stipulated for an open bed. But care must be exercised in selecting the type of cover used. The ordinary greenhouse glass cover is built for the purpose of creating a humid atmosphere to encourage the growth of plant life. But humidity is not a desirable factor in sludge drying. An improperly ventilated glass cover will sweat on the inside of the glass, and moisture will drop continually on the sludge, keeping it wet and entirely defeating the purpose of the bed. A glass cover for sludge beds should have a hinged section of the side wall, near the level of the sludge, which may be opened to permit a flow of air across the sludge.

This type of bed, while reducing the area required to one-half of that for an open bed, is not an inexpensive structure. Glass covers, of proper type, range in cost from $3 to $4 per square foot of flat bed area in place. Frequently, however, when industrial-waste-treatment plants are constructed in the vicinity of residences, it is expedient, from a psychological standpoint, to use the glass cover to remove possible complaints from nearby residents.

For large plants, where area restrictions prohibit open-bed or covered-bed drying, it may be necessary to resort to mechanical drying. This ordinarily consists of two steps, dewatering and heat drying. The wet sludge, which normally has a moisture content between 93 and 95 per cent, could, of course, be dried in heat driers, but the fuel cost to evaporate such a large amount of water is extremely high. It is considered economical, therefore, to use preliminary mechanical drying or dewatering by means of vacuum filters. These units will, in a small area, normally reduce the moisture content of the sludge from 95 to about 70 to 72 per cent in a period of a few minutes, passage around the filter drum. This reduction in moisture produces a tremendous reduction in the volume of material to be handled, and as the sludge cake with a moisture of 70 to 72 per cent can be carried on belt conveyers, the transportation problem is a simple one.

The sludge cake may be dried in several ways. The use of drum driers, in long rotating horizontal cylinders similar to lime-burning equipment, is the oldest and most simple method, but these driers require large areas and considerable power and fuel to provide the necessary drying temperatures.

The most modern method is known as Flash Drying. In this method the sludge cake is conveyed to a mixer or rabbling unit, where it is mixed with a portion of already dried material. This pulverized mixture is then blown to the top of a column through which hot gases are exhausted, and the moist particles are dropped downward through this uprising column of hot gas and reach the bottom as a dry powdery material in a condition known as commercially dry, containing 5 to 10 per cent moisture. The heat for such a system may be provided by burning digester gas from the sludge digesters or by oil, or the waste heat from an adjoining incinerator may be used.

This dried sludge may be bagged and sent away to final disposal grounds or sold for use as a fertilizer. The process may also be carried to the further step of incineration of the sludge, in which case the sole residue is a small amount of ash, a very minor proportion of the original volume of wet sludge. Figure 12-18 illustrates one form of this type of system.

A variation of this system is that of a cylindrical vertical furnace with a series of trays. The sludge is dropped on the top tray and by means of mechanical rakes is carried to the center of each tray and dropped to the next; a rising column of heated gas passes through the sludge as it travels downward.

Still another variation is a spray-drying system wherein the wet sludge is sprayed into a heated chamber and dried. Mechanical rakes at the bottom collect the dry material and remove it from the chamber.

These methods entail a considerable investment, but they may be housed in neat buildings and usually require a relatively small area. They dispose of the sludge in the most sanitary manner, and the installation gives no outward indication of its purpose to cause complaints from neighboring residents.

The dried sludge from the heat-drying processes may frequently be disposed of to the municipality, for use in its parks, or it may be used on the soil of the plant grounds. In a number of cases, heat-dried sludge is sold to those who need a mild fertilizer or soil conditioner. Sludge from slaughterhouses and tanneries treated in this way is a particularly good soil conditioner, and with a little propaganda on the part of the owners of the plant, it is possible to create a demand for it. The sale of this sludge will, to some extent, provide a revenue to offset some of the operating cost of the plant. Numerous municipalities are deriving a substantial revenue from the sale of dried sludge.

The most economical method of sludge disposal for any industrial plant is the one which will dispose of the sludge in the least offensive manner and at the least cost to the plant owner. This can be determined only by a careful study of all the factors in each case. No general rule can be laid down.

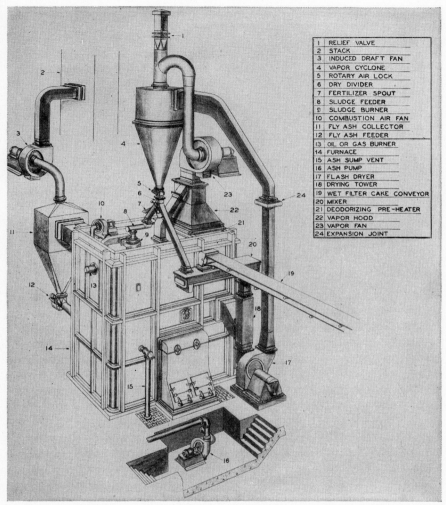

1	RELIEF VALVE
2	STACK
3	INDUCED DRAFT FAN
4	VAPOR CYCLONE
5	ROTARY AIR LOCK
6	DRY DIVIDER
7	FERTILIZER SPOUT
8	SLUDGE FEEDER
9	SLUDGE BURNER
10	COMBUSTION AIR FAN
11	FLY ASH COLLECTOR
12	FLY ASH FEEDER
13	OIL OR GAS BURNER
14	FURNACE
15	ASH SUMP VENT
16	ASH PUMP
17	FLASH DRYER
18	DRYING TOWER
19	WET FILTER CAKE CONVEYOR
20	MIXER
21	DEODORIZING PRE-HEATER
22	VAPOR HOOD
23	VAPOR FAN
24	EXPANSION JOINT

FIG. 12-18. Combustion Engineering–C. E. Raymond type Flash-Drying system for sludge. (*Courtesy of Combustion Engineering–Superheater, Inc., Flash Dryer Division.*)

PRACTICAL METHODS OF TREATMENT OF SPECIFIC WASTES

It is not the intention here to present all the ways in which various industrial wastes have been treated, but rather to give short descriptions, with flow diagrams, of methods which have been used successfully in operating plants. These are not the only successful methods that may be used, as research and development will undoubtedly produce others, but those presented will act as a guide for the treatment of a number of the more common wastes and for the construction of moderate-cost, efficient plants. A general flow diagram incorporating many of the methods used for various wastes is shown in Fig. 12-19.

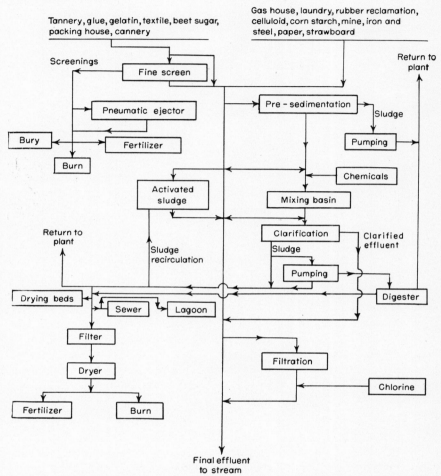

FIG. 12-19.   Composite flow sheet of typical processes for various types of industrial wastes.

Stockyard, Slaughterhouse and Meat-packing-plant Wastes

These wastes originate in the operations of slaughtering animals for food and in the preparation of animal products for the market.   They comprise the wastes from the stockyards, containing animal excreta and urine; the wastes from the killing floors of slaughterhouses, containing blood, paunch manure, bits of entrails, etc.; and the wastes from the establishments which dress the meat for market, as raw meat, or prepare portions of the animal for cooked-meat products, such as sausage. Table 12-7 shows the approximate volume of waste flows, the average analysis of the wastes, and the equivalent population represented in the pollutional strength of the individual wastes.

TABLE 12-7. STOCKYARD, SLAUGHTERHOUSE, AND PACKING-HOUSE WASTES

Type of waste*	Flow volume, gal, per unit	Typical analyses, ppm		Population equivalent per unit	
		BOD	Suspended solids	BOD	Suspended solids
Stockyards, acre............	25,000	65	175	80	180
Slaughterhouse:					
Ton on hoof..............	900	2,200	930	100	35
1 hog unit...............	100	2,200	930	18	6
Packing house:					
Ton on hoof..............	4,200	900	650	190	120
1 hog unit...............	550	900	650	24	14

* Cattle are rated as equal to 2.5 hog units. Hogs, calves, and lambs are rated at 1 hog unit each.

These wastes are usually satisfactorily treated in plants of the types commonly employed in the treatment of normal municipal sewage. Trickling filters, of both the low- and high-rate types, have proved successful. Activated sludge has also proved satisfactory for large volumes. In numerous cases, these wastes are treated in the local municipal sewage-treatment plant, either with the plant design coordinated to handle the increased percentages of suspended solids and BOD, or with pretreatment of the wastes in a separate installation to reduce the strength of the wastes to a more normal sewage strength. In some cases, the pretreatment plants are located in the packing-house areas. In other cases, as in Cedar Rapids, Iowa, and Sioux Falls, S.D., separate installations for pretreatment of the packing-house wastes are located adjacent to the sewage-treatment works. In these latter cases, a separate sewer line is laid from the packing plant to the pretreatment works and the effluent of the pretreatment taken into the municipal plant just ahead of the secondary-treatment units of that plant.

If the wastes are to be treated in a municipal plant, consideration must be given to the larger amounts of suspended solids to be removed, which directly affect the size of digestion units, pumps, sludge-drying units, etc., and the secondary units must be prepared to handle the greater amounts of BOD.   Where packing-house wastes are handled in a municipal plant, they produce an additional supply of gas which may be converted into useful energy through gas-engine generators or for other fuel purposes in the plant.

Where it is not practical to include the packing-house wastes in the municipal plant, owing to lack of proper facilities or distance from the works, and the logical discharge point is into a local stream, it is then common practice to construct the waste-treatment plant at the packing

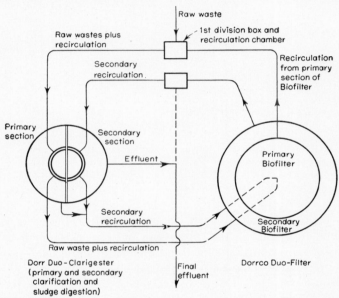

Fig. 12-20.   Flow diagram of packing-house waste-treatment plant.   Reitz Meat Products Company, Kansas City, Mo.

house.   In such cases the trickling filter or activated-sludge process may be used.   Where it is not necessary to discharge a highly purified effluent, chemical precipitation, after preliminary screening, may be sufficient.

The modern high-rate filter is a most effective type of plant for these wastes.   For the smaller establishments, especially, a unique and entirely practical type of installation has been devised, which utilizes the Biofiltration system, with recirculation of effluent.   In this plant, exemplified by the recent installation at the packing house of the Reitz Meat Products Company, near Kansas City, Mo., the use of a Duo-Clarigester and a Duo-Filter, in which the first named performs a triple purpose and the second a dual purpose, the operation has been very successful.   The Duo-Clarigester acts as both primary and secondary sedimentation unit and digestion unit, and the Duo-Filter provides two-stage high-rate Biofiltration in the one unit. The flow sheet of this plant is shown in Fig. 12-20.

As an installation of a small activated-sludge plant for the treatment of packing-house wastes, we may mention that of the Rubner Packing Company, Muncie, Ind., which treats the wastes from hog-packing operations of 350 to 500 hog units per day. This plant cost approximately $41,000 and has a designed capacity of 200,000 to 500,000 gallons per day.

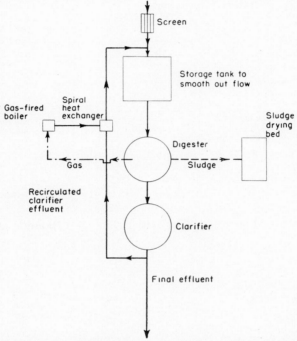

FIG. 12-20A. Slaughterhouse-waste treatment. Geo. A. Hormel Company, Austin, Minn.

The flow sheet of this plant differs from the normal flow sheet of an activated-sludge plant, shown in Fig. 12-21, and is as follows: (1) preaeration of raw wastes, (2) intermittent intensity of aeration in the main aeration units with provision for occasional aeration in the final sedimentation tank, (3) split flow of return sludge, and (4) intermixing of waste sludge in the preaeration and primary settling units.

The results stated to have been obtained in this plant are given in Table 12-8. Operating results showed an average of 4.5 cubic feet of air per gallon of waste treated. The cost of operation for the first six months of operation, including power, maintenance, interest, and depreciation on plant, was estimated at $21.93 per day, or 5.5 cents per hog unit on the basis of 400 hog units per day.

Several examples of the use of chemical precipitation have been found. At Phoenix, Ariz., the Tovrea Packing Company installed a plant which uses ferric chloride made locally from wire and chlorine. Reported

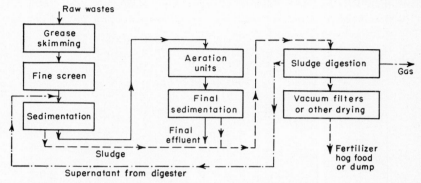

Fig. 12-21.   Typical flow sheet of activated-sludge process for packing-house wastes.

results in this plant show reductions of BOD from a raw waste of 1,448 ppm to a final effluent of 188 ppm, or 87.01 per cent, and suspended solids from a raw waste of 2,875 ppm to a final effluent of 167 ppm, a reduction of 94.4 per cent.   Ferric chloride made from 1,000 pounds of wire and

TABLE 12-8.   RESULTS OF ACTIVATED-SLUDGE TREATMENT OF PACKING-HOUSE
WASTES AT RUBNER PACKING CO., MUNCIE, IND.

Sample	Raw waste, ppm		Reductions by primary clarifier, %		Over-all results, reduction, %	
	Suspended solids	BOD	Suspended solids	BOD	Suspended solids	BOD
Composite:						
9-hr................	1,016	940	58	29	98.7	99.5
24-hr................	.....	980	....	..	....	98.3
	400	353	80.5	49	98.6	98.4
Average................	708	758	51.6	44	97.5	98.8

1,150 pounds of chlorine per million gallons was employed.   The effluent is used for irrigation, grease is recovered, and gas is utilized.   With the credit for these items, the net cost of treatment is about $25 per million gallons of waste.

At Madison, Wis., a packing house uses two-stage chemical precipitation using zinc chloride and aluminum sulfate, followed by sedimentation, lime treatment, and secondary sedimentation. A reduction in BOD from about 1,600 ppm in the raw wastes to 200 ppm in the final effluent, or 87.5 per cent, was reported. Suspended solids were reduced from 1,200 ppm in the raw waste to 80 ppm in the final effluent, a reduction of 93.3 per cent. In this plant, grease also was recovered and the sludge was dewatered on a vacuum filter and the sludge cake used for fertilizer. The effluent was stated to be clear with a slight straw color.

An interesting and important new development in the treatment of packing-house wastes has been demonstrated at the Geo. A. Hormel Company, Austin, Minn. It indicates a very economical method using natural methods only. The plant embodies a holding tank to smooth out the waste flow, a digestion tank, and a final settling tank. The digestion tank would normally have a capacity equal to one or two total days'

TABLE 12-8A

Item	Test 1			Test 2			Test 3		
	Raw, ppm	Final, ppm	Change, %	Raw, ppm	Final, ppm	Change, %	Raw, ppm	Final, ppm	Change, %
Total solids................	5,622	4,402	21.6	5,630	4,329	23.1	5,480	4,208	23.2
Volatile solids..............	1,363	390	71.5	1,665	354	78.7	2,077	384	81.5
Suspended solids..........	848	223	73.6	807	139	83.0	816	170	82.8
Total nitrogen.............	145	126	13.4	170	137	19.8	170	135	19.1
Ammonia nitrogen.........	30	105	264.0	25	119	368.0	25	114	365.
Organic nitrogen..........	115	22	81.3	146	18	87.7	145	21	84.7
5-day BOD................	1,461	76	94.8	1,948	82	95.8	1,959	108	94.5
Gas, cu ft per lb solids.....	10.5	.....	....	9.5	.....	....	6.7		
BOD removed per cu ft digestion capacity.........	0.088	.....	....	0.113	.....	....	0.115		

Anaerobic Digestion, *Public Works*, p. 44, July, 1951.

waste flow. The contents are heated to maintain a normal temperature of 90 to 92°F. The liquid overflow from the digestion tank, after settling, is recirculated to the holding tank and thence to the digestion unit. A pilot plant operated for 5 months produced such satisfactory results that a full-scale plant operating on the same plan has been projected. Results of three separate tests on the pilot plant show the interesting data in Table 12-8A. The flow sheet of this plant is shown in Fig. 12-20A.

Acid Mine Wastes

These wastes emanate from coal mines and are particularly troublesome in the coal-mining regions of Pennsylvania, West Virginia, and Ohio. The wastes from abandoned or exhausted mines create a severe problem.

The main problem is neutralization of the acid content of the wastes. The plant required is relatively simple, consisting of mixing units, chemical feeders, and sedimentation, but the cost of treatment is considerable as large amounts of lime are required. The problem of the wastes from abandoned mines is being met by sealing the mines to avoid leakage of acid wastes, but the results are not conclusive.

A secondary coal-mine waste is the fine coal particles carried away in the washing operation. The solution of this problem is by sedimentation units, usually of the mechanically cleaned type, which permit the fine coal in the wash water to settle. The sediment is then collected by the tank mechanism, and the dried sludge may be sold to power companies or briquetted with a binder and sold as fuel. A recent survey of this reclamation of coal to prevent stream pollution showed that in Pennsylvania alone a total of 36 plants have been installed or are under construction.

Cannery and Food-processing Wastes

Cannery wastes include the wastes originating in plants canning vegetables, fruits, citrus fruits, and other edible products and the wastes from the dehydration of fruits and vegetables and from general food processing. Vegetable-canning wastes include those from tomatoes, beans (both lima and string),[7] peas, corn, spinach, tomato catsup, sauerkraut, soups, pork and beans, etc. Fruit-canning wastes come from plants where all types of fruits and berries are prepared as well as from plants in which fruit juices are canned. Dehydration wastes come from the plants in which vegetables and fruits are dehydrated to be sold in that state for future hydration before use.

These wastes consist of washing waters from the raw fruits and vegetables, from the cutting and peeling rooms, where excess juices and pulp originate, and from the cooking sections and the floor washings from the cleanup operations. They are charged with dirt washed from the articles, fruit and vegetable skins, pea pods, vegetable fiber, smashed or rejected peas and kernels of corn, corn milk, etc.

Canneries operate normally as seasonable establishments if they are in a district where one crop is the rule, but in other cases they may operate on a number of fruits and vegetables in rotation as the crops mature. During the crop season the period of operation is intensive and may run 24 hours per day in order to keep up with the picking and to preserve the material before spoilage. Therefore, the volume of waste per day is usually large, but the canning season may last for only a relatively short period of weeks or months.

These wastes contain relatively large amounts of solids, many of which have a low specific gravity and will float on the surface of tanks and cause scum troubles. It has been general practice in the past to install a fine screen as the first unit in the treatment process, but as this unit does not dispose of the material, but simply intercepts it, a new unit, the Vacuator, has been developed recently. This unit assists in the removal of these light solids by means of preaeration, to encourage buoyancy, and then subjecting them to a vacuum in a closed tank to cause them to rise rapidly to the surface of the tank, where they are skimmed off and sent to the digestion tanks. A description of this unit will be found in Chap. 13.

Screening, or treatment by vacuum, will remove a large bulk of the lighter, floatable solids, but the effluent may still contain a large percentage of highly putrescible matter in the form of fine and dissolved solids and color. The wastes from corn canning, for instance, after the preliminary treatment, are usually milky white, while those from tomato canning are red.

Cannery wastes in general may be treated satisfactorily either by chemical precipitation, if not too great a degree of treatment is required, or by the trickling-filter method, if a high degree of BOD reduction and suspended-solids removal is required. In this latter method, the modern high-rate biological filter with recirculation is particularly effective in obtaining the desired result and reducing the size and cost of the plant.

When chemical treatment is employed, the usual coagulants used are lime and an iron salt, such as ferrous sulfate or ferric chloride. Such treatment may normally be expected to reduce the suspended solids 70 to 95 per cent and the BOD 25 to 75 per cent. Table 12-9 indicates the

TABLE 12-9. CHEMICAL TREATMENT OF CANNERY WASTES

Waste	Chemicals, lb per 1,000 gal			Reduction after pretreatment, %	
	Lime	Alum	$FeSO_4$	Suspended solids	BOD
Tomato..............	8.3	...	....	86.5	39.0
	4.0	1.0	....	....	50.0
Red beets...........	9.0	...	....	90.0	43.0
	10.0	...	4.0	....	59.0
	10.0	...	....	....	48.0
Corn...............	8–10	...	9–12	....	60.0
	6.0	...	3.25	....	50–75
Carrot..............	5.0	...	1.0	....	75.0
	8.0	...	....	....	75.0
Peas...............	7.5	...	3.25	....	50–75
Wax beans..........	6.0	...	2.5	....	50–75

amounts of chemicals that have produced satisfactory results on various wastes.

In treating cannery wastes by biological filters, pretreatment is required to remove as much as possible of the solid matter. The pretreated wastes may then be applied to high-rate filters with recirculation at rates as high as 20 million gallons per acre per day, the rate including the recirculated material. Owing to the short periods during which canneries normally operate, and as the ripening period of a biological filter is 3 to 6 weeks before it produces effective results, it is usually necessary to seed the filters before application of the waste flows. This is done by feeding the

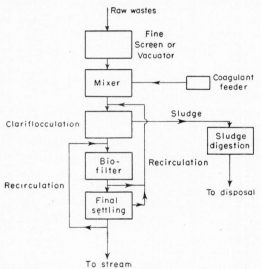

FIG. 12-22.   Flow sheet illustrating the treatment of cannery wastes.

filters with humus or raw sludge from a nearby municipal plant several weeks before the canning season opens so that the filters will be in condition to attack the canning wastes when the plant begins operations. In some cases where the cannery operates throughout the year on a series of different materials, it will probably not be necessary to seed the filters.

The sludge from the sedimentation step of cannery-waste treatment may usually be digested in the normal type of sludge digesters, although because of the tendency for rapid acid formation, it may be necessary to control the reaction in the digestion system to maintain the alkaline condition essential to rapid digestion and the production of the methane-type gas. Digesters for these wastes should be designed on the basis of the volatile-solids content of the wastes rather than to attempt to use a population factor.

In handling beet wastes, frequently so much earth is brought in with the beets that it may be considered advisable to install a unit to remove this grit and dirt from the flow, such as a grit chamber, Detritor, or Classifier.

A typical flow sheet of cannery-waste treatment is shown in Fig. 12-22. This diagram is a composite showing both the chemical-precipitation method and the biological filter with recirculation.

Cannery wastes vary in their composition and strength in different plants, owing to differences in cleanliness of the field product, the care in washing, and the manner of preparation. Table 12-10 gives an indication of the average strength and composition of several types of wastes.

TABLE 12-10. AVERAGE STRENGTH AND COMPOSITION OF CANNERY WASTES

Waste	Average volume, gal per ton of raw material	BOD (screened waste)		Suspended solids			
				Raw waste		Screened waste	
		Ppm	Tons	Ppm	Tons	Ppm	Tons
Red beet............	1,260	3,775	39.5	4,293	45	1,893	20
Tomato.............	360	2,065	6.2	2,485	7.5	505	1.5
Squash.............	.....	6,275	.....	.....	....	3,670	
Peas (raw)..........	.....	1,400					
Corn...............	.....	675					

Chemical-plant Wastes

These wastes originate in plants manufacturing chemicals or chemical products for the market. They vary greatly, depending upon the products made, from simple wastes which may require neutralization only or removal of color or other ingredients, to complex wastes such as those which arise in manufacturing establishments such as Eastman Kodak Company, du Pont Company, and other organizations which manufacture a wide variety of products.

One of the most complex problems is that of the removal of phenols and phenolic compounds from chemical-plant wastes. The outstanding example of a company with this problem is the Dow Chemical Company at Midland, Mich., where two treatment plants were installed, one for the treatment of the general wastes exclusive of the phenolic wastes and the other for the treatment of the wastes containing phenols. As the ultimate discharge point for all these wastes was a lake which was the source of potable water for large cities, complete treatment of each type of waste was required.

The plant for the treatment of the general wastes comprised the activated-sludge system, and the flow sheet was as shown in Fig. 12-23. Reports are that this plant removed 75 per cent of the objectionable odors and more than 80 per cent of the organic matter.

The plant for the phenolic wastes comprised sedimentation and trickling filters followed by activated sludge and final sedimentation and oxidation ponds before discharge to the lake. This plant, with the flow sheet shown in Fig. 12-24, is stated to remove 99 per cent of the phenolic constituent of this waste.

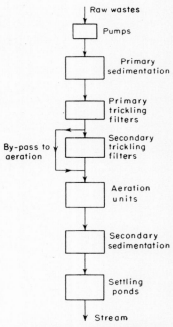

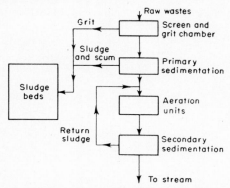

FIG. 12-23.   Flow sheet of treatment plant for general wastes.   Dow Chemical Company, Midland, Mich.

FIG. 12-24.   Flow sheet of plant for treatment of phenolic wastes. Dow Chemical Company, Midland, Mich.

Tannery Wastes

There are, in general use, two principal methods of tanning hides and skins: the vegetable-tanning process (the most common one) and the chrome-tanning process.

In the first process the wastes that arise from several stages of the operation are as follows: (1) Beam-house wastes, from the initial process of cleaning the hides and skins, which are soak wastes containing dirt, dung, blood, and other soluble matters and fats, salt, hair, and other major impurities. They are usually of a dark, dirty greenish color. (2) Lime-vat effluents, from the process of loosening the hair, which contain loosened hair, dirt, organic matter, and lime. These wastes usually have a bluish, milky appearance. (3) Warm pool wastes, which are generally similar to the lime-vat wastes but, coming from a washing step, are much weaker. (4) Dehairing machine wastes, which result from the scraping of the hides to remove the hair. They contain lime and hair. (5) Hair wastes, which are generally similar to the dehairing-machine wastes but weaker in polluting elements. (6) Fleshing-machine wastes, which are the wastes resulting from the operation of separating small and loose bits of flesh and fat from the hides. They are high in pollutional elements. (7) Deliming wastes, which are the wastes from a

TABLE 12-11. APPROXIMATE QUANTITY AND CHARACTER OF WASTES FROM VARIOUS STEPS IN VEGETABLE TANNING OF HEAVY LEATHER

Wastes	Volume per day, gal per 100 lb of hides	Total solids, ppm	Suspended solids, ppm	BOD (5 days), ppm	Total solids, %	BOD, %
Soaks*................	80	12,000	1,200	600	17	5
Limes*................	40	27,000	10,000	2,400	19	10
Warm water*..........	50	10,500	3,500	1,000	9	5
Dehairing.............	25	2,500	1,500	400	1	1
Hair washing..........	40	2,000	1,200	20	1	1
Fleshing..............	35	3,500	2,600	800	2	3
Wash wheel...........	200	1,600	450	700	6	15
Float box.............	30	300	150	25	0	0
Green stock...........	210	400	100	3	1	0
Spent tan*............	50	27,000	1,500	10,000	23	52
Bleaches*.............	40	30,000	1,200	2,000	21	8

* Denotes intermittent discharges. Others are continuous. Figures demonstrate that the intermittent discharges, which constitute only about one-third of the total liquid volume, contain almost 90 per cent of the total solids and 80 per cent of the BOD of the combined wastes.

final washing step to remove excess lime and hide substances previous to the actual tanning operation. (8) Tan-yard wastes, which are the spent tan liquors from the actual tanning. These are the worst individual wastes as they are high in color, solids, and BOD. They are usually reddish brown in color and acid in reaction. (9) Rinse liquors, which are wash waters and are similar in general character to spent tan liquor. They are frequently returned to the process for reuse.

Table 12-11 shows the average composition of vegetable tanning wastes. Data on wastes from chrome tanneries are meager. Data on an Illinois tannery indicated a population equivalent of about 36 on a BOD basis and 57 on a suspended-solids basis per 100 pounds of hides processed.   The average flow at this tannery was 1,410 gallons of liquid per 100 pounds of hides.   About 95 per cent of the total BOD, 91 per cent of the total solids, and 85 per cent of the suspended solids came from the beam-house wastes.   On a sampling test of 18 chrome tanneries in the Chicago, Ill., area in 1926, the weighted average BOD was 930 ppm and the suspended solids, 1,310 ppm.

In the treatment of tannery wastes it is customary to collect the hair, fleshings, and hide trimmings and dispose of them in that state.   In some cases they are sold to glue manufacturers.   Spent tan liquors are sometimes evaporated and sold as boiler compound.   Spent tanbark is usually burned, but may have some uses in the manufacture of white lead and paperboard.   It is frequently used as a ground covering at horse shows, circus rings, and race tracks.

Treatment of tannery wastes is usually divided into two general phases: primary treatment and secondary treatment.   Primary treatment consists of mixing the various wastes, followed by sedimentation.   It is good practice, if possible, to mix the wastes so as to produce a uniform effluent to the settling basins.   This may entail holding tanks, control valves, etc., but the result usually is simpler later treatment with less control. In some cases where primary treatment alone suffices, the weak wastes, wash waters, etc., may be discharged separately and the stronger wastes only segregated and treated.   As the chemical reactions of the individual wastes differ, coagulation takes place when they are combined.   This is an aid to sedimentation, especially in those cases where chemical precipitation is employed, as it tends to reduce the amount of added chemical coagulant.

Secondary treatment is required in those cases where wastes are discharged into streams used for potable or industrial purposes or into public sewers leading to sewage-treatment works which operate on biological processes.   In this treatment it has been found that trickling filters followed by intermittent sand filters are successful in removing color and reducing BOD.   In this connection the modern high-rate trickling filter with recirculation has a definite place, as it reduces initial plant cost. It is important that the medium for trickling filters for the treatment of tannery wastes be of an iron-free nature; otherwise, the tannic acid in the wastes reacts with the iron to form an inky-black effluent.   Reductions of suspended solids of 85 to 90 per cent, of BOD of 65 to 75 per cent, and of color of 15 to 70 per cent have been obtained with trickling filters.   The activated-sludge process has not been too successful for tannery wastes as the process is delicate and is easily upset by shock loads.   Tannery-wastes sludge is difficult to dispose of as, owing to its high lime content, it dries slowly.   It cannot be put into normal digestion tanks, as the high-lime content inhibits digestion. It may be lagooned but should be put on barren areas, as it will kill all trees and shrubbery with which it comes into contact.

The flow diagram, Fig. 12-25, indicates the general steps in complete treatment of tannery wastes. Depending upon the requirements, the treatment may stop at any point at which the desired result has been achieved.

Fermentation Wastes

These are the liquid effluents from breweries; distilleries of whisky, brandy, and other alcoholic liquors; wineries; the production of yeast; and the manufacture of alcohol from cane-sugar molasses.

The usual wastes from breweries are spent-grain mash, spent hops, keg and bottle wash, and rinse waters from cookers, fermenters, and storage or aging vats. Spent grain or mash may usually be retained on fine-mesh screens and ultimately disposed of as stock feed. Hops are also readily retained on screens to keep them out of the sewers. Keg and bottle wash waters, if sufficiently diluted, may usually be discharged into streams without further treatment. The effluents from fermenting vats, aging vats, and yeast-recovery processes are the troublesome wastes. These wastes have a very high oxygen demand and are high in proteins which decompose rapidly, producing foul odors. The composition of these wastes, from the standpoints of suspended solids and BOD, is given in Table 11-2.

Distillery wastes are the spent liquors from the vats. They also are very high in BOD. Their composition is also given in Table 11-2. Various methods of treatment have been tried on these wastes with varied success, but one of the most satisfactory, owing to the low suspended solids and high BOD content, has been that embodying predigestion, followed by high-rate trickling filters. A typical flow sheet of this type of treatment as carried out at the plant of Anheuser-Busch, Inc., in St. Louis, Mo., is shown in Fig. 12-26. For the treatment of the wastes from the manufacture of alcohol from sugar-cane molasses, which have BOD's ranging from 15,000 to as high as 50,000 ppm, the flow sheet shown in Fig. 12-14 has been worked out for an installation in Brazil.

Various efforts have been made to produce valuable by-products from these wastes and abate the pollution problem at the same time.

Wastes from wineries consist of wash waters from the crushing department, the spent lees from the wine vats, and floor washings. They are high in color and, from that angle alone, create a problem in the streams. In California much has been done in the lagooning of such wastes, and several installations have been made which recover tartrates as a by-product and simultaneously relieve the pollution problem. A flow sheet of a plant of this type is shown in Fig. 12-27.

Wastes from the manufacture of compressed yeast have a high BOD, and it has been found possible to treat them on high-rate trickling filters. Considerable work on these wastes has been done experimentally at the

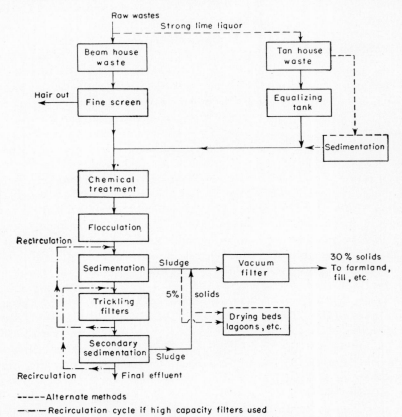

FIG. 12-25.   Flow sheet for tannery-waste treatment.

New Jersey Agricultural Experiment Station at Rutgers University, New Brunswick, N.J., by Dr. Willem Rudolfs and E. H. Trubnick and is fully reported in the literature.

Operating results on a plant for the treatment of brewery wastes at the Gulf Brewing Company, Houston, Tex., were as follows: From 1,500 barrels of beer produced daily, a total of 500,000 gallons per day of waste was discharged.   Based on the results of a pilot plant, the full-scale plant was expected to reduce the BOD about 90 per cent and suspended solids about 75 per cent. The initial BOD of the raw waste was 349 ppm and of the suspended solids, 371 ppm. The flow sheet of this plant is shown in Fig. 12-28.

The Lucky Lager Brewing Company in Azusa, Calif., finding that the local sewage facilities were inadequate to handle their wastes, decided upon their own treatment plant. This plant, of the biological type, has

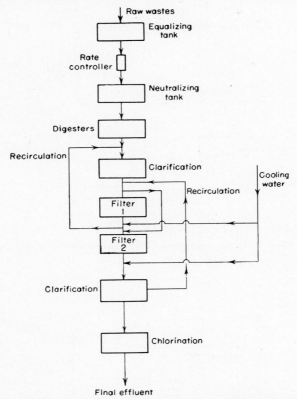

FIG. 12-26. Brewery-waste-treatment flow sheet. Anheuser-Busch Inc., St. Louis, Mo.

been very satisfactory and gives a good indication of what may be expected from this type of treatment on this type of waste.

The actual characteristics of the wastes are given in Table 12-11A.

The plant was designed on the basis of the initial assumptions, and although the actual conditions encountered were worse than the assumptions, the plant has been able to handle the wastes satisfactorily.

As illustrated in the flow sheet in Fig. 12-28A, the plant consists of the following units: (a) a control house and pumping station; (b) a rotary,

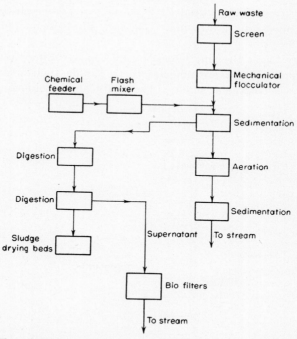

FIG. 12-27. Flow sheet for the treatment of winery wastes at Glenelg, South Australia.

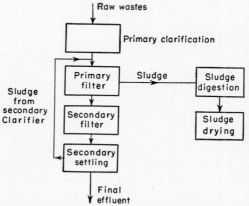

FIG. 12-28. Flow sheet for the treatment of brewery wastes at the Gulf Brewing Company plant, Houston, Tex.

self-cleaning fine screen; (3) a primary mechanically cleaned Clarifier; (4) two Biofilter beds, each with a revolving distributor; (5) a recircula-

TABLE 12-11A. CHARACTERISTICS OF BREWERY WASTES*

Factor	Initial assumption	Actual operation
Beer, produced, gal per week.................	149,000	187,740
Beer produced, bbl per week..................	4,807	6,055
Waste water treated, gal per week............	1,961,500	1,985,000
Waste water treated, gal per gal beer.........	13.2	9.5
Average flow, operating days, gal per day......	310,000	335,000
Peak flow, avg, gpm†.......................	258	302
Peak flow, max, gpm‡.......................	430	435§
Solids, total, ppm..........................	928	770
Solids, suspended, ppm......................	220	200
BOD ppm...................................	450	445
BOD load, lb per day........................	1,163	1,242
BOD population equivalent‖..................	7,756	8,280
BOD population equivalent, per bbl beer.......	10.2	8.11
Suspended solids, population equivalent, per bbl beer.....................................	4.9	3.64
Suspended solids, population equivalent‖......	3,792	3,720

* Ruben Schneider, Waste Disposal at a Modern Brewery, *Sewage & Industrial Wastes*, vol. 22, No. 10, p. 1307, October, 1950.
† Based on 12 hr for 60 per cent of flow.
‡ Based on 12 hr for total flow.
§ Frequently as high as 600 gpm, depending on packaging operations.
‖ Based on 0.15 lb per capita per day.

TABLE 12-11B. TYPICAL ANALYSIS OF TREATMENT EFFICIENCY

Item	Influent	Effluent	Reduction, %
5-day BOD, ppm...........................	445	65	88
Total solids, ppm..........................	770	379	51
Suspended solids, ppm......................	200	25	88
Dissolved solids, ppm......................	570	354	38
Volatile of total solids, %..................	67.5	44.7	67.5
Volatile of suspended solids, %.............	73.0	94.0	84.0
pH..	7.4	7.6	
Dissolved oxygen, ppm.....................	1.0	3.3	

tion pump well; (6) a secondary mechanically cleaned Clarifier; (7) a sludge-digestion tank with mixing unit and heat exchangers; (8) sludge-drying beds; (9) four final-effluent beds.

The plant is operated in conjunction with the other brewery facilities, and all of the operating personnel are regular brewery employees.

Table 12-11B gives a typical analysis of the efficiency of the treatment.

Milk-products Wastes

These wastes originate in plants handling or processing milk, among which are milk-receiving stations, where milk is pasteurized and sepa-

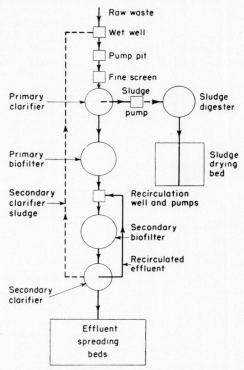

Fig. 12-28A.   Flow diagram of brewery-waste-disposal plant, Azusa, Calif.

rated; bottling works, where milk is bottled for the market; cheese factories; creameries, where butter is the main product; condenseries; dry- or powdered-milk plants; ice-cream manufactories; and general dairies.

The wastes commonly consist of various dilutions of whole milk, skim milk, buttermilk, whey from spills, drippings from processes, and the washing wastes which contain alkalies and other cleaning chemicals. There are also process wastes from the manufacture of cheese, butter, casein, and other milk products. The troublesome element in these wastes is lactose, which, if the receiving stream has insufficient oxygen for aerobic decomposition, is converted into lactic acid so that the wastes become sufficiently acid to precipitate casein which putrifies and produces strong and offensive odors.

Table 12-12 gives average approximate volumes and typical analyses of wastes from several types of plants.

TABLE 12-12.   VOLUMES OF WASTES FROM VARIOUS TYPES OF MILK AND MILK-
HANDLING PLANTS

Type of plant	Gal of waste per 1,000 lb of daily intake	Solids, ppm			Vola-tile	Oxygen, ppm		pH
		Total	Vola-tile	Sus-pended		Con-sumed	BOD (5 day)	
Receiving station.....	175	1,141	844	...	...	313	509	
Bottling works.......	250							
Cheese factory.......	200	1,528	917	751	703		998	7.0
Creamery (butter)....	110	2,422	1,141	664	483		1,246	7.7
Condensery..........	150	2,793	1,233	754	582		1,291	7.8
Condensery-vacuum pan water.........	1,500							
Dry-milk plant.......	150	2,407	540	...	...	283	485	
General dairy........	340	1,483	888	536	404		567	5.3

Treatment of these wastes may be by means of actual waste treatment or partial treatment for recovery of by-products. Whole milk may be recovered by drip savers; the whey and buttermilk may be manufactured into powder, casein, albumin, or lactose; and the waste products may be converted into stock food.

Depending upon the locality of the plant, the volume and strength of the wastes, and the condition of the receiving stream, treatment may be by one of the following methods: dilution in the stream, irrigation of waste land, septic tanks (for small establishments), trickling filters, activated-sludge or other recognized methods.

The most generally accepted method of treatment for the various types of wastes listed in Table 12-12 has been on trickling filters, and in this respect the high-rate trickling filter, with recirculation of filter effluent, has been especially effective in reducing BOD and conserving ground area. BOD reductions of 80 to 90 per cent have been obtained on such filters. The filter using the familiar revolving distributor is normally used, although on small plants the fixed-nozzle type could be employed; but the more perfect distribution of the waste over the surface of the filter area by the revolving type of distributor is said to be more advantageous for milk wastes.

Various types of filter mediums have been used in trickling filters for treating milk wastes, such as laths, cinders, gravel, spiral rings, corncobs, broken tile, quartzite, and the normal broken stone used in trickling filters for sewage treatment.   Reports of the results obtained with these various mediums indicate that a cinder bed will produce reductions of BOD of 99 per cent; all the other types show reductions above 90 per

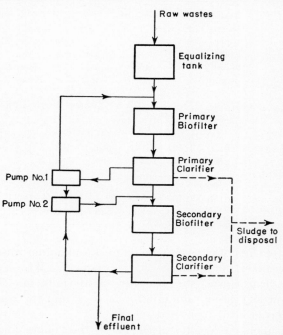

FIG. 12-29.   Flow sheet of two-stage Biofiltration plant for milk wastes.

cent, except spiral rings and quartzite, and in most cases the final BOD is within the limits required.   A flow sheet of a Biofiltration type of plant for milk wastes is shown in Fig. 12-29.   As milk wastes vary in volume and consistency during the operating period, it is advisable to provide an equalizing or balancing tank to counteract these inequalities and produce a uniform character of waste which responds best to treatment with the minimum of control on the part of the operators.

A process known as the "Guggenheim" process has been found satisfactory for treating milk wastes.   This process, controlled by Guggenheim Brothers, well-known mining operators, consists of treating the wastes with lime and an iron salt followed by several hours of aeration.

The floc which is formed in this first step is settled and recirculated through the aeration tank. The aeration period is about 4 hours and the settling, about 1.5 hours. Air requirements are stated to be about 2 to 3 cubic feet per gallon of waste, and about 100 ppm of lime and 30 ppm of ferric chloride are required. It is stated that BOD reductions of 90 per cent have been obtained by this method. Compared with the biological-filter method, this process has the disadvantage of high operating costs due to the large coagulant dosage and the cost of providing the large volume of air. It has also the disadvantage of not being able to handle shock loads without effect on the ultimate reduction of BOD. The high-rate filter, on the other hand, has proved its ability to handle shock loads for short periods better than any other method.

Paper-mill and Pulp-mill Wastes

These wastes are of two distinct types. Those from the manufacture of paper pulp present the greatest problem from a stream-pollution standpoint. Pulp is made from a great variety of materials, among which may be mentioned woods of various kinds, cotton or linen rags, straw (including wheat straw, hemp, esparto, flax, jute), reclaimed paper, and sugar-mill bagasse. The most common types of pulp are those from ground-wood, soda, sulfate or kraft, and sulfite. These, being the major pulp sources, naturally form the greatest pollution and treatment problems.

Wastes from paper mills, in which the pulps are combined with various materials such as loaders or fillers, coloring matter, and finish elements, are less difficult to treat than pulp wastes. The loading or filler materials normally used are clay, talc, gypsum, precipitated calcium sulfate, or barium sulfate, which in themselves tend to cause precipitation.

As a treatment problem, the most important wastes from the manufacture of pulp are the liquors from the digesters in which the fibers produced from the raw materials are refined. Other wastes arise in the sawing of the logs, in barking, in the reduction to chips in the preparation of the wood for the digesters and from the washers, knot-removing machines, and pulp thickeners. Wastes from the mills which prepare the actual paper from the pulps are mainly from the beaters, the regulating and mixing boxes, where fillers are added, and the actual paper machines. The wastes from the last named consist principally of fibers not retained in the sheet, and these are readily recovered by "save-alls" of different types, vacuum filters, etc. The fibers recovered are returned to the head boxes for recycling.

Table 12-13 gives an approximation of typical waste analyses.

The most difficult problem, as stated, arises from the digester liquors, particularly the sulfite-process black liquor. These liquors contain intercellular substances of the wood plus the excess chemicals used in digestion. The liquor from the sulfite process may contain as high as 48 per cent of the wood used, has a very high immediate BOD, and adds color to the stream. It is frequently acid in reaction and contains salts of lignin, which are detrimental to fish life and are also the cause of nuisance in water-filtration plants.

TABLE 12-13. TYPICAL ANALYSES OF PULP- AND PAPER-MILL WASTES

Waste from	Waste volume, gal per ton of product	BOD, ppm	Suspended solids, ppm
Pulp mill:			
Groundwood.....................	5,000	645	
Soda............................	85,000	110	1,720
Sulfate (kraft)....................	64,000	123	
Sulfite...........................	60,000	443	
Miscellaneous paper:			
No bleach........................	39,000	19	452
With bleach......................	47,000	24	660
Paperboard........................	14,000	121	660
Strawboard........................	26,000	965	1,790
Deinking of used paper...............	83,000	300	

The wastes from the sulfate process contain small quantities of mercaptans which not only have a very obnoxious odor but are said to be toxic to fish life in concentrations of more than 1.0 ppm.

Considerable study has been given to the problem of treatment of sulfite wastes, including the possibility of recovering useful by-products such as adhesives, fertilizer ingredients, alcohol, tanning liquors, and bases for dyes and for binders for road material. A recently developed by-product has been an ingredient to expedite the hardening of concrete.

Methods of treatment employed vary from the Howard process, which is a three-stage precipitation process, using caustic lime as a reagent, to the Paulson process, employing multistage evaporation. To date, neither of these has proved to be an economic success owing to the high cost of operation and small reduction of BOD accomplished.

Experimental studies on the treatment of sulfite wastes with sewage have been made, using the activated-sludge process. Fairly satisfactory results have been obtained with sewage mixed with up to 6 per cent of effluent from the Howard process and with mixtures of up to 10 per cent of raw calcium-base sulfite liquor. A great deal of investigational work has been done on sulfite black liquors, but no generally satisfactory method has yet been developed. Recovery of numerous by-products is physically possible, but the high costs of production and the limited market restrict the use of these methods except in those cases where severe pollution exists and remedial measures must be taken, regardless of the thought of possible revenue from the operation.

In the treatment of soda and sulfate pulps, better results have been obtained. These wastes are processed for the recovery of chemicals and waste heat. In this process the liquors are evaporated, burned in rotary furnaces, leached, causticized with lime, diluted with raw black liquor, and stored for later reuse in the digestion process. The two chief by-products of this operation are carbon and calcium carbonate sludge. The carbon derived is activated or otherwise conditioned and marketed as activated carbon, which is used extensively in water treatment for color and taste removal, etc.

In those sections of the country, such as the Pacific Northwest and the South, where pulp mills are concentrated and where the stream-pollution problem is intense, research organizations of the industry are making strenuous efforts to develop a process for the treatment of these wastes which not only will eliminate the pollution but will eventually prove to be economically sound from a recovery standpoint and tend to offset some of the high cost of treatment. There is no doubt that, with the intensive study being given to this problem, a satisfactory method will finally be found.

Pickling Liquors

These wastes normally come from scale-removal operations in the pickling of iron, steel, and other metallic products. The usual acid used in the pickling vats is sulfuric, but hydrofluoric and hydrochloric acids are also used, with inhibitors of various kinds to reduce the direct attack of the acid on the metals. The operation is based on the theory that the acids will mainly attack the iron oxide at the metal surface, causing a scaling of the Fe_2SO_4 and Fe_3SO_4. The metals are usually immersed in the acid solution, which is heated by steam, for sufficient time for the scaling to take place and are then removed and washed in tanks or sprayed.

The volume of wastes varies according to the method of pickling used. Strong waste liquors frequently contain 16 to 22 per cent ferrous sulfate and about 1 to 9 per cent sulfuric acid, but the wash waters will, of course, be considerably weaker.

One investigator has estimated that, in a total waste production per 1,000 tons of metal of 52 tons of strong solution and 420 tons, of wash water, the strong solution will average 18 per cent ferrous sulfate and the wash water 0.9 per cent ferrous sulfate.

An established method of treating these wastes has been by neutralization of the free acid with lime or limestone, by settling, and by discharge of the clarified solution and drying of the ferrous precipitate.

A number of other methods have been developed to produce a salable by-product, among which may be mentioned the Ferron process, crystallization by cooling, crystallization by evaporation, the Chemico process, and a more recent process for the recovery of the lime and liquid filtrate in the process. A method has been worked out by The Dorr Company in their Westport Laboratories and a process developed at the Kaiser Steel Company plant at Fontana, Calif., for treatment of such wastes.

A brief description of these methods of treatment and/or recovery should be of general interest.

The Ferron process, as illustrated in Fig. 12-30, comprises the slaking of lime in fresh water or effluent water and the treatment of the wash liquor with milk of lime in agitators at 150°F, giving a precipitation of iron hydroxide and gypsum. This mixture may be filtered through filter mediums of asbestos, paper pulp, or clay or through filter presses. The press cake is then molded or compacted, and a final drying is made to "set" the material for use.

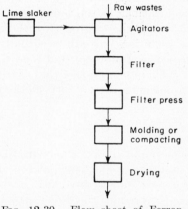

Fig. 12-30. Flow sheet of Ferron process for treatment of waste pickling liquors.

The process of crystallization by cooling involves cooling the waste liquor, which causes crystallization of copperas. The copperas is separated by centrifuging, fresh acid is added to the mother liquor, and this is reheated to the pickling temperature. Unless there is a ready sale or use for the copperas, this method of treatment is not economical.

Crystallization by evaporation comprises evaporation of the waste liquor to 28 per cent acid, at which point about 80 per cent of the ferrous sulfate crystallizes out; separation of the copperas by centrifuging; evaporation of the 28 per cent acid to 68 per cent acid, during which operation the remaining ferrous sulfate, as well as most of the impurities, crystallizes as a monohydrate; separation of the ferrous sulfate and impurities and return of them to the waste liquors ahead of the first evaporation step. The 68 per cent acid is returned to the pickling vats. This method is economical only when there is a market for the ferrous sulfate and the cost of evaporation, etc., may be balanced against the value of the recovered and reused acid.

The Chemico process is a sulfate-conversion process and comprises the following steps: (1) neutralization of the free sulfuric acid with iron oxide cinders from step 3; (2) evaporation to dryness of the neutralized liquor, which produces copperas; (3) roasting of the ferrous sulfate with pyrites and powdered coal, which produces sulfur dioxide gas and iron oxide cinders; and (4) scrubbing the sulfur dioxide and converting it into sulfuric acid in a contact plant. Owing to the high cost of evaporation, this method is not normally economical.

The process developed by The Dorr Company comprises the following steps: grinding dolomite or limestone to 200 mesh in closed circuit; thickening; adding slurry in excess to the pickling liquor and wash water and agitating in mechanical agitators; flocculation with starch; and clarification. This is purely a treatment method and produces no useful products. Figure 12-31 illustrates this method.

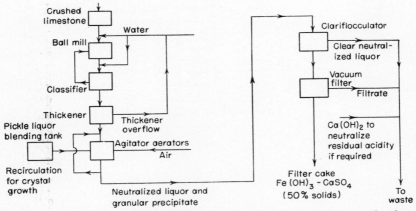

FIG. 12-31. Flow sheet of process for treatment of waste pickling liquor, developed by The Dorr Company.

When the Kaiser Steel Company plant at Fontana, Calif., was built during World War II, the location of this plant was such that it was essential that the plant be so designed that all water would be conserved and returned for reuse. This applied to the flue-dust wastes, the sewage, and the pickling wastes. To accomplish this object and produce a liquor which could be reused, the following method was developed. The acid and rinsing-vat wastes were dumped into separate sewers, both of which terminated at the pickle-liquor treatment plant. As the waste-treatment plant was designed to operate only 6 to 8 hours per day, and the day's wastes were estimated to amount to about 45,000 gallons, the spent pickle liquor and wash water were discharged into a receiving tank with a capacity of one day's total flow.   The process of treatment involved neutralization of excess acid in the waste by powdered limestone and reaction of the soluble ferrous sulfate with this material.   Calcium sulfate and ferrous hydroxide were precipitated from these reactions, and the ferrous hydroxide was oxidized to ferric hydroxide and ferric oxide by air which was forced through the slurry.   A series of three agitator mixers

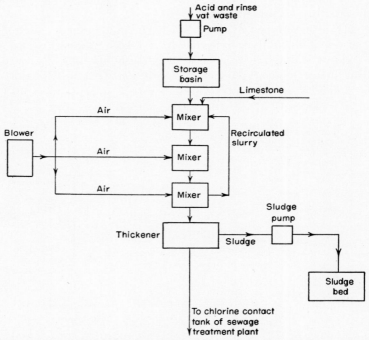

FIG. 12-32.   Flow sheet for the treatment of waste pickling liquor at Kaiser Steel Company, Fontana, Calif.

was used with partial recirculation of the slurry, and the effluent from the third mixer was passed to a thickener.   The thickener effluent flowed to the contact basin of the adjacent sewage-treatment plant, where it was mixed and chlorinated with the sewage-plant effluent and returned for reuse in the rolling mills.   The sludge was lagooned on nearby land. The flow sheet of this plant is shown in Fig. 12-32.

In a process for recovery of waste iron sulfate, developed by The Chemical Construction Corporation[34] and which is stated to be an economical method for the disposal of waste iron sulfate–sulfuric acid mixtures, the acid value of both constituents is recovered. The process briefly consists of concentrating the free acid, separating the crystallized iron sulfate by filtration, and processing the sulfate to fresh sulfuric acid.

Another recent development is that of lime treatment of pickling liquor with complete reuse of the filtrate from vacuum filters and the production of a low-volume filter cake which is readily handled. This process is said to eliminate any liquid effluent, as this is returned to the process.[35,36]

Textile Wastes

These wastes arise in the processing and preparation of fibers of cotton, wool, silk, rayon, and other synthetic materials. They form one of the largest classes of wastes as the volume of water used in the preparation of the raw materials is high. The wastes emanate not only from the

TABLE 12-14. AVERAGE VOLUME AND COMPOSITION OF VARIOUS CLASSES OF TEXTILE WASTES

Type of waste	Volume, gal per 1,000 lb of goods produced	BOD, ppm	Grease, ppm	Total solids, ppm	Suspended solids, ppm
Cotton:					
Sizing	60	820			
Desizing	1,100	1,750			
Kiering	1,700	1,240			
Bleaching	1,200	300			
Scouring	3,400	72			
Mercerizing	30,000	55			
Dyeing:					
Direct	6,400	200	....	2,600	
Basic	18,000	100	....	900	
Vat	19,000	140			
Sulfuric	5,400	1,300	....	4,300	
Developed	14,400	170			
Naphthol	4,800	250			
Aniline black	15,600	55			
Wool, scouring	Variable	1,200–22,000	3,000–25,800	.....	2,400–30,300

actual preparation of the raw basic materials but also from the later steps of dyeing, finishing, etc. Depending upon the process used, the wastes contain color, acids, alkalies, weighting agents, greases and fats, dirt, loose fibers, etc. The average volume and composition of a variety of textile wastes are given in Table 12-14.

The main pollutional load in these wastes may be removed by chemical precipitation, using common chemicals such as ferrous sulfate, aluminum sulfate, ferric chloride, lime and sulfuric acid, and calcium chloride. Textile wastes may be treated with municipal sewage if pretreatment for neutralization of acidity and high alkalinities is provided. Screens, with fine mesh, are frequently used to intercept fibers and floating materials. In one instance in the author's experience, large quantities of wool were reclaimed on a revolving fine screen in a woolen mill. The volume of this wool amounted to several barrels per day. Investigation showed that this loss was due to the use of the wool for sanitary purposes by the workers. Naturally this practice was quickly stopped by the management.

In a recent case involving rayon wastes, containing large quantities of spent black dye, the main problem was the reduction of color to a point where the effluent, when diluted with the water of the receiving stream, would not be noticeable. As the ratio of stream water to wastes was 500 to 1, it was only necessary to carry the color reduction to the point where dilution of the effluent at the ratio named disseminated all traces of color. Figure 12-33 shows the flow sheet used in the solution of this problem.

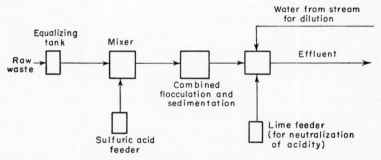

Fig. 12-33.   Flow sheet for the treatment of rayon-plant wastes for reduction of color.

Wool-scouring wastes are probably the most troublesome of all textile wastes because of the high percentage of grease which comes from the washing of the wool. Several methods of removing this grease, which is necessary before the wool can be dyed or used, have been developed, the most used being that of extraction by solvents. After removal of the grease, the resultant wastes may be treated by chemical precipitation and biological methods.

In the preparation of silk, the wastes arise in the processes of removing the natural gum from the silk and in the bleaching, dyeing, and printing operations. One of the few wastes which produces a recoverable product is that from the operation of weighting the silk with tin. In this recovery operation, the waste is treated with lime to precipitate the tin, which is then settled, dried, and reused. In a plant for this purpose, installed at the Textile Printing and Dyeing Corporation of America, at Hawthorne, N.J., the wastes amounted to about 1,600 gallons per minute and contained as much as 90 milligrams per liter (ppm) of tin salts. The final effluent contained only 2 to 3 ppm of tin salts, giving a tin recovery of 97 to 98 per cent. Depending upon the purchase price of tin and the volume of wastes, this operation may or may not be profitable for a given plant.

The recovery of waste products from textile wastes is generally not a profitable operation. There are one or two possible profit-producing operations, and while it is, of course, theoretically possible to recover any of the materials and dyes used, the actual cost of the recovery process is usually greater than the market price of a new supply of the same material.

Lanolin, or wool grease, which is used in soaps and paints, may be recovered successfully. Caustic soda may be recovered from mercerizing wastes and rayon wastes. It is stated that more than 25 million pounds of caustic soda is recovered annually in the United States from waste steep liquors in the viscose-rayon industry. As the recovered caustic solution will be about one-half the strength of the normal initial solution, it will be necessary to fortify this with new caustic to bring it to normal strength. Recovery of tin from silk-weighting operations is mentioned above.

In several states where textile industries are concentrated and the waste problems are intense, the state health authorities have formulated general requirements for the treatment of various types of wastes from typical plants. Table 12-15 gives a tabulation of the recommendations issued by the Water Commission of the state of Connecticut.

Cyanide Wastes

Cyanide in concentrations as low as 0.025 ppm has been found to be toxic to fish. It can be successfully eliminated from wastes from plating, casehardening, and other industrial processes by the addition of approximately 4.0 ppm of chlorine per part of cyanide at controlled pH's above 8.5. Chlorine also renders these wastes innocuous to sewage-treatment processes and water users. Ordinary sewage-treatment processes do not, of themselves, eliminate cyanide. Lagooning is successful if space is available. With proper acid conditions, a detention of slightly over 200 hours will substantially reduce the cyanide concentration. Reaction with ferrous sulfate to produce Prussian blue has been suggested. Where high concentrations of cyanide exist and the waste volume is large, acidification with carbon dioxide, flue gas, or carbon dioxide followed by sulfur dioxide has been used for the recovery of the cyanide. The extensive apparatus required renders these processes uneconomical for low concentrations or small volumes. Acidification with strong mineral acids and aeration have also been tried. In one plant, 4,600 gallons of plating wastes with a BOD of 15,200 ppm was treated with 10 carboys of concentrated acid and aerated for 6 hours. The resultant BOD was 3,400

TABLE 12-15. RECOMMENDATIONS BY THE WATER COMMISSION OF CONNECTICUT FOR TREATMENT OF TEXTILE WASTES

Type of waste	Process producing	Volume, gpd	BOD, ppm	Treatment of waste	BOD reduction expected, %
Cotton thread.....	Lime, scour bleaching, kier boiling, machine vat dyeing	40,000	550	Precipitation with copperas and lime	60
Finishing piece goods (cotton)	Bleaching, kier boiling, dyeing, and printing	274,000	605	Segregation of print-wash, coagulation by copperas and lime, and aeration of effluent	65
Elastic webbings and brake linings	Kier boiling, dyeing, and impregnation of linings	80,000	422	Screening, coagulation with copperas and lime, and aeration	60
Silk manufacture..	Degumming, bleaching, dyeing, and printing	1,200,000	460	Cracking of gum suds, incineration of print wastes, coagulation with ferric sulfate	65
Cotton finishing...	Bleaching, kier boiling, printing, and dyeing	80,000	540	Coagulation of wastes by copperas and lime and aeration	65
Cotton and rayon finishing	Bleaching, soap boiling, sizing, and dyeing	10,000	390	Collection of concentrated wastes, coagulation by copperas and lime, and aeration	60
Finishing cotton cloth	Alkali and peroxide boil, mercerizing, printing, dyeing, and finishing	438,000	478	Storage in open-air lagoons for a week, coagulation with ferric sulfate and lime, incineration of print wastes	65
Rayon goods......	Bleaching, dyeing, sizing, and finishing	125,000	1,920	Storage in tanks, coagulation with ferric sulfate and lime	68
Woolen cloths.....	Wool scouring, weaving, dyeing, and finishing	120,000	936	Cracking with acid, coagulation with ferric sulfate and lime	75

ppm. Thirteen additional carboys of acid and 16 hours aeration reduced the BOD to 975 ppm.

Extensive laboratory tests and several plant-scale installations have shown that cyanide can be economically and completely eliminated by the chlorination of the waste at controlled pH. The waste liquor is fed into a storage tank, and the pH is raised by the addition of lime or caustic. After thorough mixing, the waste is pumped from the tank through the injector of the chlorinator where a measured amount of

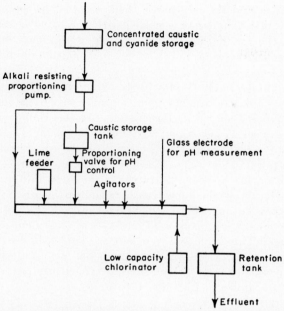

FIG. 12-34. Flow sheet for continuous treatment of cyanide wastes.

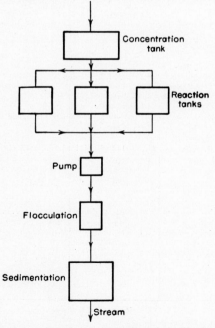

FIG. 12-35. Flow sheet for cyanide and acid-plating wastes as treated at Kaiser-Frazer Company auto plant, Willow Run, Mich.

chlorine is added and the mixture is then returned to the storage tank. To assure the maintenance of a correct pH, the caustic solution is best pumped into the circulating water. Plants of this type have been in operation for over one year, and tests by authorities have failed to show any cyanide going to the stream.

For large volumes where the flow is too great to warrant a reasonably sized retention tank, continuous operation may be carried out by means of the type of plant shown in Fig. 12-34. At the Willow Run, Mich., plant of the Kaiser-Frazer Company, cyanide and acid-plating wastes were treated by a plant comprising the units shown in Fig. 12-35.

In a recent publication of The National Lime Association[6] a table was included showing methods of treatment of some 16 different classes of industrial wastes in which lime was a beneficial agent. This table is interesting as it gives not only the character of each type of waste listed but also the composition, suggested methods of treatment, and remarks on the process. This table is given here as Tables 12-16 to 12-31. A number of flow sheets of treatment methods on various classes of wastes are included in this chapter, which are not specifically referred to in the text. These are shown in Figs. 12-36 to 12-40.

TABLE 12-16. BEET-SUGAR WASTES*

	Type of waste			
	Flume water	Process water	Lime drainage	Steffens waste
Character of wastes	High suspended solids, vegetation, dissolved organic matter	Low suspended solids, high BOD, high dissolved solids, and colloids	$CaCO_3$ slurry, some dissolved solids	Very high dissolved solids, very high BOD, low suspended solids
Composition of wastes	Dirt, sand, weeds, pieces of beets, beet tops	Sugar, dirt, sand, beet slices	$CaCO_3$, sugar	Sugars, potash, nitrogen, organic matter
Methods of treatment	Screened, grit removed, and settled; then sent to sewer	Coagulated with lime, sent to sedimentation chambers, effluent to sewer, sludge to ponds	Lime cake diluted to slurry and then pumped to ponding area	Treated to produce fertilizer and monosodium glutamate
Remarks........	Lime can be used for treating if water is to be reused	Resulting sludge from above method does not need preconditioning for vacuum filtration	....	At present the raw materials of the Steffens process (molasses) can be sold for more than the additional sugar produced from this process

* The Use of Lime in Industrial Waste Treatment, *Trade Waste Bulletin* 1 (National Lime Association, Washington, D.C.), Apr. 1, 1948, p. 9.

TABLE 12-17. CANNERY WASTES*

	Items canned†					
	Beans, wax	Corn	Peas	Spinach	Cherries	Pears
Composition of wastes:						
Waste volume, (gal per case)..	26	25	25	20	40	51
Suspended solids, ppm.........	60	980	2,800	3,500	20	310
BOD, ppm..................	240	3,000	2,400	6,000	750	450
pH........................	7.6	6.5	7.0	7.0	6.2	
Character of wastes............	Organic, suspended, and soluble; dirt and grit					
Method of treatment...........	Combined wastes are screened, the liquid is chemically treated by bath or continuous processes, lime is added, then iron sulfate or chloride, alum or zinc chloride is added. Then to coagulation tank, settling tank, with liquid discharged, and sludge to beds. Combined wastes may be sent to lagoons without pretreatment, but they require sodium nitrate treatment to prevent odors					
Remarks......................	All literature advocates use of lime, alone or with another chemical, in chemical treatment of all canning wastes. This treatment is quicker, antiseptic, and easier to control than biological treatment. In citrus canning, lime is used to reduce corrosive action of wastes on equipment					

* The Use of Lime in Industrial Waste Treatment, *Trade Waste Bulletin* 1 (National Lime Association, Washington, D.C.), Apr. 1, 1948, p. 10.

† These examples indicate range of compositions of canning wastes.

TABLE 12-18.   CHEMICAL-PLANT WASTES*

	Type of process		
	DDT manufacture	Ethyl acetate manufacture	Phosphate fertilizer manufacture
Composition of waste.........	Sulfuric acid	Sulfuric acid	SiO_2, CaF_2, H_2SiF_6
Character of waste	Highly acidic solutions from production and processing; inorganic, very corrosive	Same as DDT, no processing waste	Inorganic, atmospheric pollution, gases and fine dust
Methods of treatment	Acid solutions are stored and neutralized with lime. Effluent is sent to sewer, and sludge is ponded	Acid solution neutralized with lime. Can be handled in same way as DDT	Gases and dust treated with CaO and heated to produce CaF_2
Remarks.........	Neutralization with lime found to be more economical than recovery of sulfuric acid		Still in experimental stage; would produce a valuable by-product

* The Use of Lime is Industrial Waste Treatment, *Trade Waste Bulletin* 1 (National Lime Association, Washington, D.C.), Apr. 1, 1948, p. 11.

TABLE 12-19. COAL-MINE DRAINAGE*

	Type of waste	
	Mine drainage (abandoned and working)	Processing ("breaker water")
Composition of wastes.....	Total solids... 5,000–70,000 ppm Acidity...... 0–50,000 SO₄.......... 1,000–50,000 Iron.......... 0–13,000 Calcium....... 100– 800 Magnesium... 0– 50 pH.......... 1.2–7.0	Depending on the amount of processing, the waste water may be as acidic as mine drainage, greater in volume, and higher in total solids
Methods of treatment......	1. Neutralization of drainage with lime 2. Chemical processes for recovery of valuable by-products 3. Dilution of drainage 4. Completely closing the mine (abandoned) 5. Sealing abandoned sections of working mines 6. Diversion of surface waters from entry into mines	1. The process water is settled to remove salable coal fines 2. The process water is neutralized with lime for reuse and to prevent stream pollution
Remarks................	Using lime in treating mine water gives low cost of treatment, fast reactivity, good removal of iron and sulfur, but produces sludge. Method 3 above requires large amounts of water. Method 4 has given good results. Method 2 has given indifferent results on attempts to recover iron oxide, blanc fixe, etc.	Lime and swollen potato starch are used to improve filtration and settling properties. Lime neutralization also decreases the corrosion of equipment that handles the process water

* The Use of Lime in Industrial Waste Treatment, *Trade Waste Bulletin* 1 (National Lime Association, Washington, D.C.), Apr. 1, 1948, p. 12.

TABLE 12-20. DAIRY WASTES*

	Type of plant						
	Receiving station	Bottling works	Cheese factory	Creamery	Condensery	Dry milk	Ice cream
Composition of wastes							
Total solids...........	1,141	1,483	1,528	2,422	2,793	2,407	
Suspended solids......	.....	536	751	664	754		
BOD, ppm...........	509	567	998	1,246	1,291	485	
pH...................	.....	5.3	7.0	7.7	7.8		
Character of waste.....	Whole-milk washings	Whole-milk washings	Whey, casein, washings	Buttermilk, washings	Spoiled-milk washings	Same as condensary	Casein, milk washings
Methods of treatment...	Dilution, irrigation	Physical filtration	Biochemical process (Mallory)	Chemical and biochemical processes (Guggenheim)	precipitation and activated-sludge	Same as bottling works	
Remarks...............	All methods of treatment seem to be standardized. The Mallory and Guggenheim processes require lime in the course of chemical precipitation, and both give good results for decreasing BOD and total solids, the former decreasing BOD by 99% and solids by 50% and the latter decreasing by 90% and 50%, respectively. Lime can be used to coagulate waste from caustic washing of milk bottles. Addition of lime, copperas, aluminoferric, and mixtures of these chemicals are sometimes used to purify any wastes containing milk washings						

* The Use of Lime in Industrial Waste Treatment, *Trade Waste Bulletin* 1 (National Lime Association, Washington, D.C.), Apr. 1, 1948, p. 18.

TABLE 12-21. WASTES FROM EXPLOSIVE-MANUFACTURING PLANTS*

	Item manufactured			
	TNT		TNP	Smokeless powder
	Type of waste			
	Red	Yellow	Wash	Composite
Composition of waste	H_2SO_4, HNO_3, TNT isomers	Na_2SO_3, TNT isomers	Picric acid, H_2SO_4, HNO_3	Copper, zinc, soap solutions cleansers, lubricants, H_2SO_4, nitrogen
Character of waste	Odorless, low BOD biologically stable, acid and alkaline, turbid		Turbid, acidic, low BOD odorless	Highly turbid, acidic low BOD odorless
Methods of treatment	The wastes are mixed, diluted, and added to the sewer. The main problem is color removal		Same as TNT, except lower dilutions (1 to 650) are used than in TNT (1 to 10,000)	Lime is added to wastes, which neutralizes and settles out grease, copper, and zinc. Effluent goes to sewer and sludge is lagooned. Effective pH is 10 or over
Remarks	Dilution seems to be the most inexpensive answer to the problem. Chemical treatment is costly and only alum has shown any success as a coagulant in published results. Lime may be used to neutralize H_2SO_4 and HNO_3, from general plant drainage and product washing			Lime is the best method for chemical treatment from a cost and sludge-disposal standpoint. Acidity of waste favors use of lime

* The Use of Lime in Industrial Waste Treatment, *Trade Waste Bulletin* 1 (National Lime Association, Washington, D.C.), Apr. 1, 1948, p. 19.

TABLE 12-22. WASTES FROM FERMENTATION INDUSTRIES*

	Type of plant			
	Brewery	Distillery		Winery
		Malting	Distilling	
Character of wastes	Organic; yeast in solution and grain suspended; high BOD (to 1,000)	Organic, high in nitrogen, low BOD	Organic, acidic, very high BOD, total solids	Organic, high BOD sugars, fruit pulp
Methods of treatment	Filtered, settled; effluent discharged and solids sold as stock feed	Same as brewery except that solids are sold as fertilizer too	Same as brewery	Fruit pulp treated with lime and CaCl₂ to recover tartrates. Solids sold as fertilizer
Remarks	Physical treatment as given above seems satisfactory. Lime may be used to coagulate wastes from bottle and equipment washing. Lime as a filtration improver after primary filtration			

* The Use of Lime in Industrial Waste Treatment. *Trade Waste Bulletin* 1 (National Lime Association, Washington, D.C.), Apr. 1, 1948, p. 20.

TABLE 12-23. LAUNDRY WASTES*

Composition of waste..... Grease, dirt, starch, soda ash, soap

Character of waste....... Turbid, highly alkaline, readily putrescible, and BOD of 400–1,000 ppm

Methods of treatment.... Biological filtration and chemical precipitation (lime, alum, and ferric chloride or sulfate with sulfuric acid, to adjust pH). Under present laws, dilution is satisfactory

Remarks................ Use of lime prohibited because of nature of wastes, unless chemical processing as above is absolutely necessary. Grease removed and BOD reduced by coagulation with MgSO₄ and lime, or zeolite regeneration water and lime

* The Use of Lime in Industrial Waste Treatment, *Trade Waste Bulletin* 1 (National Lime Association, Washington, D.C.), Apr. 1, 1948, p. 21.

TABLE 12-24. PETROLEUM WASTES*

	Type of waste					
	Drilling	Oil storage	Distillation	Treating	Recovery	Miscellaneous
Composition of wastes	Oil; brine, sodium, calcium, magnesium, chlorine, SO₄, bromine	Organic sulfur compounds, acids, H₂S, SO₂; inorganic salts, sodium, chlorine, magnesium, calcium, sulfur, emulsions	Organic sulfur and nitrogen compounds, inorganic salts and alkalies, phenols, soaps, emulsions	Same as distillation and lead, copper, calcium, and naphthenic acid	Same as distillation, and mercaptides, organic esters, and iron and sulfur compounds	Oil; inorganic chemicals, HF (alkylation)
Methods of treatment	Separators, skimming tanks, evaporators, seepage, repressure producer wells	Same as drilling	Settling tanks, filters, reuse of caustic, evaporation	Same as distillation and recovery by distillation	Same as treating	Same as drilling. HF neutralized with lime
Remarks	Lime may be used to break oil emulsions preparatory to sending water to sewer; separated oil sent to seepage areas or used to repressure wells			Organic compounds used in recovery of treating chemicals. Lime may be used to neutralize H₂SO₄ and sludge if recovery is not feasible	Lime may be used to remove iron and sulfur	Includes composite from water softening, heat exchangers, and general drainage

* The Use of Lime in Industrial Waste Treatment, *Trade Waste Bulletin* 1 (National Lime Association, Washington, D.C.), Apr. 1, 1948, p. 23.

TABLE 12-25. PICKLING LIQUORS*

	Type of waste	
	Steel	Stainless steel
Composition of wastes	Sulfuric acid, ferrous and ferric iron	Sulfuric, nitric and hydrochloric acids, and iron salts
Character of wastes	Highly acidic, inorganic, toxic	Same as steel
Methods of treatment	1. Dilution and disposal to sewer 2. Neutralize with lime 3. Neutralize with lime and pond sludges 4. Cesspool or lagoon wastes 5. Recover copperas and H_2SO_4 or H_2SO_4 and hydrated ferrous sulfates, or ferric sulfate, or iron oxide, and others 6. Produce constructional material (Ferron process)	1. Same as methods 1–4, steel 2. Treat with lime to recover $Ca(NO_3)_2$, $CaCl_2$, or $Ca_3(PO_4)_2$, and metal oxide sludge
Remarks......	Method 1 would use large quantities of water. Method 5 and similar processes are still largely in an experimental stage. None use lime. Method 6 uses lime and has potentialities	Method 2 is still in the experimental stage, but shows promise since calcium nitrate has value as a fertilizer

* The Use of Lime in Industrial Waste Treatment, *Trade Waste Bulletin* 1 (National Lime Association, Washington, D.C.), Apr. 1, 1948, p. 16.

TABLE 12-26. PLATING WASTES*

	Type of waste	
	Copper plating	Chromium plating
Composition of wastes (typical analysis)	NaCN.... 15,200 ppm Na₂CO₃... 60,000 ppm Copper... 26,300 ppm	Total chromium..... 205 ppm Chromium plus 6.... 200 ppm Copper............. 3.0 ppm Nickel.............. 0.7 ppm Iron................ 0.4 ppm SO₄................. 275 ppm CN................. 0.8 ppm Mineral acid...... 208.0 ppm
Character of waste.....	Inorganic, toxic	Inorganic, toxic
Methods of treatment†.	1. Add H₂SO₄ and volatilize HCN gas 2. Add commercial lime-sulfur solution. Very good, CN goes to thiocyanate, definite yellow precipitate indicates complete reaction. Lime removes soda ash by precipitation 3. Acidic CN wastes treated with lime and copperas	1. Reduce Cr plus 6 and precipitate hydrate chromic oxide H₂O₂, Na₂O₂, KMnO₄; followed by lime, Na₂CO₃, BaCO₃, Ba(OH)₂ 2. Direct chemical precipitate of Cr plus 6. Na₂S, BaS, FeSO₄, or scrap Fe; followed by lime to neutralize 3. Miscellaneous precipitation, coagulation, and elutriation
Remarks...............	Method 2 seems to give the best results. Method 1 will contaminate the atmosphere as a result of volatilization. Method 3 is a batch process, as is method 2	The BaS method (method 2 above), followed by adding lime to pH 7.0 is easiest to observe and control. Products are precipitate containing BaCrO₄, BaSO₄, hydrated chromium oxide, and some sulfur. Cyanide can be removed in a related step as harmless salts or double salts

* The Use of Lime in Industrial Waste Treatment, *Trade Waste Bulletin* 1 (National Lime Association, Washington, D.C.), Apr. 1, 1948, p. 13.

† Treating a combination of these two wastes consists of contacting the chromium wastes with iron to reduce Cr plus 6, followed by lime treatment and addition of CN wastes.

TABLE 12-27. PULP AND PAPER WASTES *

	Type of plant				
	Pulp			Paper	Board (straw and paper)
	Soda	Sulfate	Sulfite		
Composition of waste	Lignin, resins, soda, ash, fiber; ink†	Lignin, resins, mercaptans, sulfides, disulfides, sulfates, soaps, tall oil, terpenes, fiber, ink†	Lignin, resins, carbohydrates, proteins, fats, CaO, SO$_2$, ink†	Sizing material, fillers, adhesives, fiber	Fibers, trash, garbage, nitrogen, PO$_4$
Character of waste	Organic, inorganic, toxic, suspended, and dissolved solids			See pulp	Slightly acidic, low BOD, organic
Methods of treatment	Waste liquors evaporated, burned, leached, causticized with lime, diluted with raw black liquor, and stored for reuse in the digester. Carbon and CaCO$_3$ from above used for activated carbon and calcined for causticization, respectively		1. Dilute 2. Fractional precipitation or Howard process 3. Evaporate and use as fuel (Paulson process) 4. Produce by-products: yeast, alcohol, fertilizer, acetone, etc.	1. Recirculation of wastes 2. Chemical precipitation 3. Ponding 4. Filtration	Suspended solids (30%) removed by filtration or chemical coagulation, effluent discharged
Remarks......	The above general process is necessary for the economic operation of the processes. Still, after treatment, the waste will consist of lignin, which must be removed		Methods 2 and 4 show the best futures. Both use lime and so are being given the most attention	Method 1 above is most extensively used since it cuts down BOD as much as 90%. Lime is used as a coagulant and filtration conditioner on white water wastes	Lime may be used in chemical coagulation

* The Use of Lime in Industrial Waste Treatment, *Trade Waste Bulletin* 1 (National Lime Association, Washington, D.C.), Apr. 1, 1948, p. 14.
† If deinking is part of process, these wastes may be combined with other wastes or treated by coagulation and sedimentation. Lime is best chemical coagulant for deinking waste treatment.

TABLE 12-28. RAYON WASTES*

	Type of waste	
	Acidic	Alkaline
Composition of wastes	H_2SO_4, Na_2SO_4, $ZnSO_4$, HCl, $NaHSO_4$, H_2S	Sulfides and polysulfides, colloidal sulfur, NaOH
Character of wastes	Acidic, inorganic, low BOD corrosive	Alkaline, inorganic, high BOD
Methods of treatment	The waste is split with one portion going to neutralize the alkaline waste. The other portion is treated with lime to form $CaSO_4$, which is dewatered and ponded	The waste is neutralized with a portion of the acid waste or it is oxidized in trickling filters to sulfates and thiosulfates
Remarks......	The above methods of treatment seem to be generally standard for disposing of rayon-plant wastes. Rayon-finishing wastes are treated with ferric sulfate and lime in a settling tank to remove 65 % BOD, after which the effluent is discharged to secondary settling tank. The effluent from the latter tank is discharged at an even rate into the sewer	

* The Use of Lime in Industrial Waste Treatment, *Trade Waste Bulletin* 1 (National Lime Association, Washington, D.C.), Apr. 1, 1948, p. 15.

TABLE 12-29. SLAUGHTERHOUSE AND PACKING-HOUSE WASTES*

	Suspended solids	Organic nitrogen	BOD, ppm
Type of waste:			
Killing floor	220	134	825
Blood and tank water	3,690	5,400	32,000
Scalding tub	8,360	1,290	4,600
Meat cutting	610	33	520
Gut washer	15,120	643	13,200
Sausage department	560	136	800
Lard department	180	84	180
By-products	1,380	186	2,200
Character of wastes	Organic, contain grease, hair, flesh, blood		
Methods of treatment	1. Screening and dilution		
	2. Screening, grease removal, manure removal, and dilution		
	3. Method 2 and chlorination followed by sedimentation instead of dilution		
	4. Biological filtration instead of chlorination		
	5. Chemical precipitation using lime and alum or ferric chloride to remove suspended solids and some BOD		
Remarks	Residual BOD after screening, grease removal, coagulation, and sedimentation is largely removed by chlorination, which precipitates dissolved protein. Generally, mechanical and/or biological processes are employed		

* The Use of Lime in Industrial Waste Treatment, *Trade Waste Bulletin* 1 (National Lime Association, Washington, D.C.), Apr. 1, 1948, p. 22.

TABLE 12-30. TANNERY WASTES*

	Type of waste	
	Vegetable	Chrome
Composition of wastes	Lime sludge, hair, fleshing, tan liquor, bleach liquor, salt, blood, dirt	Lime sludge, hair, fleshing, chrome, tan liquor, salt, blood, dirt
Character of wastes	Organic and inorganic, pH 7 plus or minus; high BOD; chrome wastes are higher in dissolved solids, smaller in volume, and lower in BOD	
Method of treatment	The wastes are segregated; all washes are combined. The remaining wastes are combined and allowed to settle. The effluent from this sedimentation is mixed with the total wash water and sent to the sewer. Sludge from sedimentation is lagooned to dewater it and sold for fertilizer	
Remarks......	The above method of treatment has been found satisfactory in all cases. Secondary treatment using chemical precipitation has been tried and has been successful but expensive. Processes have included flue gas (CO_2) and lime, sulfuric acid or sulfur dioxide and alum or lime or both, flue gas and ferric chloride, and sulfuric acid and ferric chloride	

* The Use of Lime in Industrial Waste Treatment, *Trade Waste Bulletin* 1 (National Lime Association, Washington D.C.), Apr. 1, 1948, p. 24.

TABLE 12-31. TEXTILE WASTES*

	Type of waste			
	Deterging	Bleach	Miscellaneous	Dyeing
Composition of wastes..	Scouring detergents, mineral matter, wool grease and sweat, textile fibers	Spent bleach, sulfuric acid, textile fibers, mineral matter	1. Starch, H₂SO, NaOH, malt (desizing) 2. NaOH, H₂SO₄ (mercerizing) 3. Tin and iron salts, (weighting) 4. H₂SO₄, vegetable matter (carbonizing)	Direct, acid, basic, sulfur, vat dyes; NaCl, Na₂SO₄, starch
Character of wastes.....	High in organic, alkaline (high), high suspended solids, easily putrescible, high BOD	Slight alkaline, low BOD, high suspended solids, inorganic and organic	1. Desizing, low volume, organic, alkaline 2. Mercerizing, alkaline, inorganic 3. Weighting, alkaline or acid, inorganic All have low BOD	Alkaline or acid, inorganic and organic, low BOD
Methods of treatment..	Wool-scouring wastes treated by adding lime followed by chlorine, or calcium hypochlorite, after being degreased. The treated waste is settled and effluent discharged	Decolorized (mixed with dye wastes)	Caustic recovered. Lime used to precipitate tin in weighting wastes	1. Dye wastes may be treated with copperas and lime to give good effluent 2. Decolorized (mixed with bleach wastes)
Remarks.................	After or without the above pretreatments, the wastes are combined and coagulation, sedimentation, and sludge removal are performed. Lime is the most common of the coagulants, being used alone or with chlorine, alum, iron sulfates, and ferric chloride. High-calcium lime is generally preferred. Primary treatment may be followed by biological filtration and secondary sedimentation. Lime is being used for some part of total treatment in practically every textile-waste-treatment plant			

* The Use of Lime in Industrial Waste Treatment, *Trade Waste Bulletin* 1 (National Lime Association, Washington, D.C.), Apr. 1, 1948, p. 17.

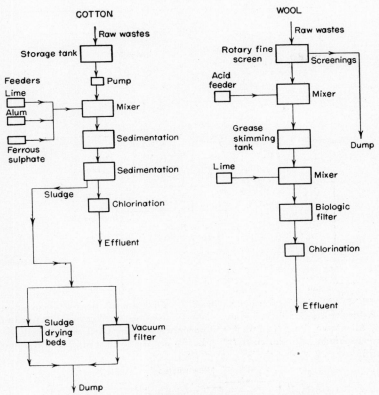

FIG. 12-36. Flow sheet for treatment of textile wastes.

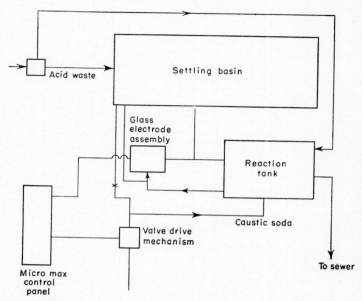

FIG. 12-37. Neutralization of acid wastes. Diagram of waste-neutralization plant for wastes from metal-finishing and plating operations at Western Electric Company plant, Allentown, Pa. The wastes are accurately maintained at a specific pH valve before discharge into the river by a Leeds & Northrup Company Micromax pH Control.

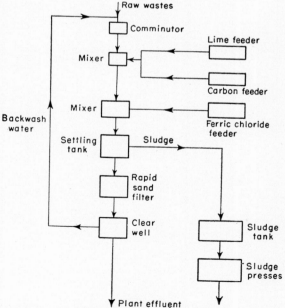

FIG. 12-38. Flow sheet of the Putnam process for treating cosmetic wastes.

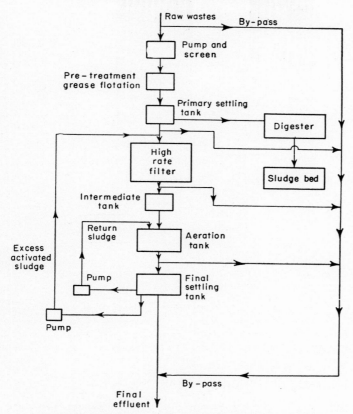

Fig. 12-39. Flow sheet of typical Bioactivation system.

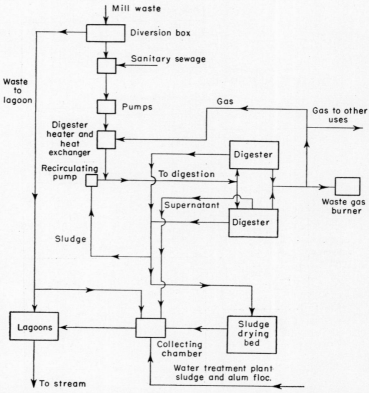

FIG. 12-40.   Flow sheet of fiberboard-waste-treatment and disposal plant.

Bibliography

1. Ryan, W. A., Economic Methods for Treatment of Industrial Wastes, Paper, Meeting, New York Sewage Works Association, Kingston, N.Y., June 6–7, 1949.
2. Oeming, L. F., General Treatment and Control Methods for Industrial Wastes, *Water & Sewage Works*, vol. 94, No. 3, pp. 105–110, March, 1947.
3. Friel, F. S., Developments in 1946 in Sewage and Industrial Waste Treatment, *Water & Sewage Works*, vol. 94, pp. 43–54, February, 1947.
4. Nelson, F. G., Pre-treatment of Carbohydrate Industrial Wastes, *Sewage Works Journal*, vol. 20, p. 530, May, 1948.
5. Barnes, G. E., Industrial Waste Disposal, *Mechanical Engineering (ASME)*, vol. 69, No. 6, pp. 465–470, June, 1947.
6. The Use of Lime in Industrial Waste Treatment, *Trade Waste Bulletin* 1, (National Lime Association, Washington, D.C.), Apr. 1, 1948.
7. Gorman, A. W., The Problem of Waste Disposal from Atomic Energy Operations, Paper, Twenty-first Annual Meeting Federation of Sewage Works Associations, Detroit, Mich., Oct. 18–21, 1948.
8. Rudolfs, W., and V. Del Guercio, Sand Filtration of Some Organic Wastes, *Water & Sewage Works*, vol. 94, pp. 349–351, September, 1947.
9. Howard, N. J., Chlorination Practice in Sewage and Waste Disposal, *Water & Sewage (Canada)*, vol. 85, pp. 11, 21, 1947.
10. Eldridge, E. F., Recirculating High Rate Filter in Industrial Waste Treatment, *Water Works & Sewerage*, vol. 88, pp. 483–490, 1941.
11. Eldridge, E. F., Industrial Waste Treatment Processes and Plant Design, Bulletin 82, Michigan State College Engineering Experiment Station, 1938.
12. Nelson, F. G., Predigestion of Industrial Wastes, *California Sewage Works Journal*, vol. 17, No. 1, pp. 27–36, 1945.
13. Mohlman, F. W., The Industrial Waste Problem: Part 1, Packinghouse, Brewery and By-products Coke Plants, *Sewage Works Journal*, vol. 19, No. 3, pp. 473–477, May, 1947.
14. Poole, B. A., Economies in Industrial Waste Treatment Plant Design, Proceedings, Second Industrial Waste Treatment Conference, Purdue University, Lafayette Ind., 1946, pp. 114–120.
15. Powell, S. T., Industrial Wastes, *Industrial & Engineering Chemistry*, vol. 39, p. 559, May, 1947.
16. Besselievre, E. B., Lime—The Medicine for Stream Pollution, Paper, Meeting, National Lime Association, Hot Springs, Va., May 5, 1947.
17. Morgan, P. F., Determination of the Type and Degree of Treatment Required for an Industrial Waste, Paper, Twenty-second Annual Conference, Michigan Sewage Works Association, Jackson, Mich., May 14–16, 1947.
18. Hart, W. B., "Industrial Waste Disposal for Petroleum Refineries and Allied Plants," Petroleum Processing, Cleveland, Ohio, 1947.
19. Besselievre, E. B., Some Examples of Liquid Industrial Wastes Treatment, *California Sewage Works Journal*, vol. 16, No. 1, 1944.
20. Symposium on Disposal of Liquid Industrial Wastes, *Sewage Works Journal*, vol. 16, pp. 1188–1192, 1942.
21. Ruchhoft, C. C., *et al.*, New Methods Proposed for Solving Industrial Waste Problems, *Civil Engineering (ASCE)*, vol. 17, pp. 59–63, February, 1947.
22. Bloodgood, D. E., Industrial Waste Problem: Part II, Strawboard, Petroleum and Distillery Wastes, *Sewage Works Journal*, vol. 19, No. 4, pp. 607–611, July, 1947.

23. Symons, G. E., Industrial Waste Disposal, *Sewage Works Journal*, vol. 17, pp. 558–572, 1945.
24. Mohlman, F. W., Sewage and Industrial Wastes in 1946, *Water & Sewage Works*, vol. 93, pp. 45–56, 1946.
25. Ryan, W. A., Industrial Waste Lagoons, *Sewage & Industrial Wastes*, vol. 22, No. 1, pp. 71–75, January, 1950.
26. Kominek, E. G., Accelerated Waste Treatment Methods, *Chemical Engineering Progress*, vol. 45, No. 7, pp. 417–420, July, 1949.
27. Heukelekian, H., Biological Oxidation of Industrial Wastes, *Sewage & Industrial Wastes*, vol. 22, No. 1, p. 87, January, 1950.
28. Hall, G. L., Biofiltration for Industrial Wastes, *Sewage & Industrial Wastes Engineering*, vol. 21, No. 3, p. 135, March, 1950.
29. Beohner, H. L., and A. B. Mindler, Ion Exchange in Waste Treatment, *Industrial & Engineering Chemistry*, vol. 41, pp. 448–452, 1949.
30. Fischer, A. J., New Vacuum Process Aids Liquid Waste Disposal, *Food Industries*, vol. 15, p. 87, 1943.
31. Industrial Waste Problems and Treatment, *Public Works*, vol. 77, pp. 25–28, 30, April, 1946.
32. Domestic and Industrial Aspects of National Water Resources Policy, A Statement of Desirable Policy with Respect to the Conservation, Development and Use of the National Water Resources, published by The Water Policy Panel of Engineers Joint Council, Mimeographed, June, 1950.
33. Kivell, W. A., and N. B. Lund, Grit Removal from Sewage, *Water Works & Sewerage*, April, 1940.
34. Bartholomew, F. J., Recovery of Waste Iron Sulfate-sulfuric Acid Solutions, Paper 50 PRI 3, Process Industries Conference, The American Society of Mechanical Engineers, Pittsburgh, Pa., Apr. 24–27, 1950.
35. Tanski, E. S., and G. R. Osterfelt, Development of Filtrate Utilization in Lime Treatment of Waste Pickle Liquor, Paper, Meeting, American Society of Mechanical Engineers, Pittsburgh, Pa., Apr. 24–27, 1950.
36. Guillot, E. F., and G. R. Osterfelt, Equipment Requirements for Lime Neutralization of Waste Pickle Liquor, Paper, Meeting, American Society of Mechanical Engineers, Pittsburgh, Pa., Apr. 24–27, 1950.

CHAPTER 13

EQUIPMENT FOR WASTE TREATMENT AND ITS SELECTION

In general, the equipment for use in plants for the treatment of industrial wastes is the same as that used in plants for the treatment of normal domestic or municipal sewage. The principal difference is in the specific application of this equipment, in the factors used in the design of the units, and in the conditions influencing the adoption of a given size, make, or type of unit or equipment.

As in all fields of engineering and industry, various manufacturers produce the necessary equipment. In general, the units developed and marketed by each manufacturer are based on a definite principle which mirrors the ideas of that manufacturer or his engineers as to the type best suited for a given purpose, from a practical or mechanical standpoint.

On the other hand, certain manufacturers are interested solely in the design of units that will perform a given task, regardless of the mechanical elements of which they may be composed; they will develop units with the idea of basic efficiency always in the foreground. Other manufacturers, who have come into the field because of the increasing volume of business brought about by the modern consciousness of public health and sanitation, devise units which utilize in some form or other a basic product of their plants. These units are a secondary line with them, the basic element being the major factor in their annual volume of business. As many of the units developed earlier have been protected by strong patents, it has been necessary for some manufacturers to produce units which circumvent the earlier patents. This, of course, does not mean that some of these units do not have merit. Many of them do.

In this chapter, the various types of equipment and units will not be discussed from the point of view of the superiority of one type over another, but rather various units available will be described so that the industrial-plant owner and his engineer may know the range and be able to select those units which seem to be the most practical, logical, and economical for his particular case.

FACTORS OF IMPORTANCE IN SELECTING EQUIPMENT

In selecting equipment for an industrial-waste-treatment plant, the advantages of one type of equipment or unit should be weighed against the others and that one (or those) selected which offers the following important advantages:

1. Low initial, over-all, and completely erected cost.
2. Least cost in operation, from the standpoint of power consumption and repairs or replacements due to wear.
3. Reputation of the manufacturer and reliability of the service organization.
4. Accessibility for repairs without requiring the emptying of tanks or basins.
5. Simplicity of construction.
6. Neat appearance and silent operation.
7. Efficiency of performance, in percentage of results produced.
8. Suitability for the available site.
9. Compactness (adaptability to adjacent units).
10. Protective devices.

Items 1 and 2, which deal with cost factors, will be discussed in detail in Chap. 16 under Initial Cost of Plant and Operating Charges and therefore will not be included here. The remaining items will now be considered.

Reputation of the Manufacturer

This is an important point. A reliable manufacturer will usually guarantee to supply his units with any part which is found defective due to poor workmanship or material within one year from the time of shipment from the factory or from the time of installation. This guarantee should be required in every case. But, again, this is not the entire story. The main point is whether the manufacturer willingly agrees to stand behind his machine after the initial period of guarantee is past, or simply writes it off his books at the end of the year. One manufacturer of this type of equipment includes in the price of his equipment a sum for service. This sum includes the services of a trained man from his field engineering division to visit the plant when the unit is installed to check it for correct installation, observe its initial operation, and make any required adjustments so that, when he leaves, it is working to the satisfaction of the owner. However, the service of this manufacturer does not cease there. Realizing that satisfied clients are his best advertisers, he sets aside a special fund for the service allotted to this particular unit, and at any time during the operation of this machine, to the extent of the amount available for service, visits will be made to the plant and adjustments made or advice given. Furthermore, the sales engineer, who has dealt with the customer, is charged with the responsibility to visit the plant when he is in the vicinity and discuss with the owner and the operator any points of operation that may have arisen. This latter service does not cease at any given time but continues indefinitely. This willingness to be of service to a client cannot be evaluated in dollars but is invaluable to any purchaser.

Accessibility for Repairs

This is important, not only as a guarantee for continued service, but from a cost viewpoint as well. If the unit is one in which all the wearing parts (those which might be subject to wear or breakdown) are located above the liquid level of the tank in which the machine is installed, they may be inspected periodically without stopping the unit or emptying the tank, and wear may be detected and corrected before a breakdown occurs. In a unit in which the parts subject to wear are submerged, inspections cannot be made until an actual breakdown occurs. This point is extremely important if gritty or abrasive elements are present in the liquid or the sediment. The machine with submerged parts which are in constant contact with these elements will deteriorate more rapidly than will one with the parts located out of this danger zone.

Simplicity of Construction

This is a self-evident point: the machine which has the fewest wearing parts will be the one which, in normal circumstances, will require the least repair and maintenance and will be subject to fewer interruptions.

Neat Appearance and Silent Operation

This may not seem important, particularly to industrial-plant owners, but it is a known fact that the trend today is to make all mechanical items, from automobiles to kitchen and shop tools, look attractive. This is a psychological factor. A clean, neat, attractive, nicely painted machine will naturally receive better care from its users than one which is sloppy or unattractive in appearance. A machine which has its lubrication devices so placed that they are readily accessible and which does not leak oil or grease not only will be lubricated properly by the attendant but will also be kept free of such soil.

For many years it was customary for the operators in mining plants to be advised when a machine was shut down by the cessation of its normal noisy operation. With the introduction of mechanical equipment into plants for the treatment of water and sewage for municipalities, considerable thought was given to its appearance and quiet operation. It was noticeable that when industrial-plant owners visited such plants and saw these neat and quiet machines in operation they wanted the same type for their plants.   In machine shops of today, cleanliness and attractive layouts are considered essentials.   The modern shop or plant is not a noisy, ear-splitting collection of throbbing, pounding units, but is usually one of peaceful quiet in which a normal conversational tone of voice will be readily heard.   Neatness and quiet action can be obtained at no extra cost.   In industrial-waste-treatment plants, which are usually erected in congested districts, these factors are important in reducing complaints from nearby residents.

Efficiency of Performance

This is an item for which the plant owner is paying hard cash.   If one piece of equipment, because of its basic design, shape, or hydraulic factor, will produce an effluent which will require less further treatment or will better satisfy the authorities, even at slightly greater over-all cost than another, it is well worth the careful consideration of the prospective purchaser.

Suitability for the Available Site

This item should normally be considered by the designing engineer. In some cases the ground at the proposed plant site is rocky or is in a low spot, where the water table is close to the surface.   In such cases a shallow tank, requiring the least excavation, will be desirable.   In other cases where a narrow piece of land is the only available site or where the waste-treatment plant must be placed between existing buildings or other structures, it is sometimes suitable to use a long narrow tank even at the possible sacrifice of some efficiency.   However, these cases are rare, and in most installations the more common circular tank, which is basically the cheapest form of construction, will be found to be adaptable.

Compactness

In many cases considerable initial expenditure may be saved in industrial-waste-treatment plants by the selection of units which may be directly coupled with other plant units or with existing buildings at a saving in ground area and construction cost.   If a square tank can be used, it is common practice to incorporate one or more walls of such a tank with adjacent units, at a considerable saving in concrete cost.   Also the area saved by the use of square tanks may be an important item.   A plant which requires, for instance, a tank area of 10,000 square feet for the treatment of wastes can obtain this entire area in a square unit with a dimension of 100 feet on each side.   A circular unit with the same surface area would require a space 113 feet square to accommodate it.

Protective Devices

In many industrial plants it is not necessary to have men in attendance on all machines at all times as the modern mechanical unit is built to operate with attention mainly for lubrication. On the other hand, if the plant is unattended much of the time, it is important that units equipped with protective devices to prevent damage and breakdown be selected. Many units are now equipped with alarm devices which, when an overload occurs, will give notice to the operator that trouble exists. If, however, he is not able to attend immediately, certain of these units are further equipped with automatic devices which, a minute or so after the sounding of the alarm, will cut off the current and stop the machine. The machine cannot again be started until the obstruction has been removed or the trouble rectified.

The points listed may seem like an unnecessarily protracted list of items to consider when an industrialist is choosing the equipment for a waste-treatment plant, but on the other hand he should realize that he is planning to build something which will entail a heavy capital expenditure and which must operate as economically as possible for a long term of years. Breakdowns and failures due to poor equipment will add materially to his overhead, which in turn will be reflected in his cost of production. It is, therefore, worth his while to scrutinize the points outlined carefully or to insist that his engineer evaluate them so that he may obtain the best equipment at the least cost.

EQUIPMENT FOR WASTE TREATMENT

The units normally used in industrial-waste-treatment plants, their variant types, and the manufacturers who supply them are so numerous that only their salient features will be outlined here.

Bar Screens or Racks

These are usually employed in industrial-waste-treatment plants where the wastes contain a considerable volume of coarse solids, such as large fibers, rags, bits of wood, fruit skins, or other large objects, which might damage or clog other units. These screens usually consist of a set of bars set in the flow channel, either at an angle of about 60 degrees to the horizontal axis of the flow or curved to the radius of a circle. The material accumulated on the bars is usually removed, particularly in large installations, by means of a mechanically operated rake, which collects the accumulation and carries it to an upper level for final removal from the plant. In many cases these rakes are controlled by time-clock mechanisms; in other cases, to save power and wear on the bars and rakes, the units are operated by automatic float controls.

There are various forms of these screens: some have curved bars, others have practically vertical bars and are equipped with rakes which travel upward from the bottom, carrying the screened solids and depositing them in cans or other containers at an upper point. The curved-bar type has a revolving rake, whereas the vertical type has toothed rakes that are pulled upward by chains or cables.

Another form of screen, which may be employed when the solids are of such a nature that they will not interfere with later processes, is a circular drumlike element set in the flow channel and consisting of bars set hori-

Fig. 13-1. The Dorrco-Sulzer screenings disintegrator. (*Courtesy of The Dorr Company.*)

zontally. Between these bars, a set of knives revolves which cuts up or macerates the solids held against the bars by the force of the flow. The cut-up material then passes through the bars on to the other units in the plant or to the sewer. One form of this unit is commonly known as a Comminutor.

In some cases where the more conventional types of bar screens are employed and the character of the screened material is such that it may be macerated and put back into the waste flow, macerators, crushers, or disintegrators are used to break up the screenings. A recently developed form of unit for this work is known as a Disintegrator and is manufactured in the United States by The Dorr Company. Figure 13-1 illustrates this unit.

Bar screens and their accessories are manufactured and sold by Dorr, Link-Belt Company, Chain Belt Company, Jeffrey Manufacturing Company, American Well Works, Yeomans Brothers Company, Worthington Company, and Chicago Pump Company, the two latter producing the Comminutor type. The float-control unit for such screens is provided by Dorr. Time clocks for screen control are supplied by General Electric Company and other companies.

Bar screens usually have bars spaced to give an opening 1 to 2 inches between the bars. They require little power to operate, one type manufactured by Dorr requiring only $3/4$ horsepower for the largest size units. The upper works of the vertical type screens are usually enclosed in steel housings, and the screenings are handled without objection from odors and unsightly solids.

Fine Screens

These units are distinguished from bar screens in that the openings range from $1/16$ inch to approximately $1/4$ inch in size. They are used to intercept finer solids than a bar screen will catch and are useful in the treatment of wastes from meat-packing plants, slaughterhouses, vegetable and fruit canneries, and other plants where the solids are finely divided. In some cases fine screens are used as the sole method of treatment. In cases where the wastes are ultimately to be handled in sewage-treatment works, they are used as a preliminary treatment.

Fine screens are of two general forms: revolving drums covered with perforated metal plates, and revolving disks also covered with perforated metal plates. The drum screens are cleaned in one of two ways. The Dorrco Fine Screen is cleansed of the solids that are caught on the surface of the drum by means of a head of water, which is built up inside the drum as it revolves and which, in escaping from the drum through the perforated plate, washes the solids from the face of the drum. This screen requires no brushes or jets of water to maintain it in operating condition and, therefore, is subject to practically no wear on its plates or clogging of the perforations. It has been used in numerous industrial-waste-treatment plants for the handling of tannery, vegetable-cannery, textile, and packing-house wastes. The Link-Belt screen, also of the drum type, is cleaned by a set of revolving brushes which travel along the top of the drum as it revolves. One form of this screen had, instead of perforated plates, a series of tightly strung wires to give a long, very narrow, uninterrupted slot.

The Disc screen is in the form of a large metal disk, set at an angle of about 30 degrees, with a central section, the whole giving the appearance of a Pilgrim's hat. The solids are caught on the face of the disk and, as this revolves, are carried around to the top where they are brushed off by a set of revolving brushes.

When screens are brushed from the side of the plates on which the screenings are held, soft solids tend to be crushed and forced into the perforations, thus making it necessary to clean the plates occasionally with steam, hot water, or kerosene.

Another form of screen now used in the screening of cannery wastes is the vibrating screen, similar to a type used in metallurgical operations. This screen is manufactured by the Link-Belt Company.

Grease and Scum Removers

Certain industrial wastes contain large percentages of grease and fine solids with low specific gravity which cause excessive float or scum on tanks and vessels. It is considered advisable to remove this material, and in many plants such a unit is employed for this purpose, particularly for wastes from vegetable and fruit canneries, paper mills, etc.

These units are of several forms. Some are merely enlargements of the channel through which the waste flows, permitting the solids to settle or rise to the surface, from which they are then skimmed. Other units are provided with air-diffusion plates set in the bottom, through which compressed air is admitted which, in rising, carries with it the light material, grease, etc., which collects on the surface.

A more recent form of grease and light-solids remover, which has been effective in fruit and vegetable cannery, petroleum, and other industries, is known as the Vacuator, a product of The Dorr Company. This unit is a closed circular tank, about 12 feet deep. As the waste material is about to enter the tank, it is subjected to a short period of aeration by means of a mechanical aerator, which tends to coat the fine particles, grease, etc., with air, thus giving them greater buoyancy. After entering the tank, the aerated material is subjected to the pull of a maintained vacuum equivalent to 9 inches of mercury. This causes the air-encased solids to rise immediately to the surface, and at this point they are removed by two continuously rotating scum skimmers and are discharged down a separate scum pipe. The clarified liquid flows away at a level below the scum, to further treatment. This unit, owing to the aeration and vacuum, is able to operate at very much higher rates than ordinary settling units. Figure 13-2 illustrates this unit.

Sedimentation or Settling Units

In practically every waste-treatment method or plant, sedimentation is a basic element, whether the wastes are treated with chemical coagulants to expedite precipitation of fine solids or whether gravitation alone is depended upon to bring down the bulk of the settleable solids in a reasonable period of time, normally considered to be 2 to 4 hours.

As the objectives of sedimentation have been covered in the preceding chapter, the variant forms of sedimentation tanks used in recognized waste-treatment processes will be discussed here.

There are two general forms of such tanks: (1) the circular tank, with revolving sludge-collecting mechanism, and its variant form, the square tank, with the same type of mechanism; (2) and the rectangular tank, which has a length equal to several times its width. The question of which type is best suited for a given project is not a subject for this chapter.

The circular tank is usually fitted with a mechanism consisting of a central shaft, or column, to which arms are attached equipped with

Fɪɢ. 13-2.   Sewage-treatment plant at Palo Alto, Calif., showing the Dorrco vacuator in the background.   (*Courtesy of The Dorr Company.*)

scraper blades which pass close to the tank bottom to collect the settled material. These units are driven by means of a motor located at the center of the unit on a supporting superstructure, which revolves the central shaft or column through a train of gears usually enclosed in an oil bath. In other types of circular units, the arms are carried around the tank by means of a motor carriage running on the wall of the tank itself or on rails laid on it. Some types operate by means of a sprocket at the end of the upper arm extension, which pulls the arm around the tank by means of a chain laid in the effluent channel.

The method of feeding these tanks is either from the center upward through a hollow central column or pier from which the flow radiates outward to a weir around the entire periphery, or from a central feed-well fed by a pipe brought in under the liquid level from the side of the tank. One type of tank employs a central drive unit to rotate the arms but, instead of using the normal scrapers on the arms, employs a chain-scraper mechanism operating on one arm, which pulls the settled solids to the center of the tank. Still another form employs the central-drive type with radial arms but utilizes suction to draw solids up into the arms through nozzles similar in form to those of the common household vacuum cleaner.

Circular sedimentation units, or "Clarifiers" as they are now commonly called, are produced by Dorr, Link-Belt, American Well Works, Carter, Infilco, Walker Process Equipment Company, and other companies.

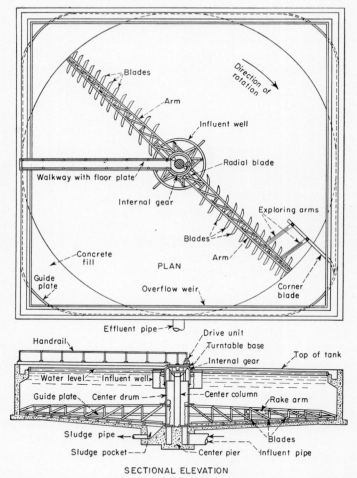

FIG. 13-3.   Diagrams of Dorrco Squarex siphon-feed clarifier with peripheral overflow weir.   (*Courtesy of The Dorr Company.*)

Differing from the circular center-driven type is the perfectly square tank, fed either from the center with siphon feed to a weir around the entire periphery of the tank, or from one side to a weir on the opposite side.   Figure 13-3 illustrates this type.

The rectangular type of tank, used where ground conditions dictate or where personal preference prevails, is usually equipped with a mechanism composed of a chain running over sprockets located at the top and bottom of each end of the tank and driven by a motor located at the top of the tank, through another set of chain and sprockets. At intervals, plates or boards which scrape along the bottom of the tank and pull the settled material to the sludge hopper at one end are affixed to the chain in the tank. As mechanical limitations control the width of these tanks, it is necessary, when a very wide tank is required, to employ two or more mechanisms in the same tank. In such cases an auxiliary cross collector of the same type is necessary, to collect the sludge from the several hoppers and carry it to a common point.

Another form of rectangular tank is cleaned by means of a traveling carriage which moves along the walls of the tank, from which a framework is suspended which carries scraper blades which move the sludge on the tank bottom. In one form of this tank, known as the Monorake, the carriage is propelled by means of stainless-steel cables which pull it along and return it to the head end of the tank by reverse switches. Figure 13-4 illustrates this unit. In other forms of this type, the carriage is moved along by means of a motor, located on the carriage, driving a wheel which runs on rails laid on the wall of the tank. Still another form, developed in Germany and known as the Mieder type, consists of a heavy traveling carriage with means for transferring it from one tank to another when cleaning is considered necessary.

Mechanisms for rectangular tanks of the several forms, chain and traveling carriage, are marketed by Link-Belt, Chain Belt, Jeffrey, American Well Works, Dorr, and Hardinge.

A recently developed form of sedimentation unit combined with aeration to assist in flocculation has been found effective in increasing the removal of suspended solids and adding oxygen to the sewage. Two of these units, known as the Oxidator and the Aerator-Clarifier, are marketed by Process Engineers and Dorr, respectively.

In some small plants it has been advantageous, from the standpoints of economy and ease of operation, to incorporate the sedimentation step with the digestion phase in one tank. Such a unit, known as a Clarigester, was developed originally by John F. Skinner and later taken over by The Dorr Company. It is, in effect, a mechanized Imhoff tank, as it involves the same general principles of that well-known unit, with the added advantages gained by the mechanical collection of sludge and mixing of sludge in the digestion compartment.

In this unit sewage enters the top, or sedimentation compartment, at a central feed well and flows radially to the peripheral overflow weir.

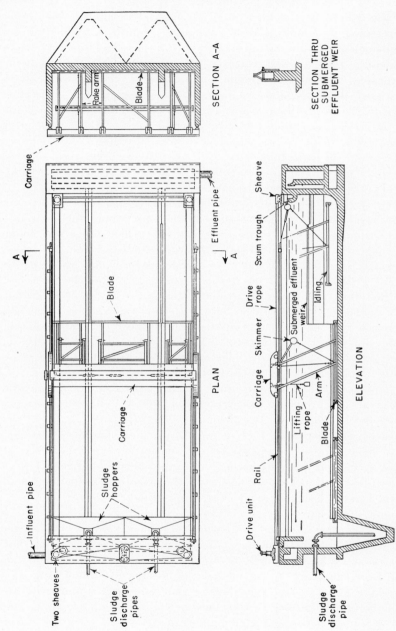

SECTION A-A

SECTION THRU SUBMERGED EFFLUENT WEIR

PLAN

ELEVATION

FIG. 13-4.   The Dorrco Monorake Clarifier mechanism for rectangular settling tanks.   (Courtesy of The Dorr Company.)

The sludge in this compartment is continuously collected by the familiar revolving type of mechanism with sludge scrapers. These scrapers move the sludge to a central opening in the concrete sloping diaphragm which separates the upper sedimentation compartment from the lower digestion compartment. The sludge drops through this opening, which is provided with a seal to prevent the resurgence of solids or the escape of gas. At the top of the digestion compartment, attached to the same central shaft, are two arms, with uprising fingers, which tend to break up scum which forms under the diaphragm and to prevent matting of fibrous material. At the bottom of the digestion tank is a second set of arms

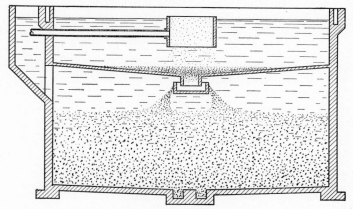

FIG. 13-5. Diagrammatic sketch illustrating the principle of operation of the Dorr Clarigester (combined clarification and digestion). (*Courtesy of The Dorr Company.*)

which stir up the sludge and maintain it in a semifluid state, permitting its ready discharge from the unit. The gas, which is developed in the digestion compartment, flows up into a well at the side of the tank and is collected in a metal gas dome at the top. The unit, in most cases, is provided with a small centrifugal pump which pumps the scum collected from the water level in the sedimentation compartment down into the digestion compartment. Figure 13-5 illustrates the principles of this unit.

Although this unit has the same basic principles as the Imhoff tank, it is more economical to build and operate, as it does not require the steep slopes on the sedimentation compartment or the thin involved walls and complicated concrete of the earlier tank. Likewise, the mechanical collection of sludge eliminates the hand squeegeeing of the slopes of the sedimentation compartment, the digestion compartment is provided with the modern means of circulating sludge and breaking scum, and reaction control and heating may be applied.

Owing to structural limitations, the unit is made only in sizes up to 40 feet in diameter, which restricts its use to the smaller plants, unless duplicate units are installed. In cases where sedimentation with digestion of sludge is the sole required treatment, this unit may comprise the entire plant. By installing it with the water level in the sedimentation compartment about 8 feet above ground level, the sludge from the digestion compartment may be discharged to sludge-drying beds at ground level by the hydrostatic head in the unit. This arrangement eliminates, in many cases, the need for sludge pumps.

In those cases where previous flocculation of wastes, either with or without coagulants, is decided upon, it has been found advantageous to combine the flocculation step in the same tank as the sedimentation. The unit used is known as a Clariflocculator and consists of a circular tank, in the center of which is a circular well of steel or concrete equipped with revolving flocculation paddles. The waste to be treated enters this well at the top and is subjected to the normal flocculation period of 30 to 40 minutes; then the entire flow passes out of the open bottom of the flocculation compartment into the sedimentation compartment, which extends under the flocculation compartment. The solids and floc thus formed settle to the bottom of the sedimentation compartment at the most desirable point, close to the sludge hopper, and are collected by the revolving arms of the sludge-collecting unit and carried, as in any ordinary sedimentation unit, to the central sludge well. Figure 13-6 illustrates this unit.

This unit has the advantage of reducing the amount of concrete required, as the flocculation compartment is entirely within the area of the sedimentation unit. Furthermore, it incorporates the basic principle of flocculation—that the flocs once formed should not be subjected to an increase of velocity by being passed through a pipe or other restricted opening. It has been observed in many instances that industrial-waste flocs are relatively fragile and, if subjected to high velocities or impact against obstructions, become dispersed and that it is difficult, and sometimes impossible, to reassemble them. In the unit under discussion, the flocs pass through the unobstructed bottom of the flocculation chamber directly into the settling compartment below.

Recently, for small plants, an interesting development has been to make dual use of the volume and area in a settling tank by placing a metal diaphragm across the tank which extends above the water line and down to the level of the sludge-raking arms. The raw waste is fed into the central influent well, which occupies one side of the diaphragm, and flows radially outward to the overflow weir, which is equal in length to one-half the circumference of the tank. The final effluent, in those cases where

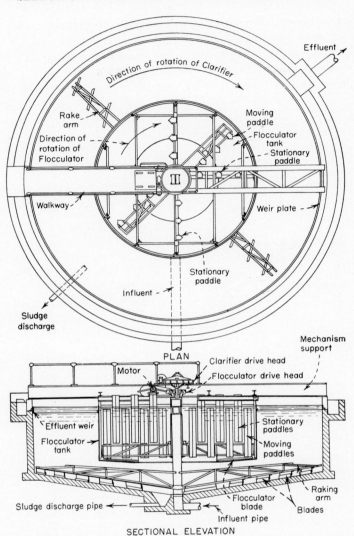

FIG. 13-6. Diagrammatic drawings of the Dorrco Clariflocculator.   (*Courtesy of The Dorr Company.*)

secondary sedimentation is required, is brought back to an influent well on the opposite side of the diaphragm, and this liquid also flows radially outward to the secondary overflow weir, which occupies the other half of the circumference of the tank.   As the sludge from both the primary and secondary settling steps falls to the bottom of the same tank, it is collected by the one sludge-collecting mechanism.

In certain cases, where the plants are small, the Duo-Clarifier may be combined with the digestion compartment below known as a Duo-Clarigester, in which both primary and secondary settling and digestion are carried out in one unit. Where secondary treatment by biological filtration is adopted, the trickling filter plus the Duo-Clarigester com-

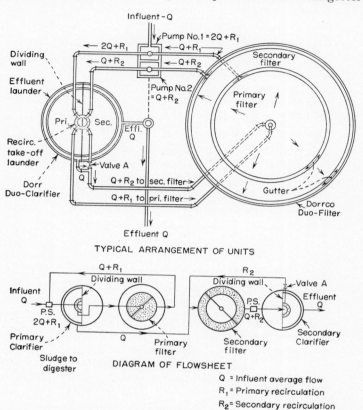

FIG. 13-7. Diagrams of Biofiltration process plant equipped with Dorrco Duo-Clarifier and Duo-Distributor units. (*Courtesy of The Dorr Company.*)

prise the entire plant. The advantages of this unit from a control and operation standpoint can be readily appreciated. Figure 13-7 illustrates the flow sheet used when this principle is employed. Plants of this type offer great economies in usage of ground area, which is frequently an item of importance in industrial-waste treatment.

Sedimentation units are usually designed, after studies and tests on the individual waste have been made, on the basis of detention, but in recent years it has become evident that detention alone is not a correct criterion and that area has more effect on the percentage of removal of settleable solids than depth. Detention, without some controlling factor, may result in a totally ineffective solids-removal method.

Let us assume that for a given case we need a settling tank with a total detention volume, based on a selected number of hours of the average daily flow, of 10,000 cubic feet. If detention alone is used, this volume can be obtained in a tank 10 feet square by 100 feet deep, but the flow line in such a tank is so short that practically none of the suspended solids would be removed. On the other hand, a properly designed tank, having the same volume but with a depth of 10 feet and a surface area of 1,000 square feet, or a circular unit 36 feet in diameter and 10 feet deep, would produce a result in accordance with modern expectations. It has therefore become the custom, adopted generally by the engineering departments of many states and by other authorities who control the design of waste-treatment plants, to combine the detention period with an area unit of flow, in which the total volume that may be handled by 1 square foot of tank area is restricted to a given figure, usually between 800 and 1,000 gallons per square foot of tank area per day. Thus, a waste flow of 100,000 gallons per day, with a required settling-tank rate of 800 gallons per square foot, would require a tank with an area of 125 square feet.

An important factor in the efficiency of sedimentation units is the means of bringing the flow into the tank and of discharging it. This may be done in a variety of ways, some of which are effective and others not. The diagrams in Fig. 13-8 illustrate some of the common ways of feeding and discharging from tanks.

Type A is ineffective because there are, as shown, dead areas in the tank and short-circuit points between the ends of the influent and effluent weirs. Type B is ineffective because the holes through which the influent enters the tank tend to cause streaming of currents across the tank, causing unequal distribution. Type C is ineffective because of possible fanlike streaming and short-circuiting across the tank and dead areas.

Type D is effective because the influent enters at the central feed well at the top and flows radially outward to a complete peripheral weir. This type, however, has a disadvantage in that the influent is directed against one side of the wall of the influent well, which tends to set up diverse currents that make the flow uneven in its travel to the outer edge of the tank. Type E is the most effective because the influent comes into the tank at the bottom, rises upward in a hollow center pier or shaft, and spills over the top in an even volume on all sides; thus, it flows equally in all directions radially outward to the periphery.

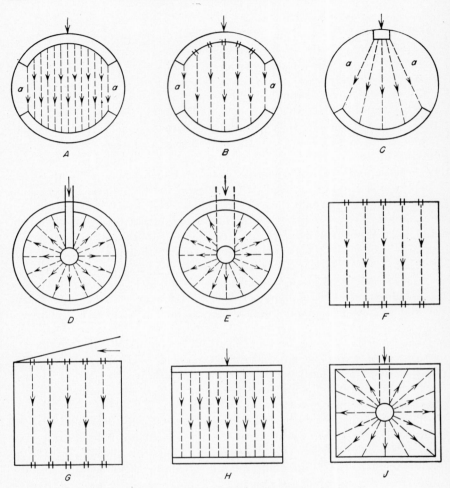

"*a*" in diagrams indicates dead areas and dashed lines indicate stream flow

FIG. 13-8.   Various methods of arranging influent and effluent flow for sedimentation tanks.

For square tanks, type F is ineffective because of the streaming and short-circuiting effect caused by the liquid jetting through relatively small ports. Type G is ineffective because the flow approaches the inlet channel at an angle and tends to flow more definitely through the ports or over the weir at the left-hand side of the tank, thus causing unequal flow and velocity conditions in the tank.

Type H is usually effective if the weir is perfectly level or is of the V-notch type, which tends to distribute the flow equally. Type J is the most effective as the flow enters from the bottom of the tank, is distributed uniformly at the top of the central inlet, and flows equally and radially to the peripheral weir.   This type is also the most effective from a hydraulic standpoint, as the velocity of flow into the tank is at its highest point at the point of entry at the top of the central upflow column, and from that point the velocity drops constantly as the flow approaches the effluent weir.   Thus, the solids tend to settle in a parabolic line and form a conical pile close to the center of the tank, requiring the shortest time to bring them to the central sludge pocket.   Also, as the solids settle faster as the flow approaches the overflow weir, the influence of uprising currents is nullified, and the solids will stay down in the tank and will not pass over the effluent weir to cloud the final discharge. In cases where an influent channel approaches at an angle, as in type G, it is advantageous to place deflector vanes in the channel to force the flow to even out as it passes through the various ports.   This will prevent the short-circuiting that is common to this type of influent.   This design is used regularly in the Dorr Detritor and has operated satisfactorily in installations of all sizes.   As the sedimentation unit is one of the most important units in a plant, a designer should give considerable thought to the details of entrance and exit of tanks.

Combination Units

As previously mentioned in this chapter, the most recent development in sedimentation units is the incorporation of an aeration section.   It has been found that a short aeration period, usually between 30 minutes and 1 hour, with a small amount of air accomplishes the same general effect as flocculation without coagulants, in flocculating or agglomerating fine suspended matter and colloids, giving greater efficiency of solids removal and BOD reduction in primary sedimentation.   This treatment also has the ability to scrub out and dilute entrained gases which might cause odor nuisance; it freshens and conditions the raw waste, thus creating improved general conditions during subsequent treatment; it deemulsifies and floats grease; and it mixes and disperses small batch discharges of toxic or otherwise objectionable industrial wastes.   It is believed that this type of treatment will be especially beneficial with septic or stale wastes, keeping down odors and assisting in the later oxidation.

Several state departments of health are now encouraging the installation of means for preaeration where a degree of treatment in excess of that normally effected by primary treatment is required and in cases where the raw sewage or wastes are very strong.

Standards now being prepared by a group of states in the Upper Mississippi and Great Lakes area include preaeration.   The general statement in these proposed standards for the guidance of 10 states is as follows: "Flocculation of sewage by air or mechanical agitation, with or without chemicals, is worthy of consideration when the raw sewage is strong, or when it is desired to reduce the strength of the sewage to such a degree that subsequent treatment units can produce a satisfactory plant effluent."

It is interesting to note that these standards also propose to state: "A unit should be so designed that it may be removed from service without affecting any settling unit."

A recently developed unit, marketed by Dorr, covers just these points and should have considerable application in the treatment of industrial wastes, where the agglomeration of solids will be of benefit and where aeration will not act to make the solids float instead of settle.

This new unit, called the Dorrco Aerator-Clarifier, comprises a standard circular, mechanically cleaned settling tank with a steel central well in which the aeration step is performed. In this well, porous diffuser tubes, through which compressed air is admitted, are supported on a grid of pipes, the number of tubes varying with the size of the unit. These tubes are readily removed for inspection without interrupting the flow through the tank. At the bottom of the aeration well is a large opening through which the aerated wastes pass directly into the lower settling compartment. Therefore, there is no possibility of fracturing light flocculent materials by transferring them at high velocities from the aeration chamber to the settling compartment as might occur if the two chambers were entirely separate units. Likewise, as the bottom of the aeration unit is open, grit and other solids cannot collect in it.

Another recently developed unit with a similar purpose is known as the Process Oxidator, developed by Process Engineers, of California. In this unit, the air is supplied through diffusers mounted on a rotating manifold in the aeration compartment, but because this diffuser arrangement revolves with the mechanism it cannot be serviced readily without stopping the unit and lowering the water level.

It is evident that these units indicate a trend in plant practice which, while increasing the initial cost to a very small degree, will increase the efficiency of removal of solids and also assist in preventing odors due to stale or septic wastes.

Other preaeration units are produced by Pacific Flush Tank Company, American Well Works, and Walker Process Equipment. These, however, differ materially from the two just described, those of the two last-named companies being mechanical-aeration units which are entirely separate from the settling tanks. In these there would appear to be the danger of fracture of light floc by high-velocity transfer from one unit to another and of the deposition of grit and solids in the aeration section if no sludge-collection equipment were installed there.

Sludge-digestion Units and Systems

Except in those cases where heavy charges of chemical coagulants are used, the solids taken from the sedimentation units in the form of sludge are usually pumped to sludge-digestion units, in which the natural decomposition of the organic matter is carried out in the presence of heat, to maintain a temperature conducive to rapid anaerobic bacterial action. These digestion tanks now are usually closed units, with either steel or concrete roofs. In most cases they are equipped with means to maintain the sludge in agitation to prevent stratification of the solids entering and also to inoculate incoming fresh material with active bacteria from the older sludge, thus decreasing the time required for the complete decomposition of the organic matter. In some cases, this agitation is done by means of motor-driven agitator units suspended in the tank, which are devised to circulate the entire contents of the tank from one level to another. In another form, the circulation is by means of a pump which draws sludge from the bottom, or other level, of the tank and pumps it back into the upper levels. Digestion units may be either single or two stage. In the single-stage type the entire digestion cycle is carried out in the one tank, and the gas (an important product of modern controlled digestion) is collected at the top of the tank in a steel dome or under a cover which floats upon the liquid.

In the two-stage type, the first, or primary, digester is usually a tightly closed tank, with a concrete or steel-dome roof. The raw sludge is pumped into this tank, which is usually provided with stirring mechanisms or means for circulation and with heat exchangers or other means of applying heat to the contents. After remaining in this first tank for periods of 15 to 30 days, the sludge passes over automatically into the second tank, together with the gas, which has collected at the top, and the supernatant liquor. In the secondary tank, which is normally neither agitated nor heated, quiescent settling takes place, and the digestion cycle is completed. The only effluent from the two-stage system is from the secondary tank and is the supernatant, equal in amount to the amount of sludge pumped into the primary tank. As the secondary tank is quiescent, the concentration of solids and BOD in this supernatant is usually much less than it is from the agitated single-stage system.

The theory of the two-stage system, the two tanks of which contain the same volume as one single-stage unit, is that in controlled digestion the bulk of the gas, the main by-product of the bacterial breakdown of the organic matter, occurs in a relatively few days, 15 to 20, and the completion of the digestion takes a longer time. The secondary tanks are usually provided with steel covers, which rise and fall according to the volume of gas accumulated in them. In those cases where it is proposed to make use of the gas as a fuel, the gasholder covers are provided with sufficient lift, up to 19 feet on large units, to act as reservoirs to provide the engines or other units with a constant supply. The use of this type of system eliminates the need for auxiliary gasholders, which are required when the secondary units are provided with fixed covers or when low-lift covers with little storage capacity are used. Figure 13-9 illustrates one form of the two-stage system.

Sludge-digestion units are marketed by Dorr, Pacific Flush Tank, Hardinge, Carter, Chicago Pump, Infilco, Link-Belt, Walker Process Equipment and other companies and are normally supplied with all the essential protective devices to prevent the escape of gas and to eliminate the danger of explosions within the tanks.

Digesters are heated in several ways. Some are heated by means of hot water passed through coils of pipe laid around the wall on the inside of the tank, the water being heated by the type of hot-water boiler commonly used in the home and made by Bryant, Basmor, American Radiator Company, and others. In this system, illustrated in Fig. 13-10, the water is heated in the boiler, usually by burning the digester gas as fuel, and is forced through the digester coils by a pump and then returned to the boiler for reheating. The temperature of the hot water sent to the digester is usually 125 to 130°F, and the cooler water, returning to the boiler, ranges from 105 to 110°F, showing a drop of only about 20 degrees in the digester. Thus an optimum temperature of 90 to 95°F is maintained in the digester contents; the temperature at which it has been observed that bacterial activity is sustained at its maximum efficiency. In the coil system it has been found that, if the ingoing water is at a temperature much above 130°F, the sludge has a tendency to bake on the coils; the heat-transfer capacity is materially reduced as long as this coating continues. Another heating system employs heat-exchanger units, made of vertical rows of pipe suspended in the tank and connected at the top to the hot-water and return-water lines. This system is advantageous, as the coils may be removed for inspection, cleaning, and painting simply by uncoupling the unions at the top and lifting the banks of pipe out of the tank. Coils laid around a tank wall cannot be inspected or repaired without emptying the tank and entering it. The methane gas formed in sludge digestion is toxic, and to enter a tank which has not been thoroughly evacuated of gas is extremely dangerous.

Another method of heating is to inject hot water or steam directly into the tank contents; however, there is danger that the heat will not be

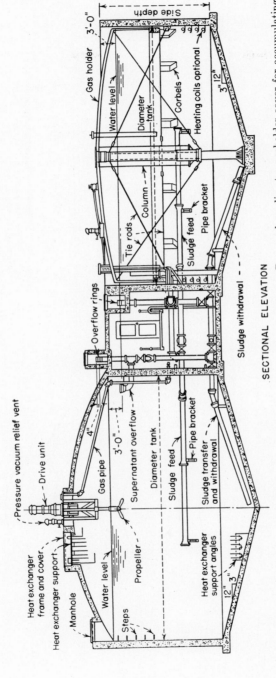

FIG. 13-9. Diagram of Dorr Multi-digestion (two-stage) system with type B secondary digester gasholder cover for accumulating and storing gas. *(Courtesy of The Dorr Company.)*

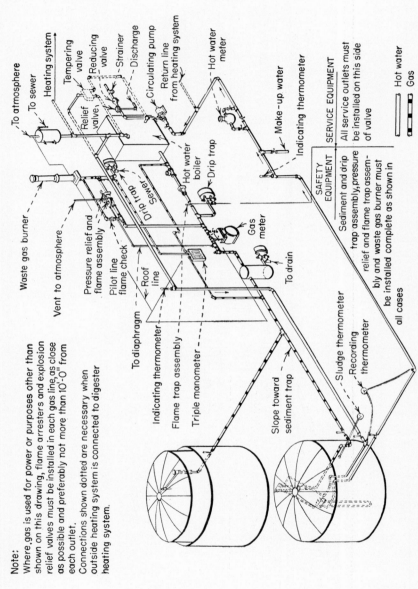

Fɪɢ. 13-10.   Arrangement of safety and service equipment for hot-water heating system.   (*Courtesy of The Dorr Company.*)

thoroughly dispersed through the mass of sludge. When suspended vertical heat exchangers are used, the units are placed in close promixity to the mixers or agitation units so that the sludge is thrown directly against the heat coils and is then dispersed through the tank, assuring an even temperature throughout the entire volume.

The latest units for sludge heating are of the external type, in which the sludge or the supernatant liquid from the digestion tank is passed through a heat exchanger and is then sent back into the tank to carry the necessary BTU to heat the contents. A recent form of this type known as the Spiral Heat Exchanger, consists of two thin-walled metal concentric spiral passageways in a circular metal body. Hot water is passed through one spiral and the sludge or supernatant liquid through the other; the heat is transferred through the thin metal wall without dilution of the liquid or any contact between the water and the sludge or supernatant. Figure 13-11 illustrates this unit.

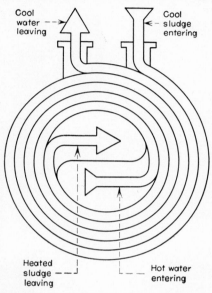

Fig. 13-11. Diagram of spiral heat exchanger for sludge digesters. (*Courtesy of The Dorr Company.*)

One of the important phases of operation of modern sludge-digestion units is the maintenance of the sludge in an alkaline state at all times, *i.e.*, at a pH of 7 or above. In the normal operation of a digester, the sludge passes through an acid-fermentation stage during which hydrogen sulfide, with its common rotten-egg odor, is formed. This gas is not only obnoxious but has no fuel value, and the sludge in this state digests very slowly. On the other hand, it has been found that, if the tank contents are maintained on the alkaline scale, the entering sludge, which is normally about 3 per cent of the total tank volume, is prevented from becoming acid, and the resultant by-product of this alkaline digestion is an appreciable volume of methane-type gas which has a very definite fuel value. Alkalinization can generally be accomplished by adding an alkali, usually lime, to the tank until the entire contents are alkaline. In most cases this may have to be done only during the initial stages of operation, for perhaps 2 to 3 weeks, after which the tank, having been put into alkaline balance, will remain in this condition for extended periods without further addition of alkali.	In some cases this initial condition of alkalinity is accomplished merely by dumping lime into the top of the digester, but in larger installations automatic chemical dry feeders are frequently provided, which inject this alkali when needed in uniform amounts over definite periods.

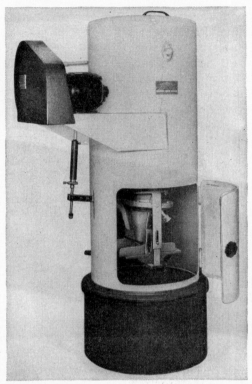

FIG. 13-12.	Universal Feeder, Model UF-3, with door open, showing oscillating throat and feed tray. (*Courtesy of Omega Machine Company, Division of Builders Iron Foundry.*)

Chemical Feeders

Where chemical precipitation of fine solids is required, neutralization of acid wastes or, as mentioned above, correction of digester reaction is normally carried out by installing a rapid or Flash Mixer in a small tank, to give a period of 10 to 20 seconds mixing.	The chemical is discharged into this mixer unit in dry powder form and is rapidly spun into the mass of liquid.	The feeders used for this work are of several types (Fig. 13-12 illustrates one form) and usually are comprised of a vertical container superimposed on a rotating disk or sliding platform on which the chemical falls. By means of knife-edge adjustable blades or vibration, the amount of material discharged from the disk or belt is regulated. In some cases the powdered chemical is dropped first into a small mixing or dissolving chamber under the mixer and made into a solution and then passed to the rapid mixer. Lime, aluminum sulfate, ferrous sulfate, and other dry chemicals may be fed through these feeders. They may be obtained from Omega, Infilco, Wallace & Tiernan, Permutit, Bacharach, and others.

These feeders are usually provided with graduated scales or guides whereby the amount of chemicals to be fed per hour may be accurately set. They are ordinarily provided with integral hoppers, but these seldom have a large capacity, and in plants which require the use of large amounts of coagulants per day, extension hoppers should be provided that hold sufficient coagulant to last at least for one shift of the operators. It is common in large plants to have large extension hoppers or storage bins above the feeders, which hold sufficient material to supply the machines for periods of weeks or more.

In selecting dry chemical feeders for use with hydrated lime, the hopper should be provided with an agitating device, as lime has a tendency to pack or "arch." If no agitation is provided, an obstruction may form that completely prevents the material from reaching the feed device.

Flocculation

This term is applied to the process of adding coagulants to liquids which contain suspended or colloidal solids in order to coalesce these fine solids into larger particles to aid in their settlement. Many wastes contain finely divided solids that are individually invisible to the eye but which in bulk form a cloudy or milky appearance. The addition of certain chemical agents causes these particles to agglomerate into larger particles, giving the appearance of light, flocculent individual units. These flocs, when first formed, are very minute and light and do not settle rapidly. The use of coagulants, however, tends to bring them together into larger particles. In the ordinary tank where coagulants are used to produce this effect, the small flocs settle very gradually and do not impact with others and the clarification effect is meager.

Some years ago it was found that if these small light flocs could be gently agitated, so that they passed up and down and sidewise through all the zones of a tank, they impacted on each other and stuck together to form more compact and solid masses. In this form less surface area was exposed to maintain them in suspension, which, added to their greater specific gravity, caused them to settle rapidly. As these flocculent particles passed through the various zones of the tank, they tended to pick up other small light particles, much in the same manner as a sponge passed through a body of water will pick up small particles. This agitation process has made it possible greatly to increase the percentage of fine solids that are removed from a liquid. And because these larger particles settle quickly to the bottom of the sedimentation basin, smaller basins can be used. In practically every case where fine solids are present in industrial wastes, flocculation will be of material assistance in freeing the liquid from them.

In those cases where color, in colloidal suspension, is the troublesome ingredient, it may be appreciably reduced. In color removal, the fine flocs have the property of absorbing color from the solution. The treatment is one of changing the isoelectric concentration of the liquid so that the particles come out of solution in fine suspension. The efficiency of the process depends upon changing the hydrogen-ion concentration, or pH, to the optimum point, where the solids will coalesce. Usually this action takes place at or near the neutral point, or pH 7, but sometimes the best results are obtained at a pH slightly below or above the neutral figure.

The action of the mechanical unit known as the Flocculator is as follows: After the coagulants have been mixed with the liquid in a rapid mixer, the chemically dosed mass is passed into a tank equipped with a series of paddle wheels which revolve slowly, causing the small pin-point particles first formed to pass through all zones of the tank; as this action proceeds, the adsorption of other particles and the growth of the flocs can readily be seen with the naked eye. Eventually a point will be reached at which these particles, despite the effort of the paddles, will begin to settle, and the surrounding liquor will begin to clear. This is known as "cracking." When this occurs, flocculation is practically completed. The liquid then flows into the sedimentation basin, and as soon as the effect of the agitation of the paddles is dissipated, the flocs settle rapidly to the bottom of the sedimentation unit.

The first form of this type of flocculation was developed by Dorr and initiated at the water-treatment plant at Richmond, Va. This first plant, in which financial expediency decreed that the rows of paddles should be placed transversely of the tank, proved so successful that the units paid for themselves, in the savings of chemicals, in the course of a few years. Although other manufacturers have produced flocculation basins with paddles running parallel to the flow through the tank, the basic idea of transverse paddles has continued to produce the best results. The detention time in the average flocculation tank is 30 to 45 minutes, depending upon the material to be handled. The time can be determined by laboratory tests, best made in a model unit of the same general type as the actual installation. Laboratory models for this type of test are obtainable from The Dorr Company.

The basic advantage of flocculation is that it makes more efficient usage of the coagulating agent. In the older plants, before flocculation was developed, what we now know as excessive volumes of coagulants were required to achieve a satisfactory result. Because the coagulant was merely dumped into the liquid, without coming into contact with all the fine particles, much of it settled to the bottom without reacting on the solids. With modern flocculation, chemical requirements have been reduced 30 to 40 per cent or more, and in practically all cases a saving can be shown that is sufficient to pay for the flocculation equipment in a period of but a few years. Also, as stated earlier, it has become possible to reduce materially the size of the sedimentation basins in many instances, thus adding an economy to plant construction.

The principle of mechanical flocculation has become so well established that practically every water-treatment and industrial-waste-treatment plant and many sewage-treatment plants use flocculation in some form or another. In numerous cases where the suspended solids in the raw liquid are of appreciable size, it has been found that, by merely subjecting the liquid to a period of flocculation without the use of coagulants, suspended-solids removal can normally be increased 15 to 20 per cent over unassisted sedimentation. The modern flocculation unit comprises a series of rows of paddles, preferably four or more, set on shafts and, if possible, installed transversely in the tank, spaced at reasonable distances apart, and with a short baffle extending downward between each two rows to give a downward trend to the water in each section.

The paddles on each shaft are set at an angle of 90 degrees with each other, and the paddles on the following shafts are each set at 90-degree angles with those on the preceding shaft. This setup tends to give a barrel-rolling effect to the flocs which assures their passage through all zones of the tank, giving them the maximum contacting and adsorbing effect. The paddles are mounted on shafts which extend through the wall at one side into a dry well, in which the chain drives are located. This arrangement is essential, as in many cases the liquid after dosing with coagulants is slightly acid and corrosive and is destructive of the wearing surfaces of the chains and sprockets of the drive unit. Likewise, the dry well enables the operator to give proper lubrication and to inspect the drive details at any time.

In one form of unit, to assure proper lubrication of the shaft bearings in the tank itself, each bearing is equipped with an automatic lubricator which holds sufficient lubricant for one year's operation and is sealed so that no grease or oil enters the liquid.   The average speed of the paddles is variable, but it is usually set to give a tip speed of the paddle blade of 1.2 feet per second, which, as has been demonstrated by numerous installations, is sufficient to keep the light flocculent particles in suspension but is not sufficiently violent to break up the flocs.   In some cases the units are provided with variable-speed drives, but practice has indicated that this is an unnecessary expense as, once determined, the speed best suited for a given installation is seldom changed.

As explained earlier in this chapter, under Sedimentation Units, the flocculation principle has been incorporated into one tank with the sedimentation unit in a unit known as the Clariflocculator which conserves space and saves construction cost.

Flocculation units of all types operate at low speed; therefore their power demands are small, 2 to 3 horsepower usually being sufficient for a fairly large unit.

Flocculation units using transverse paddles are marketed by Dorr and other companies, and units with paddle rows parallel with the direction of flow through the tank are obtainable from various manufacturers, among which may be mentioned Chain Belt, Link-Belt, Carter, Chicago Pump, Dorr, Infilco, and Jeffrey.

Sludge Pumps

To remove the settled solids, or sludge, from sedimentation tanks, it is usually necessary to provide pumps.   As this material is of small volume compared with the volume of waste liquid, the most favored type of pump for this service is the plunger or piston-type displacement pump.   The basic theory of the modern mechanized sedimentation unit is that the sludge deposited in it should be removed continuously in an amount equal to the rate of deposition.   As this rate varies from time to time and it is not desirable to pump too fast from a tank, the plunger type of pump with adjustable stroke offers the greatest advantage in control.   A centrifugal pump is ordinarily a single-speed unit, pulling sludge at a given rate. In cases where the deposition is slow, the centrifugal pump may create a vortex in the sludge deposit and pull the lighter liquid instead of the sludge.   In most modern sedimentation units a small sludge pocket is provided, and the sludge-pumping operation is so adjusted that this pocket will always be filled with sludge to feed the pump and avoid this vortex.   Plunger pumps are made in single- and multiple-plunger types. Single-plunger units will normally have a capacity of 75 gallons per minute at full stroke, and a duplex unit will handle 150 gallons per minute.   The stroke may be adjusted by revolving a cam which changes the length of stroke of the plunger without requiring a change in the driving motor speed.

While the basic theory of the modern sedimentation tank, a relatively shallow unit, is to remove the sludge as fast as it is deposited, in actual practice this is difficult to obtain without continual manual control of the pump capacity; therefore, it has become common practice to equip these pumps with electric time-clock controls, set to start and stop the pump at given intervals, run it for a short period, and then let it rest for another period. In the initial operation of a plant, the determination

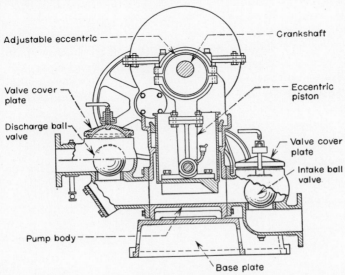

FIG. 13-13. Diagram of Dorrco Simplex (single-plunger) sludge pump. Capacity 75 gallons per minute. (*Courtesy of The Dorr Company.*)

of the proper timed interval requires adjustment of the pump stroke and the control unit. But once the correct timing is determined, the pumping operation becomes entirely automatic. The pumps are usually provided with suction and discharge-pipe openings of a minimum of 4 inches in diameter so that any objects in the sludge may be readily handled. The suction and discharge valves are ordinarily of the ball type, some using rubber-covered lead balls, with valve-box lids which can be quickly opened in case an obstruction occurs. The average Simplex pump with a 3-horsepower motor will normally handle 75 gallons per minute against a total discharge head of 30 feet. A Duplex pump with a 5-horsepower motor will handle 150 gallons per minute against the same head. Figure 13-13 illustrates one form of Simplex sludge pump.

Pumps of this type are available from Domestic, Marlow, Dorr, Carter, Chicago Pump, and other companies.

Centrifugal Pumps

The centrifugal pump is commonly used for pumping raw wastes or final effluent, if that is required. The "open-type impeller" is recommended, as in any but the very smallest sizes it will handle any solid that comes to the plant, particularly if there is a bar screen ahead of it to catch any unusually large articles. It is good practice to install two such pumps, even though the flow may be small, so that if trouble occurs with one pump, the other will be available for service. In some cases where the flow varies, it is considered good practice to install a group of pumps, each of a different capacity, so that, if the load increases beyond the capacity of one pump, another one of proper capacity will be automatically brought into service. Centrifugal pumps suitable for handling industrial wastes are made by a large number of manufacturers, among which may be mentioned Worthington, Allis-Chalmers, Fairbanks-Morse, Chicago Pump, Peerless, Yeomans, DeLaval, Economy, Infilco, and Carter.

Sludge Drying

Drying the sludge from industrial-waste-treatment plants for final disposal frequently offers difficulties. In some cases, where large areas of waste land are available, the sludge, particularly if it is high in lime, may be disposed of on this land. In most cases, however, sufficient land is nonexistent or the local health officials object to such a method of disposal and other methods must be resorted to. These methods have already been discussed in Chap. 12, under Sludge Drying. Therefore we shall be mainly concerned here with the units available for the various processes.

In large plants, where land area is at a premium, or where some by-product use of the sludge is to be made, consideration may be given to heat drying of the sludge. Several units perform this type of drying.

In the one known as the Flash-Drying system, the sludge, after it has been partially dewatered on vacuum filters, is ground up with some of the already dried material. The advantage of this particular unit, marketed by Dorr in all foreign territories, is that the sludge may be dried for use as a fertilizer, or the process may be carried to complete incineration for final disposal as a small amount of ash.

Another form of heat drier consists of multiple hearths or diaphragms in a circular structure. The sludge is admitted at the top and is raked from the individual trays by a revolving scraper and dropped to the next tray. An uprising column of heat dries the sludge as it passes downward from one tray to another until it reaches the bottom. This type of unit is furnished by Nichols Engineering Company and is known as the Nichols-Herreshoff furnace.

A third type is one which comprises a circular hollow shell into which the sludge is sprayed and, owing to the applied heat, falls to the bottom as dried particles and is there collected by a revolving rake. This type is handled by Komline-Sanderson.

Still another type of drier is that known as the revolving kiln, which is a long tubular cylinder, laid almost horizontally, with the entrance end slightly higher than the exit end. The sludge is admitted at the upper end, and as it rolls down the length of the tube, hot gases passing upward dry it. The main disadvantages of this type is the length of the tube and the area required for its installation.

To prepare sludge for handling in any one of these driers, it is necessary partially to dewater it by other means. Normally wet digested sludge has a water content of 94 to 97 per cent, and to evaporate all this water by heat is extremely expensive. To reduce this cost, it is common practice to precede the drying unit with a vacuum filter which pulls the occluded water from the sludge mass and will reduce the moisture to a point where it is then economical to employ heat drying. (Vacuum filters are described in detail in Chap. 12.) The average vacuum-filter installation is so designed that it will receive wet sludge and reduce it to a form of cake which will have a moisture content of 70 to 74 per cent. The digested sludge before filtration is liquid and can be handled only by pumps, whereas the sludge cake can be handled on a belt conveyer or can be spaded. Figure 13-14 illustrates a modern vacuum-filter installation for sludge.

The accessory equipment for a vacuum filter consists of vacuum pumps, compressors, filtrate pumps, etc., and is usually furnished by the manufacturers of the filters. For small plants, several companies produce "package" plants which contain all the needed elements, filter and all its accessories, mounted on a common bedplate and operated by a single motor. These units are especially suitable for small industrial-waste sludge-disposal problems. Figure 13-15 illustrates one form of package unit.

Sludge is applied to the filter surface at various rates, according to the character of the material to be filtered. Normally, rates of 2.5 to 5 or 6 pounds of dry solids per square foot of filter surface per hour have been found successful. The rate, however, should be determined by the filter manufacturer who, when provided with sufficient data as to the nature, moisture, etc., of the particular sludge to be handled, will be able to

advise as to the proper size of unit to be used.   The main cost of maintenance on a vacuum filter is the replacement of the filter medium.   Owing
to clogging and wear, these cloths, usually of cotton duck or wool flannel,
develop holes, and it is then necessary to replace them.   A run of 400 to
600 hours is considered a normal life for these cloths.   The operation of

Fig. 13-14.   Oliver vacuum filter, 5 feet 4 inches by 10 feet long, handling sewage
sludge at Westerly Sewage Works, Cleveland, Ohio.   (*Courtesy of Oliver United
Filters, Inc.*)

replacement is not costly.   One plant, which has had filters in operation
for a period of 8 years, reports a cost for new filter cloths of $22.50 each
and the labor required to replace a cloth at 2.5 hours.   Vacuum filters of
this type are manufactured by Oliver United Filters, Eimco, Conkey,
and other companies.
    In an attempt to eliminate the replacement of filter cloths, a new filter
has recently been developed which, instead of using a cloth medium, uses
long tightly wound springs which pass entirely around the drum and over

a shaft at the take-off point (see description on page 157). This unit was developed and is marketed by Komline-Sanderson.

Aeration of Wastes

In treating certain wastes, it has been found effective to use the activated-sludge process, in which a volume of air is blown or otherwise induced into the sewage to oxidize the organic matter. A certain pro-

Fig. 13-15. Self-contained package vacuum-filter unit. (*Courtesy of Oliver United Filters, Inc.*)

portion of the active sludge from the final settling tanks after the aeration step is returned to mix with the raw wastes to initiate rapid bacterial action. The compressed air which is usually admitted at a pressure of 8 to 10 pounds per square inch is supplied from air compressors or blowers. As the solids in the waste tend to settle in their passage through the aeration tanks, it is customary to add sufficient air to induce a continuous circulation of the mass to prevent settlement of the solids until they reach the settling tank. Naturally, this use of air as an agitation unit entails the use of much more air than is actually necessary to supply oxygen to the wastes, and this is usually the largest single item of expense in the operation of an activated-sludge plant. It is common practice, depending upon the strength of the waste, to supply air in a volume equal to

1.5 to 2.0 cubic feet of air per gallon of waste treated. Thus a flow of 100,000 gallons per day would require 100,000 to 150,000 cubic feet of air, or a blower or compressor with a capacity of 70 to 110 cubic feet per minute. For larger flows, this figure would be multiplied in proportion.

The air is usually supplied to the wastes through porous tiles set in concrete or metallic containers along the bottom of the tank and fed through pipes leading down from the main air supply. As iron and other materials, in time, clog the small interstices in these plates, it is necessary to remove and clean them. In tanks with fixed plates, this operation requires the draining of the tank, which puts it out of service during the cleaning operation. The tiles for these diffusers are manufactured by The Carborundum Company and the Norton Company and are usually 1 foot square and 1 to 1½ inches in thickness. They are made with different porosities to suit different conditions.

To eliminate the need for emptying the aeration tanks to service the diffusers, the Chicago Pump Company has developed what is known as "swing diffusers." These are tubular diffuser elements, mounted on pipes and extending outward horizontally from these pipes. The air-supply pipe coming down from the top of the tank acts also as the supporting pipe and is hinged at its connection with the main air-supply line so that the entire section may be swung up out of the liquid for inspection or cleaning without interrupting the operation of the unit or affecting any of the adjacent diffuser units.

For smaller plants, to avoid the expense of air compression and the installation of the diffuser system, several companies have developed mechanical aerators, which are primarily in the form of tubes extending downward into the liquid and in which impellers revolve, in some cases arranged to circulate the liquid in the tank to bring it into contact with the atmosphere to absorb oxygen and in others, to pull air down into the liquid for the same purpose. Owing to the mechanical restrictions on the sizes of impellers and the effective area in a tank, these units are suitable mostly for small plants. Units of the mechanical type are marketed by American Well Works, Chicago Pump, Yeomans Brothers, Vogt Manufacturing Company, and others.

In a recent development, resulting from work done by The Dow Chemical Company in their waste-treatment plant at Midland, Mich., the air required for oxidation is induced by means of a series of injectors placed close to the bottom of the tank. The waste liquid being forced through these injector nozzles forces the air necessary for the oxidation through the jet into the liquid. This system, marketed in the United States by American Well Works and in foreign countries by Dorr, has the advantage of not requiring any large compressors or other heavily powered units, and results of operating plants show considerable economies in operation over other diffused-air systems.

An ingenious aeration device was developed some years ago by Dr. H. J. Kessener, a well-known engineer of the Netherlands, and has been successfully used, particularly in Holland, in treating packing-house and creamery wastes. The unit comprises large stainless steel combs. These combs are revolved rapidly and are so placed that the tines extend only

Fig. 13-16. Kessener brush aerator for activated sludge. Invented by Dr. H. J. Kessener, Holland.

an inch or so below the surface of the liquid. As the comb revolves, it sprays the liquid into the air in very fine bubbles which come into contact with the oxygen in the atmosphere as they fly through it. This type of unit requires no blowers, compressors, tiles, or piping and only a very small amount of power to operate the comb. Figure 13-16 illustrates this unit.

Trickling Filters

These units are not new but are perhaps one of the oldest used in the treatment of sewage and industrial wastes. Trickling filters, either of the rectangular or circular type, were used in Great Britain for the treatment of various wastes many years ago. For a more complete discussion of the filters the reader is referred to Chap. 12, where they are described in detail.

In the original form of trickling or sprinkling filters, the waste passed through the filter bed only once and the bacteria had only that one opportunity to work on the organic matter. Consequently, to provide more time for this bacterial action, the bed was made 6 to 10 feet in depth. After experimentation on this type of filter, it was found that wastes to be properly treated could be applied to the beds at a rate of only 1 million to 2 millions of gallons per acre per day. Thus a waste of 100,000 gallons per day would require a bed with an area of 2,128 to 4,356 square feet for adequate treatment. In the case of very strong wastes, even more area was required. Consequently, for large volumes of wastes, the cost of construction of trickling filters was very high. As the common earlier method of applying the sewage was from a dosing tank, which operated intermittently, the entire area of the filter bed was unwetted for prolonged periods, and this permitted the larva of the Psychoda fly to develop. While these flies are not necessarily harmful, they are a nuisance around any plant, getting in the eyes and ears of the operators. A second bad feature of this earlier type of filter was that as the mass of bacterial jelly became heavy it broke away from the stones, and unless the filter was followed by a sedimentation unit, there were times when, as this sloughing occurred, the filter effluent would be as bad as the raw waste or sewage.

In the older type of filters, particularly those with fixed nozzles, the spray of waste being sent up into the air was subject to unequal distribution on the filter bed by wind and also odors were disseminated into the atmosphere. The nozzles also became clogged with grease formations in cold weather, and in some plants the entire time of one or more men was required to clean the nozzles.

About 1894, a unit of the revolving type with radial arms extending from a revolving center column was developed in England. The unit was turned by the action of the sewage jetting from orifices in the arms. This system was superior to the fixed-nozzle type as the waste was discharged downward to the stone from a very low elevation, instead of being thrown into the air. Distribution was more uniform, and no odors were present in the vicinity of the plant. However, these early units were still fed from dosing tanks, and the revolving units rested idle for varying periods, permitting fly larva to develop. For many years, this type was not used in the United States because it was felt that in the colder northern climates the beds would freeze and the revolving units become inoperative. Several were installed with complete housings over them, but these structures were very expensive.

With the modern developments in the theory of the trickling filter, the revolving distributor has now come into common and increasing use in this country. The distributor now normally consists of a hollow central revolving column through which the waste to be treated enters. This column rests on large ball bearings so that low heads of 1.5 to 2 feet will cause it to revolve. Two or more hollow radial arms are attached to the central column and extend to the periphery of the bed. Each arm is equipped with special spray nozzles, provided with splash plates, diverters, or disks, which tend to fan out the liquid so that adjacent sprays will meet as they leave the arms or touch the bed surface, to provide complete coverage of the area. The units are turned by the jetting action of the liquid discharging from the orifices in the arms. It has now been recognized that continuous dosing of filter beds produces better results and gives higher area capacities than the dosing tank which is passing from favor. In modern plants, the waste to be treated flows directly from the effluent channel of the settling unit to the distributor unit, thus keeping it in continual motion, and the bed surface being continually wetted drowns out the larva of the filter fly.

With the increased knowledge of the action of the trickling filter and in the belief that the unit is capable of producing a greater result than had been realized, several newer types have been developed.

Two basic systems have been developed, using this high-capacity rating. The earlier one, developed by Jenks and known as the Biofiltration system, with later developments by Ward, consists of returning one portion of the filter effluent back to the primary settling unit and a second portion of the effluent from the final settling tank back to a point just ahead of the filter, where it is recirculated through the filter. Thus, if the waste equals 100,000 gallons per day and the BOD is such that a recirculation rate of three times is deemed necessary, and if the split recirculation system is used, as mentioned above, the primary settling tank area will be based upon a total flow passing through it of 100,000 gallons plus the recirculation of one-half the total recirculated volume, or 150,000 gallons. The same volume of flow will likewise be handled by the final settling tank. The filter, however, will handle both the flow of waste of 100,000 gallons per day plus the entire recirculation of 300,000 gallons, or a total of 400,000 gallons. The distribution unit on the filter, therefore, will be designed to handle this volume.

In the Biofiltration system, the recirculation is continuous, 24 hours per day. Because the raw waste will at times be less than the normal rate, or may stop entirely during the night, the distribution unit must be so designed as to handle both the maximum volume of 400,000 gallons per day and the minimum, which will be the recirculation volume, of 300,000 gallons per day. To do this automatically, so that the distributor unit will revolve at all times, without the need of manual control, The Dorr Company has designed a special distributor unit for this type of operation.   Figure 13-17 illustrates a unit of this type.

The other basic system is known as the Aerofilter system and differs from the Biofiltration system in that the recirculation is taken from the filter effluent line to a point just ahead of the filter.   Also in this system, instead of continuous recirculation of a given volume, the recirculation ratio is usually varied during the day to maintain at all times a certain

FIG. 13-17.   Dorrco revolving distributor for trickling-filter beds, showing special double-compartment arm for automatically adjusting to varying rates of flow.   (*Courtesy of The Dorr Company.*)

definite volume of flow through the distributor and filter; therefore, the recirculation fluctuates in accordance with the fluctuations in the rate of flow of the raw wastes.   In the Biofiltration system the recirculation pumps always operate at the same speed and capacity and require no attention or adjustment.   In the Aerofilter type the recirculation pumps must be of a type in which flow and speed may be changed, which requires a complicated electrical control, operation of the pumps at less than their normal rated speed and capacity, higher power usage, or constant manual attention to regulate the pumps.

In these systems the recirculation adds a slight additional cost to the initial plant and the operation.   But, as the filter beds, which are the item of greatest cost in a plant of this type, are very much reduced in size, the saving in these beds will usually offset the slight additional cost of recirculation.   Because the pumps are of the low-head type (12 to 15 feet), motor sizes are small and the efficiency when operating at full load and speed is high.

For wastes with high BODs, the modern high-rate filter has many applications.

Filter Bottoms

As it is essential that trickling filters be constructed so as to drain continuously and not permit the waste to back up in them, it is customary to provide an underdrain system in the form of a complete floor of ceramic or vitrified blocks with apertures in the top.   The filter stone rests on these blocks, and because the apertures are of fair size they do not clog, and the filtered liquid passes out of the bed through these underdrains as fast as it reaches the bottom.   Numerous forms of underdrains are made by different manufacturers, but all have the same general principle. A form of underdrain, which is equally satisfactory and which can be made on the job, is in the form of thin slabs of concrete, say 12 to 18 inches long by 2 inches thick, which are set on edge on the filter-bed floor and interlock with each other to form a grid.   The filter stone is placed on top of them.

The design of a filter is important.   The selection of the filter medium is one of the most important factors, and in general the material should be broken stone, of a character which will not oxidize or become soft.   Stone of irregular shapes is the most effective as it affords a better holding place for the bacterial jelly.   Flat stones or smooth pebbles are not as effective. The best medium is broken traprock which will not disintegrate.   The following specifications for trickling-filter stone will be found satisfactory.

The aggregate shall be crushed stone of a quality that will withstand the disintegrating effects of the weather and of the applied waste.   The aggregate may be granite, limestone, or traprock and shall be of such quality as to generally satisfy the following requirements:

Not more than 3.0 per cent wear; not more than 0.7 per cent absorption; minimum specific gravity, 2.00; minimum hardness, 12.00; crushing strength, 15,000 pounds per square inch; calcium carbonate (if limestone), not less than 8.3 per cent; sulfate as SO_4, not over 1.2 per cent; organic matter, none; loss, sodium sulfate (20^4 cycles), not over 10 per cent; and pyrites, trace. Sizes shall be as follows, using a round screen: retained on 3 inch but passing $3\frac{1}{2}$ inch, not more than 5 per cent; passing 3 inch and retained on 2 inch, not less than 50 per cent; passing $4\frac{1}{2}$ inch, not over 5 per cent; passing 1 inch, not over 3 per cent.   Soil and clay not permitted. Stone shall be produced by one operation of crushing and screening unit, and recombining will not be allowed.   Important: Before placing, stone should be thoroughly washed to remove all dirt, dust, and loose fines. Placement should be carefully done, especially the layer immediately above the underdrains to prevent crushing or cracking them. Stone at the surface of the bed to be carefully leveled to avoid hills or hollows.

Chlorination

Many state and other health authorities require, as a final measure of protection against the escape of pathogenic organisms or disease germs, that the final effluent be sterilized with chlorine or chlorine-containing compounds. This sterilization is usually effected by 20 to 30 minutes detention in a small contact chamber in which chlorine gas is admitted by one of the commercial type of chlorination machines manufactured by Wallace & Tiernan, Builders-Providence, Everson, Fischer & Porter, and others. The use of chlorine gas is the simplest method, as no manual handling of the chlorine compound is required and the cylinders are readily handled and procured. The gas may be obtained in cylinders which contain 150 pounds of chlorine; for larger units, cylinders containing $\frac{1}{2}$ ton and 1 ton are available. The amount of chlorine residual required in the effluent is usually determined by the state or other health authority; a residual of 0.5 ppm is average. Chlorine is also sometimes used to dose the raw waste to inhibit septic action or to create conditions favorable to further chemical treatment.

Bibliography

1. Knowles, C. L., Industrial Wastes from the Equipment Manufacturers Viewpoint, *Industrial & Engineering Chemistry*, vol. 31, pp. 1338–1345, 1939.
2. Equipping Plants for Trade Waste Disposal, Editorial Review, *Chemical & Metallurgical Engineering*, vol. 38, No. 9, pp. 524–530, September, 1931.
3. Pearson, A. O., Instrumentation of Sewage Treatment Processes, No. 5, Control of Industrial Waste Treatment, *Sewage Works Engineering and Municipal Sanitation*, vol. 20, No. 9, pp. 432–433, September, 1949.
4. Demarest, E. L., and W. D. Kohlins, Equipment for Waste Disposal Problems, Paper, Meeting, American Institute of Chemical Engineers, Houston, Tex., Feb. 27, 1950.
5. Instrumentation for Waste Treatment, *Bulletin* 7301, Brown Instrument Co., Philadelphia, Pa.
6. The Sewerage Manual, Public Works Magazine, Fifteenth Annual edition, 1949.
7. Modern Equipment and Materials for Industrial Waste Treatment, *Sewage Works Engineering and Municipal Sanitation*, vol. 20, No. 3, pp. 139–144, March, 1949.

CHAPTER 14

COAGULANTS AND CHEMICALS

The treatment of industrial wastes involves the consideration of several methods, and it is the responsibility of the engineer or technician engaged to solve the problem to study each and decide which, for the project in hand, is most desirable both from practical and economic standpoints or from the requirements set up by public officials. Some wastes respond either to biological treatment or to chemical precipitation. In such cases it is essential for the investigator to set up a balance sheet, taking into account all the factors, so that he may arrive at a conclusion satisfactory to his client and to the authorities.

There are numerous factors to be considered in such a study. Even if test results or the past experience of others indicates that chemical treatment is effective, this is not the entire answer. While the plant for chemical treatment may be, and frequently is, less costly to construct than a plant for biological treatment, the cost of operation of the plant may be an entirely different story. The daily cost of supplying an appreciable amount of chemical may, over a year's time, amount to a large sum of money which, together with the extra labor cost usually entailed in the handling of chemicals, may show that another type of plant, perhaps of the biological type, even with the higher initial plant cost, will be cheaper on an annual cost basis.

In recommending chemical treatment, the availability of the chemicals specified must always be taken into consideration. If an industrial plant is located in an isolated district, distant from railroad or other transportation facilities, the cost of transporting the necessary chemicals may be an expensive item, which must be added to the actual cost of the chemical.

In those cases where the recommended chemicals are not available in the immediate neighborhood of the plant, it will be necessary for the plant management to provide means for storing an adequate supply to maintain the plant in operation. This supply must be sufficient to last until a new supply is ordered and received at the plant. Sometimes a large bulk of the chemicals must be stored, which not only involves a considerable outlay of funds but also requires expensive storage space. Likewise, there is the possibility that certain chemicals, such as lime, will deteriorate when stored for long periods, thus rendering them less effective.

261

When laboratory tests are made on wastes, a certain chemical compound will frequently produce a better and quicker result than another. This compound may be readily available to the laboratory in the small quantities used in test work, but it may be difficult to obtain it in necessary quantities to handle a large volume of waste at short notice or at a moderate price.

In test work the addition of 2 grains of chemical per gallon of waste to be treated may seem infinitesimal, as the 2 grains represent only one three-thousandth of a pound.   But when this is translated into plant practice, the chemical requirement to treat a waste of, say, 250,000 gallons per day, at 2 grains per gallon, would be 72 pounds per day.   This particular chemical may cost 10 cents per pound at the nearest railroad base but must be transported to the plant at a cost of $2.50 per ton. The annual cost of this chemical will, therefore, be in the neighborhood of $2,661 per year.   Another chemical, which may be procured locally, costing say 1.5 cents per pound delivered at the plant, may require 4 grains per gallon to do the same work as the chemical first recommended. The total daily amount required will be 143 pounds, but the annual cost will be only $782.93.   The difference in cost of these chemicals, plus the cost of providing a large stock of the higher cost chemical and the necessary storage bins, etc., would go a long way toward paying the fixed charges on a larger initial plant or paying for the extra equipment which might be required to handle the second chemical.   By assuming that the difference in annual cost of these two chemicals, $1,879, is the interest at 5 per cent on a capital sum of $39,580, the industrial owner could well afford to spend some additional money on a plant that uses the cheaper chemical.

Also, let us consider that a method has been worked out which uses only 4 grains per gallon of the 1.5-cent chemical; for 250,000 gallons of waste per day, the annual cost is $782 per year.   At 5 per cent, this is the interest on $15,640, and the industrial-plant owner could actually afford to spend this amount on a plant of another type which required no chemicals, no storage, no transportation charges, and less manual attention.

These factors are particularly important if the waste problem is one in a country other than the United States.   In many countries, where chemical industries have not reached the stage of development as those in this country, and where the majority of the chemical compounds must be imported, the financial viewpoint becomes much more important. The ocean freight, insurance, and other charges on foreign shipments, plus the excise taxes, customs duties, wharfage fees, and handling charges at the port of destination, are frequently so high that a common chemical in the United States may cost two to three times more when delivered in

another country.   In such cases, if it is possible, an investigator, before
making any definite recommendations, should endeavor to obtain data
from the U.S. Department of Commerce, the chambers of commerce of
the country involved, or the consular staff of that country as to the availability and local cost of the chemicals he is considering recommending.
Then these costs should be balanced against the use of a method which,
although perhaps costing more for the plant, does not require this expensive material.

It is not uncommon for shipments to a foreign country to require a
month or more for the actual transportation and to take 2 to 3 months
more after arrival at the foreign port to be cleared through the local
customs and made available for use.   To avoid shortage, the foreign
plant must anticipate all these delays and lay in a stock of the needed
chemical, which will carry him over any interval between the time he
sends an order to the foreign supplier and the time his local customs
officials actually release the material.   In the present unstable conditions
in many countries, 2 to 6 months or more may be needed to obtain the
necessary permit to import the material and then more months to procure
the necessary exchange to enable the seller to get his money when the
goods are shipped.

It is important for an investigator to ascertain if any industries near
the site of the proposed waste-treatment plant turn out wastes containing
chemical elements which may be useful as coagulants.   If such wastes
are available, not only will the supply be ample, but the other industry
will be delighted to sell its waste product at a low price as it solves its
waste-disposal problem at the same time.   For instance, ferrous sulfate
is a common and usually effective coagulant for industrial wastes of many
kinds.   It is likewise a waste product of steel and iron mills, galvanizing
plants, wire mills, etc., which exist in many localities.   If ferrous sulfate
can be used to produce the desired result, even though a larger quantity
of it may be required than some other less common chemical, it will pay
the industrial plant requiring it to purchase the wastes liquors of a nearby
metallurgical mill.   Thus a constant, low-cost supply is assured.

In recent years, a number of chemical-coagulant compounds have been
developed which, when tested against other more common chemicals,
offer a quicker and better result with the usage of a small quantity.
These new compounds, in many cases, are admirable solutions to a problem.   On the other hand, while they may be available in one section of
the country, they are generally proprietary compounds made by one
concern only and must be obtained from that company.   This means
that, for plants in distant parts of the country or in foreign countries, the
transportation and other charges added to the original basic cost will

make these chemicals very costly. In such cases the weighting of the various factors suggested earlier in this chapter should be given careful study.

This brings to mind a specific case. A salesman came to the author's office to discuss a marvelous coagulant. He had with him a small bottle containing a black liquid, said to be an industrial waste. He also had an ordinary laboratory test tube, about ½ inch in diameter and 4 inches long. Filling this with the black liquid, he took his penknife and dug out a small amount of white powder from another bottle. Putting this into the test tube, he shook it. In a few minutes, a precipitate appeared; shortly after, the upper liquor became entirely clear. It was, indeed, an interesting demonstration. On questioning him as to the actual cost of such treatment, he replied that it was minute as so little of the coagulant was required, only that on the end of the knife blade. But when this small amount of chemical, costing 10 cents per pound, was translated into the treatment of a waste of appreciable volume, say 100,000 gallons per day, the annual cost was staggering. Actual tests in the laboratory with this coagulant compared with more common coagulants, such as aluminum sulfate and lime, showed that only the rare plant owner could afford to use it.

A list of the flocculating agents ordinarily tried on every waste problem submitted to a prominent organization specializing in the development of economical and practical methods of treatment is given in Table 14-1. In some cases, a preliminary test-tube sample will show immediately whether or not certain of these coagulants will be worth further investigation.

As these coagulants and chemicals require special types of equipment to handle them and as the volume required in storage bins, etc., varies, Table 14-2 gives the details of the manner in which a number of the chemicals normally used in waste treatment are shipped, the forms in which they are available, their weight, the most satisfactory materials to be used in the equipment handling the basic compounds, and the usual strength of the common market varieties.

Likewise, some of these chemicals are harmful to humans and must be handled with care and kept away from the hands and skin of the operator. Sulfuric acid, hydrochloric acid, and chlorine are dangerous substances, and ferric chloride is very corrosive; therefore, special feeding appliances must be employed. If vacuum filters or other mechanical devices are used, the piping or parts which come into contact with these chemicals must be resistant.

Lime may be fed by any one of the numerous automatic feeders, but as it has a tendency to cake or arch over at the small exit from the hopper,

TABLE 14-1. COAGULANTS AND PRECIPITANTS USED IN TESTS ON INDUSTRIAL WASTES

Name of coagulant	Symbol	Common or trade name
Common agents		
Aluminum sulfate..........	$Al_2(SO_4)_3 \cdot 14H_2O$	Alum
Calcium oxide.............	CaO	Quicklime
Calcium hydroxide.........	$Ca(OH)_2$	Hydrated lime
Ferrous sulfate.............	$FeSO_4 \cdot 7H_2O$	Copperas
Calcium carbonate.........	$CaCO_3$	
Sulfuric acid..............	H_2SO_4	Oil of vitriol
Hydrochloric acid..........	HCl	
Ferric chloride.............	$FeCl_3$	Anhydrous ferric chloride
Clay......................		
Diatomaceous earth........		
Boothal...................		
Bentonite.................	$H_2O(Al_2O \cdot Fe_2O_3)$	Colloidal clay
Uncommon agents		
Barium chloride...........	$BaCl_2$	
Calcium chloride...........	$CaCl_2$	
Cataphoresis (electrolytic action)..................		
Chlorinated lime..........	$Ca(OCl)_2 \cdot 4H_2O$	
Activated carbon..........	C	Aqua Nuchar, Hydrodarco
Glue......................		
Lead acetate..............	$Pb(C_2H_3O_2)_2 \cdot 3H_2O$	
Phosphoric acid............	H_2PO_4	
Sodium chloride...........	NaCl	Salt
Ammonium aluminum sulfate	$Al_2(SO_4)_3 \cdot (NH_4)_2SO_4 \cdot 24H_2O$	Ammonia alum
Ferric sulfate.............	$Fe_2(SO_4)_3 \cdot 9H_2O$	Ferrifloc-Ferrisul
Sodium aluminate..........	$Na_2O \cdot Al_2O_3$	Soda alum
Sodium silicate............	$Na_2O \cdot SiO_2$	Water glass
Common combinations of flocculating agents		

Lime followed by aluminum sulfate
Lime followed by ferrous sulfate
Aluminum sulfate followed by sodium silicate
Clay, limestone, marl, or bentonite plus any other agent where ample but slow settling floc is formed
Aluminum sulfate followed by lime
Ferrous sulfate followed by lime

TABLE 14-2. COAGULANTS AND STATISTICS REGARDING THEIR HANDLING

Chemical	Shipping containers	Available forms	Weight, lb per cu ft	Suitable handling materials	Commercial strength
Activated carbon...	Bags	Black granular powder	15	Dry: iron, steel Wet: stainless steel, rubber, silicon iron	
Aluminum sulfate..	100-, 200-lb bags;	Ivory-white powder	38–45	Dry: iron, steel	15–22 % Al₂O₃
	300-, 400-lb bbl, car load	Ivory-white ground	60–63	Solution: lead, rubber, silicon iron, asphaltum	
	Bulk; car-load, barrels	Ivory-white lump	62–67		
Ammonium aluminum sulfate	Bags, barrels, bulk	Lumps	64–58	Lead, Duriron rubber, stone-	11 % Al₂O₃
		Nut	62	ware, silicon	
		Pea	65	iron	
		Powdered	60		
Bentonite.........	100-lb bags	Powder	60	Iron, steel	
		Pellets			
		Mixed sizes			
Calcium hydroxide.	50-lb bags, 100-lb barrels, bulk carload	Pulverized	40–70	Rubber, iron, steel, asphal-	85–99 % Ca(CH)₂
		White powder	26–48	tum, cement	63–73 % CaO
Chlorine..........	100-, 150-, 200-lb cylinders; ½-, 1-ton cylinders; tank cars	Green-yellow gas or light orange liquid	......	Dry: steel, copper, iron Wet: silver, glass, lead, hard rubber	99.8 % Cl₂
Ferric chloride.....	5-, 13-gal carboys	Dark brown sirupy liquid	......	Rubber, glass stoneware, synthetic resins	37–47 % FeCl₃ 12–17 % Fe
Crystals	300-lb bbl	Yellow-brown lumps	......	As above	59–61 % FeCl₃ 20–21 % Fe
Anhydrous.......	500-lb casks; 100-, 300-, 400-lb kegs	Green-black powder	......	As above	98 % FeCl₃ 34 % Fe
Ferrous sulfate.....	Barrels	Green crystals, granules, lumps	63–66	Concrete, tin, lead, wood, asphaltum	55 % FeSO₄ 20 % Fe
Potassium aluminum sulfate	Bags, barrels, bulk carload	Lumps	62–67	Lead, lead-lined rubber, stone-	10–11 % Al₂O₃
		Ground	60–65	ware	
		Powdered	60		
Sodium aluminate..	100-, 150-lb bags; 250-, 325- 400-lb drums; solution also	White to greenish yellow crystals Liquid 27°Bé	50–60	Iron, steel, rubber plastics	55 % Al₂O₃, 35 % Na₂O plus 5 % excess NaOH
Sodium silicate.....	Drums, trucks, tank cars	Opaque viscous liquid	......	Cast iron, steel, and rubber	38–42°Bé (Activated brands also available)
Sulfuric acid.......	Bottles, drums, carboys	66°Bé solution 60°Bé solution	......	Concentrated: steel and iron Dilute: lead, porcelain, glass, rubber	66°Bé, 93.2 % H₂SO₄ 60°Bé, 77.7 % H₂SO₄

which interrupts the flow to the feed mechanism, therefore all lime-feeder hoppers should be provided with an agitating device to shake the lime down to the feed device. Aluminum sulfate may be fed by the same type of dry feeder, but the agitator is not required.

FIG. 14-1. Omega loss in weight feeder and lime slaker. Rate of feed: 250 pounds per hour. Note special electric water heaters. Front view with doors open. City of Richmond, Va. (*Courtesy of Omega Machine Company, Division of Builders Iron Foundry.*)

Bentonite, clay, or diatomaceous earth may also be fed by the ordinary type of dry feeders. Chlorine is fed as a liquid, usually through hard-rubber piping. Ferric chloride cannot be fed by dry feeders because it is highly hygroscopic, and a dry feeder makes a mush of it which will not feed. Solution feed is required. The small pressure-pump solution feeders manufactured by a number of concerns are adaptable for this chemical.

Ferric sulfate is also hygroscopic but may be fed through a dissolving pot with agitation. Ferrous sulfate, although mildly hygroscopic, will

cake in storage.   The crystal type can be fed by dry feeders to a mixing
or dissolving pot, which is ordinarily an integral part of a dry-feeder unit.

Sodium aluminate and sodium carbonate, or soda ash, may be fed dry,
but agitators are required in the feed hoppers.   Sodium silicate, being a
liquid, must be fed by solution feeders.   This material is difficult to

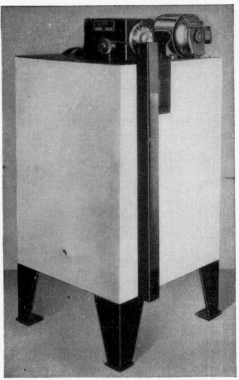

FIG. 14-2.   Model PFS1H-100 precision feeder with synchronous-motor drive, slow-
speed agitator, and low-level alarm.   Rate of feed: 0.16 to 16 gallons per hour.   (*Courtesy of Omega Machine Company, Division of Builders Iron Foundry.*)

handle, as if not properly mixed, it forms a jell which cannot be fed.
Sulfuric acid must be fed by liquid feeders.   Figures 14-1 and 14-2
illustrate modern forms of dry solution feeders.

When a recommendation is made for use of any of the coagulants or
precipitants discussed, the manufacturers of feeders and all other equipment with which the raw coagulant or a solution of it may come into contact should be carefully advised of the coagulant that is to be used so
that they may provide equipment which will operate satisfactorily with
that material.   For some coagulants, an additional expense may be

entailed in the first cost of the equipment, but longer life and continued operation will be assured, with the minimum of replacements due to corrosive or destructive action of the material.

Bibliography

1. Pearse, L., Chemical Treatment of Sewage, *Sewage Works Journal*, vol. 3, No. 6, pp. 997–1108, November, 1935.
2. Rohland, P., The Colloid Clay Process for Trade Waste Treatment, *Chemiker-Zeitung*, vol. 37, p. 754, 1914. *Wasser und Abwasser*, vol. 9, p. 38, 1914.
3. "The Use of Lime in Industrial Trade Waste Treatment," National Lime Association, Inc., Washington, D.C., 1947.
4. Howard, N. J., Chlorination Practice in Sewage and Trade Waste Disposal, *Water & Sewage (Canada)*, vol. 85, p. 21, November, 1947.
5. Buswell, A. M., Reaction of Sodium Nitrate in Stabilizing Organic Wastes, *Sewage Works Journal*, vol. 19, p. 628, July, 1947.
6. Besselievre, E B., Lime—The Medicine for Stream Pollution, Paper, Meeting, National Lime Association, Hot Springs, Va., May 5, 1947, *Sewage Works Engineering and Municipal Sanitation*, vol. 19, pp. 19–20, 26, January, 1948.
7. Reidl, A. L., Limestone Used to Neutralize Acid Wastes, *Chemical Engineering*, vol. 54, pp. 100–101, July, 1947.
8. Weston, R. F., Activated Carbon in Sewage and Industrial Waste Treatment, Thesis, New York University, 1939.
9. Brintzinger, H., and H. Schlegel, The Purification of Waste Water by Hydrogels, *Kolloid-Zeitung*, vol. 70, p. 321, 1935.
10. Eldridge, E. F., Role of Chemicals in Industrial Waste Treatment, *Water Works & Sewerage*, vol. 89, pp. 341–346, 1942.
11. Ferguson, R. H., Lime in the Treatment of Trade Wastes, *Chemical Age*, vol. 32, No. 7, July, 1924.
12. Carpenter, L. V., L. R. Setter, and J. J. Coates, Use of Sulfur Compounds for Treatment of Water and Industrial Wastes, *Journal, American Water Works Association*, vol. 31, No. 8, pp. 1400–1416, August, 1939.
13. Ockershausen, R. W., Principles of Chemical Treatment of Industrial Wastes. Lecture, Second Annual Sewage Works School, State College, Pennsylvania, June 13–17, 1949.
14. Enslow, L. H., Sewage and Trade Waste Problems Solved by Chlorine, *Chemical & Metallurgical Engineering*, vol. 38, No. 9, pp. 531–533, September, 1931.
15. Olin, H. L., *et al.*, Bentonite as a Coagulant for Sewage and Industrial Wastes, *Water Works & Sewerage*, p. 535, December, 1942.
16. Snell, F. D., and Cornelia C. Snell, Chemical Treatment of Trade Wastes: IV, Wastes from Organic Ester Synthesis, *Industrial & Engineering Chemistry*, vol. 30, No. 3, p. 200, 1928.
17. Moberg, A. R., and E. M. Partridge, Ferric Alumina: A Modern Development in the Field of Coagulants, *Industrial & Engineering Chemistry*, vol. 22, p. 163, 1930.
18. Elder, A. L., and S. W. Stahl, Ferric Oxide Hydrosols as Coagulants in Waste Treatment, *Industrial & Engineering Chemistry*, vol. 31, p. 925, July, 1939.

CHAPTER 15

HANDLING INDUSTRIAL WASTES IN MUNICIPAL SYSTEMS AND CHARGES THEREFOR

The question of whether or not a municipality or district should handle the industrial wastes of any or all industrial plants, of whatever type, in its communal sewerage systems and treat them in its present or future sewage-treatment works is an important one. The justice of this question is also open to much discussion.

A number of pertinent factors related to this question should be considered. These are, in general, practicability, policy, expediency, and justice. Many municipalities have unwisely agreed to handle industrial wastes from factories within their boundaries, without due consideration of these factors, later to be brought face to face with difficulties and expenses which throw an unjust burden on the people of the town. Indiscriminate acceptance of this burden, without proper recompense, is not a wise or expedient policy since it frequently throws upon the local taxpayers the expense entailed in providing greatly increased plants plus the heavy operating costs. However, it is equally unfair to assume that each and every industry must treat its own wastes separately and discharge the equivalent of clean water into the sewers. Industries have a definite place in municipal economy and a right to have their individual problems evaluated on their respective merits.

Sometimes a municipality, in its eagerness to encourage industrial development, perhaps because of a rival adjacent city, agrees to handle the wastes of industries without previous inquiry into their nature and effect. The wastes may be of such character that their inclusion in the city system will require a much more complex and expensive treatment plant than would be required for the normal domestic sewage. Or the indiscriminate inclusion of industrial wastes of some types may require that a city enlarge its plant materially or even entirely change the method of treatment to counteract the inhibiting character of the wastes upon the processes formerly employed.

Invitations or agreements to include industrial wastes are usually made in the belief, often true, that the revenue and economic advantages brought to the city by the industry will offset the extra cost to which the city may be put. New industries frequently bring added population to a city in which a large labor pool does not exist. This will mean increased business for the stores and shops of the city in general, additional taxes for the city treasury, more business for the local post office, more homes to be built, etc. The industry itself will frequently bring more revenue to the city in the form of taxes on its property, on the water to be furnished, and in prestige with its intangible value.[26]

Sometimes, when a large industrial plant indicates that it may locate in a small community, it may be assumed that such an industry will become the largest single local employer of labor. It thus would supply a greater portion of all the money circulating in the town. The municipal authorities may take the attitude that, because of the importance of the industry as a revenue producer, it is to the city's interest to accept the burden of treating the wastes free of charge. Only a sound, unbiased, and careful investigation of the nature and volume of the wastes that will be discharged by the industry will determine whether this premise is sound or not.

Generally speaking, there is no justification for a city to agree arbitrarily to handle the wastes of any industry if this will entail an extra burden for the taxpayers. After investigation, by technicians thoroughly skilled in this work, and after weighing all the factors to ascertain what effect the wastes may have on the various elements of the sewerage system, some agreement may be reached whereby the industry is bound to eliminate from its wastes those elements which it is believed will be harmful. In large cities where, owing to the location of industrial districts, there is no other possible outlet for factory wastes than into the sewers and where the wastes are of diverse character, the proper authorities should thoroughly discuss the desirability of taking all these wastes into the system without the assumption of some of the burden by the industries themselves.

Industry, in general, knows that its liquid wastes are a source of expense. Usually they do not contain substances which may be reclaimed at a reasonable cost, and the sole desire of the industry is to dispose of them in the best and cheapest manner. The cost of waste treatment is not a productive factor in plant operations but, instead, adds to the overhead and thus becomes an item, sometimes a considerable one, in the unit cost of production. Every industry will welcome any means that will solve this difficulty in a reasonable way and at a low cost.

One way to solve this problem is for the industry to treat its wastes only to the extent that they will not damage or interfere with the structures of the sewerage system or be inhibitory to the processes employed in the sewage treatment and for the city to assume the burden of handling the partially treated wastes in the municipal system. In this way, the plant owner is able to construct a cheaper plant than would otherwise be the case. However, it is believed that the plant owner should make some payment for the handling of the resultant wastes. If the wastes are of such character that they will not damage the structures of the sewerage system and may be treated by the normal methods employed to treat domestic sewage, they may be taken into the municipal system on the basis of a fair charge for the handling.

THE FACTORS INVOLVED

The question of what is a "fair" charge[6] for handling industrial wastes in a municipal system is susceptible to much argument and discussion. No general rule or formula can be logically applied. What is right and fair for one city may be entirely unjust in another, not only for the industrial-plant owner but also for the taxpayers of the city. Such a vast number of factors enter into the determination of a charge for handling wastes that every municipality must accept the responsibility for working out its own formula. A number of cities in the United States and elsewhere have formulated charge bases for their particular problems. These will be discussed in this chapter, with the advantages and disadvantages of each. However, it is logical to list here the factors which enter into the determination of a basis for a charge; each of which must receive due consideration and study.

1. The type of sewage disposal or treatment method employed by the city:
   a. Discharge into a stream—dilution only. Will the addition of industrial wastes cause this method to be discontinued and a more complex one employed? This determination will usually be made by the department of health of the state in which the city is located, if the stream is one entirely within the state boundaries; if the stream is an interstate watercourse, one of the interstate agencies may have jurisdiction, or even the Federal authorities may exert some power.
   b. Preliminary treatment, such as screening, degritting, degreasing, as its sole treatment. To what extent will the inclusion of an industrial waste affect this treatment or require its elaboration?
   c. Primary treatment only—preliminary as above plus sedimentation and sludge digestion. Will the inclusion of wastes require additional degrees of treatment?
   d. Complete treatment—preliminary plus primary plus secondary treatment by chemical precipitation, biological treatment with trickling filters of either high or low capacity, or activated

sludge. Will the inclusion of industrial wastes react on these methods to an extent which will cause a change in the method of plant operation, enlargement of its component units, or abandonment of the plant?

2. The capacity of the existing sewage-treatment plant and the percentage of that capacity required for the treatment of the present waste volume. Has the present plant the capacity for absorbing industrial wastes without increase or addition?

3. The character of the wastes to be handled:
   a. The volume—of each individual waste and total volume.
   b. The periodicity of flow of each waste, whether for short periods during the day, or uniformly over the daily operating period of the industrial plant.
   c. The percentage of suspended matter and settleable solids and their nature.
   d. The BOD of the combined and individual wastes.
   e. The content of toxic, destructive, or inhibitory elements present in the wastes and their nature and volume.

4. The local municipal policy toward industry:
   a. Whether the city government feels obligated or committed by precedent to care for industrial wastes in the local system.
   b. Whether they feel it expedient, economically or politically, to handle the wastes of certain plants or types of industry.
   c. Whether, after a study of the factors in 1, they find that the existing sewerage systems and appurtenances will handle any excess volume or if new units or additional grades of treatment will be required by the inclusion of any or of certain types of wastes.
   d. The amount of taxes that will be contributed by the industrial plant to the general city funds.
   e. The influence of certain local organizations, such as boards of trade, chambers of commerce, and service clubs interested in attracting industry to the town, in compelling the local authorities to agree to handling industrial wastes.
   f. The effect upon local public health by the inclusion of wastes into the city system.

5. After an evaluation of the foregoing factors, additional factors must be considered which will enter into the formulation of a fair charge to the various industries.
   a. A charge for the entire load contributed by the industrial plants on the basis of
      (1) The volume of waste contributed daily.

(2) The load of suspended or settleable solids contained in the waste.

(3) The BOD of the wastes.

(4) The chlorine demand of the wastes, *i.e.*, the amount of chlorine that will be required to treat the wastes either before or after treatment in the city plant.

b. A charge for the excess load contributed by the industry in relation to the composition of the normal sewage of the city on the basis of

(1) Excess volume of wastes over normal sewage.

(2) Excess load of suspended or settleable solids.

(3) Excess BOD over that of the normal sewage.

(4) Excess chlorine demand.

The above factors are the units in a formula covering only the daily operating costs of the plant. In order, however, to arrive at an equitable charge, consideration must be given, in any formula or rate, to the other charges that may be incurred by the handling of the industrial wastes. These factors are as follows:

1. Fixed charges. Whether industrial owners should pay a proportional part of such charges, *i.e.*, interest on treatment-plant investment and amortization for obsolescence of plant.

2. Charges for maintenance. Whether the industry shall pay its proportional share of the maintenance charges on large sewer systems, where such charges and costs are kept separately from sewage-treatment costs.

3. Initial cost of plant:

   a. Whether, in those cases where a city agrees to handle certain industrial wastes in an existing sewage-treatment plant, the industry should pay back charges for its proportional share in the original cost of the plant, on the basis of volume or composition of wastes contributed.

   b. Whether an industry should pay the entire cost of construction of new plant units or for additional degrees of treatment required because of the inclusion of its wastes, or only its proportionate part as represented by the ratio of its volume or load to the city's total volume or load.

4. Rebate or reduction of taxes to industry

   a. Whether the total amount of taxes paid by an industry should be deducted from the total of any charges arrived at for handling its wastes.

 b. Whether only the proportionate part of the taxes paid by an industry as represented by the proportion of the city taxes used for sewage treatment and maintenance shall be deducted from the total of any charge arrived at by the city.

5. Adjustment for beneficial wastes discharged by an industry. In some instances an industry may discharge a waste which would

 a. Tend to flush out low-velocity sewers, keep them from clogging, and thus reduce the maintenance cost to the city.

 b. Neutralize wastes contributed by other industries to a point where the flow of wastes from those industries would then not be harmful to structures or inhibitory of processes.

 c. Precipitate sulfides from the sewage.

6. Adoption of a standard for the wastes to be admitted to sewerage systems and treatment plants.

 a. Whether maximum limits of suspended or settleable solids, BOD, etc., shall be set up by local or state agencies and an industry required to pay a charge for all in excess of these limits.

 b. Whether, with such maxima set up, an industry can build its own treatment plant and reduce its waste to the city standard and thus avoid payment of additional charges to the city for handling its wastes in the public system.

7. Consideration of charges to an industry that receives no other benefits from city works but yet pays large taxes to it. In some cases the taxes paid by an industry (*i.e.*, oil fields) might well be in excess of any charge that might be assessed for handling these wastes in a city plant. This might result in the city treating the wastes free if all taxes paid were rebated.

8. Consideration of the possibility that industries which have common or mutually reacting wastes would join together in districts or plants to consolidate their several wastes and turn out an effluent within the maxima set, thus avoiding any charge for handling their wastes in the city system.

9. Extent of requirements arbitrarily calling for pretreatment of any or all wastes before their discharge into any public system.

10. Devising of a basic formula taking into account all the various elements which might be used by any particular municipality in arriving at the charges to be made according to the polluting or disturbing elements contributed by any of its industries.

11. Recommendations for an enabling act (if required) by the state legislature to permit any particular city, county, or other political agency to set up regulations and devise formulas for charging for industrial-waste handling.

12. Recommendations that conferences be held between municipal officials, industrial-plant management, engineers, and local business groups to arrive at a logical and equitable basis of charge.

It will be seen from this extensive list of factors that it is impossible to arrive at one formula for basing charges for industrial-waste treatment in public systems which will be applicable to all cases. Some of the general factors may be included, but in every case the intangible factors must be considered as well and the charge tempered by their merit. In order to arrive at some basis for charges, it has been necessary for certain cities to adopt formulas, but if these are arbitrarily applied they will, undoubtedly, work an injustice on some industrial plants and be too easy on others.

Volume of wastes alone is not a correct basis for a charge. Many plants discharge large volumes of wastes that contain only a small amount of solid matter and have a low BOD. Other plants may discharge a relatively small volume of wastes which contains a high percentage of organic matter or has a high BOD. The latter will put much more of a load on the city treatment facilities than the waste of greater volume but lesser strength. Therefore, if a charge for volume alone is made, the industry with the small volume of high-concentration wastes will be unduly favored and will pay less in proportion to the treatment-plant cost involved than the industry having the large volume of low-concentration wastes. As the high-concentration wastes will require more exact and expensive treatment than the low concentration, this division of costs will be unfair. Volume is relatively cheap to handle in a sewage-treatment plant, but the removal of BOD and the handling of large volumes of sludge are the most costly operations in any plant.

The dual function of a sewage-treatment plant is to remove the suspended matter and to reduce the BOD and other polluting elements of the liquid wastes entering it. The size of the plant units for handling suspended solids and BOD is directly related to the total amount of these constituents in the wastes and in the ability of the method selected to remove or reduce them.

It would seem advisable, therefore, and more equitable for all concerned —regardless of the type of treatment required—to make a general basic charge against industries on the basis of the amount of suspended solids and BOD contributed to the sewage load, whether this charge be on the basis of the total load thus imposed or only on that part of it which is in excess of the percentage of these same elements in the normal city sewage. It is the strength and character of the waste that should basically govern in arriving at a charge for services rendered.

As the cost records of sewage treatment cannot be set up readily to separate the plant costs for handling any particular proportion of the wastes entering it without great expense for continuous analyses and tests, the charges for the basic elements of suspended solids and BOD are logically related to the cost per million gallons created for handling the sewage in the plant. This rate may be merely the cost of the daily operating items of the plant, comprising labor, electric current, lubricants, repairs, chemicals, chlorine, etc. It may also, and more equitably, include a proportion of the fixed charges of the plant, which include interest on the investment, amortization of the debt created to build the plant, maintenance, and replacements.

As a normal treatment plant is designed for sewage which has a relatively low BOD and suspended-solids load as compared with most industrial wastes, two ways are suggested for establishing the two basic factors of a charge. These are known as the "excess-load" charge and the "normal-load" charge.

In determining the excess-load charge, the normal suspended solids and BOD content of the sewage are ascertained. The loads of these constituents in the industrial waste to be handled in the plant are likewise determined. In both cases, these are normally stated in parts per million, in which 1 part per million is equal to 1 gallon per million gallons or, on a weight basis, 8.34 pounds. The charge is then based on the extent to which the industrial waste in question exceeds the loads in the normal sewage. Thus if the normal sewage has a suspended-solids content of 275 ppm and a BOD of 300 ppm and the industrial waste to be treated has a suspended-solids content of 400 ppm and a BOD of 800 ppm, the industry would be charged on the basis of contributing 125 ppm of suspended solids and 500 ppm of BOD additional load. Thus, that portion of the industrial waste which has the same concentration as the municipal sewage would be handled in the city plant without charge, and the industry would pay only for the excess. As sewage-treatment-plant costs are ordinarily reported on the basis of the cost of treatment per million gallons handled, and as the amounts of total suspended solids removed and BOD reduced by the plant are usually given, it is quite simple, if the concentration of the industrial wastes is known, to figure the excess contributed by the industry. With the cost per million gallons of sewage treated and the amounts of suspended solids removed and BOD reduced put into units of 100 pounds of each, a cost figure can be arrived at.

The second method, normal-load charge, consists of charging the industry for the total load of suspended solids and BOD contributed in its wastes, regardless of the strength of the city sewage. In this method, the industry pays the entire cost of removing and reducing these two constituents from its wastes, and the city only provides the facilities for treatment. Which of these two methods is the more equitable for a particular problem requires the evaluation of many of the factors enumerated earlier.

Table 15-1 is a compilation of data selected from authoritative sources reporting actual figures from operating plants of various types and sizes in several sections of the country. It gives the sewage strength in suspended solids and BOD, the efficiency of the plant in removing and reducing these elements, the cost of treatment per million gallons, and the cost per unit of suspended solids removed and BOD reduced, based on the million-gallon cost of treatment. It will be noted that regardless of the size and type of plant, there is a remarkable uniformity in the cost of removal and reduction of these two elements. The table includes data on 37 plants, and it is interesting to note the following average figures based on the information in the table.

Cost of operation per million gal treated...............	$20.00
BOD reduced:	
Ppm...	171.3
Lb per million gal..................................	1,306.54
No. of 100-lb units of BOD reduced...................	13.0654
Cost of reduction per unit of BOD...................	$1.53
Suspended solids removed:	
Ppm...	193.08
Lb per million gal..................................	1,569.33
No. of 100-lb units of suspended solids removed.........	15.69
Cost of removal per unit of suspended solids............	$1.27

FORMULAS AND RATES

Numerous cities in the United States and abroad have established formulas for charging for handling industrial wastes, based on various combinations of factors. Some of these are worthy of mention.

Buffalo, N.Y., Formula.[3] In 1943 this city adopted a service charge for wastes based on the volume and concentration. This formula is

$$R = FP_c(C - N_c) + FP_s(S - N_s)$$

where R is the rate of special charge, in cents per 1,000 cubic feet of waste volume; F is a factor for converting the parts per million to pounds per 1,000 cubic feet, which when worked out is 0.0622; P_c is the contract price of chlorine, in cents per pound. C is the concentration of the chlorine demand of the waste, in parts per million; N_c is the normal dry-weather chlorine demand of the raw sewage, in parts per million as received at the sewage-treatment plant; P_s is the cost in cents of chemicals for sludge conditioning and of power for solids disposal per pound of suspended solids received in the raw sewage at the treatment works; S is the concentration of suspended solids in the waste, in parts per million; N_s is the amount of normal grit-free suspended solids in the raw sewage received at the treatment works.

The factor P_c may vary from year to year according to the contract price for chlorine, and the factor P_s may also vary according to the current price of chemicals and power involved in the disposal of solids as determined from operations for the previous one or two years. The factors C and S may be established by analysis (periodic or otherwise) to obtain the average concentrations to be applied for any agreed length of time. The factor P_s as used in this formula does not apply except in cases, such as in Buffalo, where the sludge is dewatered on vacuum filters, with chemical conditioners, and dried otherwise than on open sludge beds.

The average results cited at Buffalo show a chlorine demand of 5.6 ppm and a suspended solids content of 157 ppm. The special charge made per 1,000 cubic feet of waste amounted to 0.136 cent for each part per million of chlorine demand and 0.00305 cent for each part per million of suspended solids determined in the sewage analysis.

This formula was developed especially for Buffalo, where the treatment consists of primary sedimentation, with prechlorination, sludge digestion, dewatering of conditioned digested sludge on vacuum filters, and incineration of the filter cake only. It makes no charge for volume, nor does it recognize the efficiency of the process in reduction of BOD. It is stated to have worked successfully for this city.

New Brunswick, N.J. Formula. An ordinance passed by the city council in February, 1944, based this formula on the premise that all industrial and other liquid wastes should be treated at the recently constructed sewage-treatment plant without pretreatment by the industries. The rate set forth in the ordinance was as follows:

The charges for factory effluents or industrial wastes discharged into the city sewers or tributaries thereof shall be fixed and determined according to flow, suspended solids, and chlorine demand, according to the following schedule of rates: $22 per million gallons, $5 per ton of sludge, and $5 per 100 pounds of chlorine demand.

This formula, or rate schedule, takes no account of BOD load, but charges only for volume, suspended solids, and chlorine demand. This is not entirely equitable as some wastes have small volume and are low in suspended solids but very high in BOD, which puts a severe and costly load on the plant or on the receiving stream in order to supply the oxygen to stabilize the wastes to prevent nuisance.

The Wright Formula.[4] This formula was proposed by Dr. S. R. Wright, head of the Civil Engineering Department of the University of Texas.

TABLE 15-1. OPERATING COSTS OF SEWAGE-TREATMENT PLANTS AS RELATED TO REMOVAL OF BOD AND SUSPENDED SOLIDS FOR ESTABLISHING CHARGES FOR INDUSTRIAL WASTES

Plant location	Type of plant (see key)	Cost of operation per million gal	BOD, ppm						Suspended solids, ppm					
			Raw sewage	Effluent	Ppm removed per million gal	Lb removed per million gal	No. of 100-lb units removed	Cost per unit removed	Raw sewage	Effluent	Ppm removed per million gal	Lb removed per million gal	No. of 100-lb units removed	Cost per unit removed
Rockville Centre, N.Y.	AcS	$59.68	288	41	247	2,060	20.6	$2.90	234	25	209	1,743	17.43	$3.42
Hartford, Conn.	S & D	14.90	137	119	18	150.1	1.5	9.92	117	25	92	767.3	7.67	1.94
Anderson, Ind.	Gugg	17.73	157	13	144	1,200	12.0	1.47	233	26	207	1,726.0	17.26	1.02
Jackson, Mich.	AcS	18.73	122	7	115	959.1	9.59	1.95	191	17	174	1,451.0	14.51	1.30
Marion, Ind.	AcS	24.16	184	13	171	1,426.14	14.26	1.69	178	12	166	1,384.44	13.84	1.74*
Minneapolis-St. Paul, Minn.	SIM	9.56	200	120	80	667.20	6.67	1.43	315	86	229	1,909.86	19.09	0.50
Gary, Ind.	AcS	8.79	132	7.2	125.5	1,047.00	10.47	0.84	228.8	5.9	222.9	1,859.00	18.59	0.47
Galesburg, Ill.	TrF	15.94	165	30	135	1,126.00	11.26	1.42	193	32	161	1,343.00	13.43	1.18
Elizabeth, N.J.	S & Bg	7.91	240	143	97	809	8.09	0.97	194	64	130	1,084.00	10.84	0.73
Aurora, Ill.	SDTF	14.86	120	14	106	884.04	8.84	1.68	196	21	175	1,459.5	14.59	1.02
San Bernardino, Calif.	SDTF	8.98	170	6	164	1,368.00	13.68	0.65						
Findlay, Ohio	AcS	28.14	405	21	384	3,203.00	32.03	0.88	427	11	406	3,386.00	33.86	0.83
Pasadena, Calif.	AcS	19.86	149	13.2	135.8	1,133.00	11.33	1.75	303	27	276	2,303.00	23.03	0.86
Muskegon Heights, Mich.	AcS	33.20	357	9	348	2,902.00	29.02	1.05	305	6	299	2,493.6	24.94	1.33
Springfield, Ill.	AcS	15.28	203	13	190	1,584.6	15.84	0.97	199	10	189	1,576.3	15.76	0.97
Belvedere, Ill.	AcS	63.72	200	5	195	1,626.30	16.26	3.92	198	3	195	1,626.3	16.26	3.92
Chicago Heights, Ill.	AcS	16.33	236	16	220	1,835	18.35	0.89	320	20	300	2,502.0	25.02	0.65
Decatur, Ill.	SDTF	7.12	199	24	175	1,459.5	14.59	0.49	209	37	172	1,434.0	14.34	0.49
Elgin, Ill.	SDTF	13.79	123	34	89	742.3	7.42	1.86	196	27	169	1,409.5	14.09	0.98
Urbana-Champaign, Ill.	SDTF	16.11	314	28	286	2,385.0	23.85	0.67	211	33	178	1,484.52	14.84	1.09
Danville, Ill.	CP	15.73	185	87	98	817.3	8.17	1.92	148	58	90	760.6	7.61	2.07
Waukegan, Ill.	CP	19.22	195	95	100	834.0	8.34	2.31	201	50	151	1,259.00	12.59	1.53
DeKalb, Ill.	SDTF	30.82	255	36	219	1,826.46	18.26	1.68	211	42	169	1,409.46	14.09	2.11†

TABLE 15-1. OPERATING COSTS OF SEWAGE-TREATMENT PLANTS AS RELATED TO REMOVAL OF BOD AND SUSPENDED SOLIDS FOR ESTABLISHING CHARGES FOR INDUSTRIAL WASTES—(*Continued*)

Plant location	Type of plant (see key)	Cost of operation per million gal	BOD, ppm						Suspended solids, ppm					
			Raw sewage	Effluent	Ppm removed per million gal	Lb removed per million gal	No. of 100-lb units removed	Cost per unit removed	Raw sewage	Effluent	Ppm removed per million gal	Lb removed per million gal	No. of 100-lb units removed	Cost per unit removed
Washington, D.C.	S & D	4.39	171	117	54	450.3	4.50	0.97	180	89	91	759.0	7.59	0.58
Ft. Dodge, Iowa	SDTF	27.94	825	74	751	6,263.3	62.63	0.44	616	59	557	4,645.0	46.45	0.60†
Massillon, Ohio	S & D	15.65	151	77	74	617.2	6.17	2.50	244	86	158	1,318.0	13.18	1.18
Buffalo, N.Y.	S & D	8.25	127	101	26	216.8	2.17	3.80	168	110	58	484.0	4.84	1.78
Cleveland, Ohio:														
Southerly	SDTF, AcS	15.71	138	41	97	808.98	8.08	1.94	194	69	125	1,042.50	10.42	1.50
Easterly	AcS	17.31	192	9	183	1,526.22	15.26	1.13	246	13	233	1,943.22	19.43	0.99
Westerly	S & D	15.20	260	210	50	417.0	4.17	3.64	262	179	83	692.22	6.92	2.20
Toledo, Ohio	S & D	8.83	189	124	65	542.1	5.42	1.63	194	93	101	842.34	8.42	1.05
Medina, Ohio	SDTF	60.92	567	54	513	4,278.00	42.78	1.42	263	62	201	1,676.34	16.76	3.60
Ann Arbor, Mich.	AcS	43.25	216	40	176	1,467.84	14.67	2.94	200	23	177	1,476.18	14.76	2.92
San Diego, Calif.	S & D	14.35§	152	95	57	475.38	4.75	2.51	360	120	240	2,001.60	20.01	0.71‡
Racine, Wis.	S & D	11.93	171	103	68	567.12	5.67	2.09	170	80	90	750.6	7.50	1.59
Battle Creek, Mich.	S & D	11.81	.....	.....	.....	.....	.....	.....	284	84	200	1,668.0	16.68	0.70
Dallas, Tex.	SDTF	4.80	324	46	278	2,318.52	23.18	0.207	348	71	277	2,310.18	23.10	0.207

Notes

* 1947 report gives 1.804 per 100 lb.
† Includes cannery wastes.
‡ Includes packing-house wastes.
§ Gross cost before deduction for sludge sales.

Key to Symbols of Types of Plants

AcS   Activated sludge.
CP   Chemical precipitation.
Gugg   Guggenheim process.
S & Bg   Sedimentation and barging to sea.
S & D   Sedimentation and separate digestion.
SDM   Sedimentation-digestion-magnetite filters.
SDTF   Separate digestion with trickling filters.
TrF   Trickling filters.

It is primarily based on the premise that the industries will partially treat their wastes before they are discharged to the city system. It is also partially based on the excess-load theory. The formula is

$$F = 1 + \frac{0.5R(S - 150)}{150}$$

or

$$F = 1 + \frac{R(S - 150)}{300}$$

where F is a factor by which the regular volume rate is multiplied; R is the ratio of the annual cost of treatment to the total annual cost of the entire system; and S is the suspended solids in the industrial waste, expressed in parts per million by weight. The following is given as an example: Assume that the cost of primary treatment is $20,000 per year and the annual operation cost of the entire system is $50,000. Then R in the above formula becomes 0.4. An industry contributes a waste containing 750 ppm of suspended solids. Substituting in the formula, F then is 1.8. In fixing the charge for this industry, the regular rate per 1,000 gallons should then be multiplied by 1.8; in other words, the industry should pay 1.8 times as much per unit of volume as another user who contributes only domestic sewage. This formula is based on the theory that a charge will be made to all users of the system and the industries will pay according to their concentration of wastes.

Where complete treatment is provided in the plant, an additional term is added to the formula to take care of BOD. Dr. Wright assumes the average domestic sewage BOD to be 200 ppm and adds the term to the formula to compensate for the additional BOD of the wastes. He states that "the added cost due to a heavy organic content would be

$$\frac{BOD - 200}{200}$$

times the normal organic load." However, as it is common practice to credit approximately one-third of the BOD as being reduced in primary sedimentation units of proper design, the added cost due to the extra load on the secondary-treatment units is only two-thirds of the total organic load in the industrial waste. Therefore, the factor by which the volume rate must be multiplied in those cases where complete treatment is provided may be expressed as follows:

$$F = 1 = \frac{R(S - 150)}{300} + \frac{2R(BOD - 200)}{3 \times 200}$$

which when simplified is

$$F = \frac{300 - R[(S - 150) + (\text{BOD} - 200)]}{300}$$

where F is the factor by which the volume rate is multiplied; R is the ratio of cost of treatment to the total cost of operation of the sewerage system; S is the suspended solids in the industrial waste, in parts per million; and BOD represents the 5-day BOD of the industrial waste, in parts per million. An example of the application of this formula is as follows: R is assumed to be 0.6. A local packing house discharges a strong waste with a solids content of 1,000 ppm and a 5-day BOD of 3,000 ppm. Under these circumstances, F would be 8.3 times the unit volume rate for ordinary domestic sewage. With this formula, an industry which discharged a waste low in suspended solids and BOD would receive an adjustment in the rate charged.

California Formula. This formula, developed by Harold S. Gray, consulting engineer of California,[12] is based upon making a charge to industry for treating wastes in the municipal system but taking into account all taxes paid exclusive of those paid by industry. This formula may be set up as follows:

$$K = M - (S + s) = M - S\left(l + \frac{t}{T}\right)$$

where T is all the taxes paid to the city exclusive of those paid by industry; t is the taxes paid by industry; S is the cost of operating the sewage works before industry contributes, paid by T; s is industry's share of the sewage-works operation cost without industrial wastes added, paid by t; M is the cost of operating the sewage works with the industrial waste added; and K is the extra cost assessed to industry for handling its wastes.

Belleville, Ill., Formula.[14] In developing a formula for this city, containing several industries with highly polluting wastes, Dr. George S. Russell, consulting engineer of St. Louis, produced the following one:

$$R = R_b + [0.002 \times (\text{BOD} - 200)]R_b$$

where R is the rate per 100 cubic feet of waste; R_b is the basic rate per 100 cubic feet of waste; BOD is the parts per million in the raw waste.

The sewage of Belleville had an average BOD of 200 ppm. This was established as the norm, and an extra charge for volume of wastes was made in accordance with the above formula in those cases where the BOD exceeded the 200-ppm norm. On the basis of this formula, the accompanying table of rates was established.

TABLE 15-2.   MONTHLY RATES

Cu Ft of Waste Treated per Month	Charge per 100 Cu Ft, Cents
First 13,000	20
Next 13,000	15
Next 27,000	12.5
Next 27,000	9.6
Next 54,500	7.2
All over 134,000	6.6

Added to these basic figures an additional charge of one-fifth of one per cent was made for each part of BOD in which the industrial-waste concentration exceeded the 200-ppm norm.

As the engineer realized that these costs would enter into the cost of the various products of the industries contributing, he reduced the charges to costs per units of product. These could be used by each industry in revising its cost of production figures due to the waste-treatment program. They were established as follows:

Beer	7.2	cents per barrel
Packing house	16.0	cents per hog killed
Laundry	21.0	cents per 100 lb of clothes washed
Catchup manufacturing	0.33	cents per case
Spaghetti manufacturing	1.2	cents per case

Allegheny County, Pa., Formula.[5]   When the joint treatment project for Pittsburgh and contiguous cities in western Pennsylvania was set up, John F. Laboon, chief engineer of the authority, realizing the extremely high industrial load that would be contributed to the proposed system in this congested industrial section, developed a series of rates based upon volume and an additional formula to take care of the extra load of suspended solids, BOD, and chlorine demand imposed by handling the industrial wastes in the proposed sewage-treatment plant. The rates are shown in Table 15-3.

TABLE 15-3.   QUARTERLY RATES

Gal of Waste Treated per Quarter	Charge per 1,000 Gal, Cents
First 100,000	18
Next 1,000,000	12
Next 2,250,000	9
All over 3,350,000	7

To establish a norm for the formula so that additional charges could be made to the above basic rates, the suspended solids were established as 275 ppm and the BOD as 300 ppm, and an extra charge was made for all in excess, computed as follows:

$$F = 1 - R\left[\frac{0.75(S_i - S_a)}{S_a} + \frac{0.25(B_i - B_a)}{B_a}\right]$$

where F is the factor to be applied to the basic rate; R is the ratio of quality cost to total annual cost, or 0.15; S_i is the suspended solids in the waste from the particular industry, in parts per million; S_a is the average suspended solids of all the sewage, or 275 ppm; B_i is the BOD of the waste from the particular industry, in parts per million; B_a is the average BOD of all the sewage, or 300 ppm. The increase in cost on the basis of this formula is predicated on the actual treatment costs of the excess volumes and suspended solids and BOD loads. The charge is nominal. On the basis of a suspended-solids content of 500 ppm and a BOD of 500 ppm, the additional charge would be 11.7 per cent of the total bill on the volume basis.

Over and above the surcharge for suspended solids and BOD, an additional charge will be made for wastes possessing an excessive chlorine demand. Until the actual chlorine demand of the sewage to be treated can be determined upon completion of the proposed plant, the rate formula is established as follows:

$$R_c = FP_c(C_i - C_a)$$

where R_c is the surcharge rate for chlorine demand, in cents per 1,000 gallons of waste; C_i is the chlorine demand of the wastes from a particular industry, in parts per million; C_a is the average chlorine demand of all the sewage, in parts per million; F is the factor for converting parts per million to pounds per thousand gallons, or 0.00835.; P_c is the contract price of chlorine, in cents per pound.

A review of these formulas shows how opinions differ as to the manner of arriving at the surcharge to be made to basic rates to recompense a municipality for handling industrial wastes. As shown by Table 15-2, it is relatively simple to arrive at a basic charge on the basis of volume alone, and any city which has a sewage-treatment plant will undoubtedly have a fairly accurate record of the costs of treatment on a volume basis. But the consideration of the elements, other than volume, which make industrial wastes more troublesome and costly to treat than sewage requires the evaluation of many additional factors which differ in practically every case. The tangible factors such as suspended solids, BOD, and chlorine demand are usually matters of analysis and calculation, but the intangible factors—the policy and expediency factors—as described earlier, cannot be reduced to a formula; each one must receive consideration in each case.

Numerous other examples of charges that are made, both in the United States and elsewhere, can be found, based on volume, regardless of other factors. A few of these are enumerated here.

Marion, Ind.[24]   The charge made for the disposal of cheese whey by digestion is $1 for each 500 gallons of whey hauled from the dairy plant. The net cost to the industry is $6.50 to $13 per 1,000 pounds of whey, depending upon the concentration of the wastes.

Germiston, Transvaal, South Africa.[21]   The charge for accepting trade effluents into the sewers includes the cost of pumping the plant effluent, the cost of purification of the waste, and the cost of sludge disposal.   The costs are based on treatment-plant records per load unit of aerobic treatment of the city sewage and the cost of sludge digestion per pound of dry volatile matter.

Durban, Natal, South Africa.   Here the charge made for the admission of trade wastes into the municipal sewer system is 2 shillings per 1,000 imperial gallons (1,200 U.S. gallons) discharged, with a minimum charge of 5 shillings per month.   Wastes are required to meet the following standards: temperature not to exceed 110°F, suspended solids not to exceed 400 ppm, pH not to exceed 6 to 10.

Baltimore County, Md.   Wastes from two distilleries in Maryland are discharged into the sewers on the following basis: $1.37 per 1,000 gallons of stillage dumped into the sewers and $25 each per week for inspection and maintenance of the sewers.

Dewsbury, England.[21]   Trade wastes are admitted into the sewers on basis of a charge of 4 pence per 1,000 imperial gallons.

Halifax, England.[21]   Charges for handling wastes without preliminary treatment vary from £6 to £20 per million imperial gallons according to the type of waste.

Huddersfield, England.   The charge is 2 pence per 1,000 imperial gallons untreated or after preliminary screening.

Brighouse, England.   The charge is fixed according to treatment and varies from 1 penny to 6 pence per 1,000 imperial gallons.

Keighley, England.   Dyeing and scouring wastes are handled at 2 pence per 1,000 imperial gallons; wool-washing wastes, at 1 shilling 6 pence per 1,000 imperial gallons.   No charge is made if full treatment is given to wastes before discharge into the sewer system.

Morley, England.   The charge is 2 pence per 1,000 imperial gallons.

Ossett, England.   The charges for general trade wastes are 2 pence per 1,000 gallons; for wastes from butchers, tripe dressers, fellmongers, piggeries, etc., they are 4⅖ pence per 1,000 imperial gallons; and for wastes from steam boilers, they are 12 shillings per annum.

Elland, England.   The charge for handling gas-plant liquor is 1 shilling 9 pence per 1,000 imperial gallons.

Golcar, England.   The charge is 4 pence per 1,000 imperial gallons.

Linthwaite, England.   The same as Golcar.

Heckmondwike, England. When no preliminary treatment is given, the rate varies from £3 to £10 per million imperial gallons according to the class of waste.

Saddleworth, England. The charge is 5 pence per 1,000 imperial gallons for wastes from woolen mills and allied textile trades and 2 pence per 1,000 imperial gallons from dye works and allied trades.

Shipley, England. The charge for wool-washing refuse is 4½ pence per 1,000 imperial gallons after preliminary treatment, 5½ pence without treatment; piece scouring and dyeing wastes, 3½ pence per 1,000 imperial gallons; leather wastes, a fixed annual charge; carbonizing, cleaning clothes, picker wastes, 3 pence per 1,000 imperial gallons; spent gas liquor, 1 shilling 9 pence per 1,000 imperial gallons; and miscellaneous wastes, fixed annual charge.

Certain American cities have established a policy toward the admittance of industrial wastes to their municipal systems. The following are a few of these:

Durham, N.C., requires partial treatment by chemical precipitation before discharge to sewer. Also flow must be proportioned over 24 hours. No charge is made for treatment of wastes.

Winston-Salem, N.C., accepts all wastes into the sewer system without any requirement for pretreatment and without charge.

Fort Worth, Tex., requires meat-packing plants to give fine screening and sedimentation.

San Antonio, Tex., takes all wastes with pretreatment or at an extra charge.

Lodi, Calif., excludes winery wastes from the municipal system. These are treated on land by the industry.

Austin, Minn., excludes slaughterhouse and packing-plant wastes. These must be treated separately by the industry.

Mason City, Iowa, same as Austin.

Cedar Rapids, Iowa. Slaughterhouse and packing-plant wastes must be passed through grease traps and fine screens and then conveyed in a separate sewer system to the municipal plant where they are given further treatment at the expense of the industry.

Wisconsin State. The policy is to require industry to reduce the strength of its wastes to that of the average municipal sewage before discharge into the sewerage system.

Madison, Wis., requires slaughterhouse and packing-plant wastes to be screened and treated by chemical precipitation before discharge into the municipal system.

Milwaukee, Wis., accepts all wastes and excludes only those similar to acid wastes which damage structures. Wastes from gasoline and oil stations are excluded. Industries with settleable wastes are required to screen and settle them. Grease wastes must be passed through grease traps. Owing to great variety of wastes, many wastes neutralize each other. Iron and acid wastes from steel mills assist in the activated-sludge process used in the municipal plant.

Peoria, Ill., accepts brewery, cannery, packing-house, and commercial-solvent plant wastes but excludes distillery wastes. These are treated separately by the industry.

Decatur, Ill., accepts starch-plant wastes without extra charge.

Dayton, Ohio, receives all wastes except cyanide wastes. These are treated by the industry producing them.

Cleveland, Ohio, takes in all types of existing wastes without requiring pretreatment and without charge.

Indianapolis, Ind., same as Cleveland.

Perth Amboy, N.J., same as Cleveland.

Worcester, Mass., same as Cleveland.

Bibliography

1. Gray, H. F., The Responsibility of the Municipality in the Industrial Waste Problem, *Sewage Works Journal*, vol. 16, No. 6, pp. 1181–1188, November, 1944.
2. Hurley, J., Trade Effluent Policy, *The Surveyor (England)*, vol. 103, pp. 343–345*ff*. 1944.
3. Symons, G. E., Special Charge Formulas for Industrial Wastes in Municipal Sewage, *Water & Sewage Works*, vol. 96, No. 5, pp. 200–203, May, 1949.
4. Wright, S. R., Sewerage Service Charges, Bulletin 98, Agricultural & Mechanical College of Texas, College Station, Tex., 1947.
5. Laboon, J. F., *et al.*, Report on the Proposed Collection and Treatment of Municipal Sewage and Industrial Wastes by the Allegheny County (Pa.) Sanitary Authority, *Water & Sewage Works*, January, 1948.
6. Besselievre, E. B., What Is a Fair Charge for Handling Industrial Wastes? *Engineering News-Record*, vol. 34, pp. 825–828, June 14, 1945.
7. Smith, H. F., Solving the Problem of Billing for Sewage Disposal, *Water Works & Sewerage*, pp. 22–24, January, 1941.
8. Charging Industries for Treating Liquid Wastes, *Public Works*, p. 46, October, 1939.
9. Jenks, H. N., Salad Bowl Wastes Treated at Converted Plant, *Sewage Works Engineering and Municipal Sanitation*, p. 666, August, 1947.
10. City Bases Sewage Charge on Industrial Waste Characteristics, *The American City*, vol. 59, pp. 57, 77, April, 1944.
11. A Report of Procedure for the Handling of Industrial Wastes, Committee on Industrial Wastes, California Sewage Works Association, *California Sewage Works Journal*, vol. 17, 1945.
12. Financing Industrial Waste Collection and Disposal, Symposium, Twenty-first Annual Meeting California Sewage Works Association, Stockton, Calif., May 19–21, 1948.
13. Palmer, C. L., Regulation of Industrial Usage of Municipal Sewers, *Sewage Works Journal*, vol. 19, No. 5, p. 811, September, 1947.

14. Russell, G. S., Selling Sewer Rental to Industry, *Water & Sewage Works*, vol. 96, No. 5, pp. R-112–113, May, 1949.
15. Uhlmann, P. A., Charges to Industries for Treating Their Wastes in a Municipal Plant, *Public Works*, vol. 75, No. 12, p. 23, December, 1944.
16. Indiana Cities and Industries Share Costs of Sewage Disposal Service, *Engineering News-Record*, vol. 135, No. 14, p. 452, Oct. 4, 1945.
17. Formula Sets Industrial Waste Treatment Fee at Buffalo (N.Y.), *Sewage Works Engineering and Municipal Sanitation*, pp. 543–544, October, 1944.
18. Charges for Industrial Wastes, City Ordinance 667, Anaheim, Calif., Feb. 29, 1944.
19. Childs, J. A., and G. J. Schroepfer, A Review of Sewer Rental Fees and Charges, *Sewage Works Journal*, vol. 4, pp. 1006–1040, 1932.
20. Cities Levy Special Charges for Industrial Waste Treatment, *Sewage Works Engineering and Municipal Sanitation*, vol. 16, No. 12, p. 615, December, 1945.
21. Hodgson, H. J. N., Sewage and Trade Waste Treatment, Report to Government of Australia, Adelaide, Australia, August, 1938.
22. Symons, Geo. E., and F. W. Crane, Special Sewer Service Charges for Industrial Wastes, *Water Works & Sewerage*, March, 1944.
23. Paulus, C., The Effect of Industrial Wastes on the Trend of Sewage Treatment, *Sewage Works Journal*, July, 1944.
24. Backmeyer, D., Disposal of Cheese Whey by Digestion, *Sewage Works Journal*, vol. 20, No. 6, pp. 1115–1118, November, 1948.
25. Hurley, J., Accepting Trade Effluents into Sewers, *The Surveyor (England)*, Sept. 3, 1948.
26. Besselievre, E. B., Will That New Industry Be of Real Benefit to Your City? *The American City*, November, 1929.
27. Schroepfer, G. J., Determination of Fair Sewage Service Charges for Industrial Wastes, *Sewage and Industrial Wastes*, vol. 23, No. 12, pp. 1493-1515, December, 1951.

CHAPTER 16

FACTORS IN THE DEVELOPMENT OF LOW-COST PLANTS

An industrial-waste-treatment plant is, in most cases, a capital invest-ment and a continuing expense for an industrial-plant owner. At the present time, except in a few instances, a return on this investment which would make it an attractive financial subject is not practical. As research into the reuse of the by-products and components of various wastes progresses, no doubt means will be developed which will show, in many cases, that an industrial-waste-treatment plant may be built with some hope of making it a lesser drain on the profits of a commercial organization.

As that day has not yet arrived, those who are charged with the responsibility of solving industrial-waste problems and designing the necessary treatment plants must scan with care all known methods of treatment and work out for their clients a plant with as low initial and operating costs as is consistent with the production of the desired result. Low initial cost, *i.e.*, cost of plant construction, is not the only concern, as the continuing annual charge for the operation and upkeep of the plant and the fixed charges on the initial investment must also be taken into consideration. It is sometimes more practical, from an economic standpoint, to spend more money on the first construction than might seem warranted, with the aim that the daily operating charges will be materially reduced. The old adage that the cheapest is not always the best holds true in industrial-waste-treatment studies.

It would be a wise policy for any engineer or investigator, when pre-sented with an industrial-waste problem, to work out several solutions and make a careful economic study of each. Then he may present these data to his client so that he can decide which type of plant will suit his needs. If his client chooses the plant which is cheapest in first cost, regardless of the annual cost, the engineer need not feel responsible.

In evaluating the costs, a number of factors must be taken into consideration:

1. Initial cost of plant.
   a. Cost of necessary equipment and apparatus.
   b. Cost of installation of the equipment.
   c. Cost of excavation required for the plant.

   d. Cost of preparing the ground at the site. This is particularly important if bad conditions are encountered and piling or other subsurface supporting structures must be provided.

   e. Cost of form work. This is particularly important if the tanks and other structures are of an involved design, requiring thin complicated walls, etc.

   f. Cost of concrete for the construction, in place.

   g. Cost of electric connections—wiring, controls, etc.

   h. Cost of land occupied.

   i. Cost of covering tanks, if required.

   j. Cost of necessary buildings.

  2. Cost of operation of the plant.

   a. Cost of electric power required daily.

   b. Cost of chemicals required in the treatment (if any).

   c. Cost of maintenance of the equipment.

   d. Cost of labor required to operate the plant.

   e. Cost of repairs and supplies.

  3. Fixed charges.

   a. Interest on the investment in the plant.

   b. Amortization, for plant obsolesence.

These points will be discussed briefly.

INITIAL COST OF PLANT

This is not confined to the actual cost of the equipment, priced at some given shipping point, but includes the following items of importance:

1. The actual cost of the equipment, f.o.b. railroad cars, at some given point.

2. The cost of shipment from the shipping point to the purchaser's plant. This is extremely important for shipments going to a foreign country or from port to port in the United States by ocean carriers. Ocean carriers have the option of charging for transportation of shipments on the basis of either their weight or their cubic contents when packed for overseas shipment, whichever results in the greater revenue for them. Not only is a boxed or crated item heavier than the unit alone, but also the cubic volume when measured on the outside dimensions of the container is usually much more than the cubic volume of the machine, and the charge if made on a cubic foot basis may easily run into a considerable sum. Ocean carriers usually allow a volume of 40 cubic feet per ton of weight for freight-calculation purposes. Therefore, units which are manufactured with the thought of foreign sale or ocean shipment in mind should be disassembled and packed into small-volume units, instead of being completely assembled in the shop and shipped as complete machines.

This so-called "stacking" will show a considerable saving both in local and overseas shipments. In estimating the cost of a unit, particularly one which must be shipped abroad, the price quoted should indicate the approximate cost of putting the packed unit on board the vessel. After a shipment, based on "f.o.b. railroad cars" at a given port, reaches the dock area at that port, certain additional costs must be added to put it aboard a vessel.

In addition to the actual shipping costs, there are the fees for preparation of marine documents; consular fees collected by the consul of the country to which the shipment is destined, for his work in preparing the necessary papers to secure admittance of the shipment to that country on its arrival; handling charges to take the shipment from the railroad cars to the vessel; special handling charges if the packages are very heavy which may require the use of special equipment, such as cranes, tackle, or other items, to lift the units from the dock and lower them into the hold or to the deck of the ship; marine insurance to protect the shipment against loss or damage during transit. Also at the receiving end, there are charges for unloading, dock fees, duties, etc., which the customer must pay. The manufacturer can usually furnish the purchaser with a reasonably accurate estimate of the charges to put the shipment on board a vessel at the home port, but the buyer must figure the local costs for himself. As these charges and costs vary according to the weight, type, and manner of packing of the equipment, it is important that this information be given to the buyer so that he can arrive at a true cost of the various types laid down on his dock.

3. The cost of erection of the unit into its final structure. This is a basic item in balancing the cost of one type of unit against another, which is extremely important but frequently neglected. Some units of equipment which are received entirely disassembled require considerable skilled mechanical labor to reassemble the parts, to weld or rivet them together, and to fasten them into place. Because of the present high cost of this type of labor in practically every country, this item alone may add considerably to the cost of a piece of equipment. Certain manufacturers prepare their units for shipment in such a way that, although the cubic volume of individual parts is kept to a minimum by careful packing, precision parts which require careful and skilled assembly are usually shipped as complete units, thus eliminating much of the need for skilled mechanical labor on the job. In out-of-the-way places it is sometimes difficult to obtain the skilled labor necessary for assembly of precision parts, and in many cases it must be brought to the job at considerable expense. Any reliable manufacturer will be glad to inform the purchaser of the approximate cost of installing his equipment.

All manufacturers will be willing to discuss these points with the purchaser and give him reliable data on the various costs. This information should be called for when bids are being received on equipment and used as the initial basis for comparison of prices.

Equipment and Apparatus

The modern industrial-waste-treatment plant, like the modern municipal sewage-treatment plant, will contain much mechanical equipment and various units of apparatus for the automatic control of operations. With the rising cost of manual labor, the machine is fast coming into its own as an economical, practical, and reliable way in which to accomplish a given objective. Modern equipment is usually built to operate satisfactorily for long periods of time; during that time, it will, with reasonable care and attention, perform its duties well. It will not ask for an annual increase in wages, it will not wish to cut down its working hours, it will not require an annual holiday, and it will stay on the job, come storm or fair weather, day and night. It is not subject to strikes at the whim of a well-salaried union official, and it will not engender picket lines to prevent its operation.

Many types and varieties of mechanical equipment are adapted to this work. These are fully discussed in Chap. 13. Suffice it to say, however, that, while most of the well-known items of equipment perform their work well, basic differences in their construction enter into the initial and operating expenses of a plant.

Mechanical equipment should be of a type built to serve a definite purpose, regardless of the component parts required in its fabrication, and each part of the unit should be sturdily built of such materials as will best withstand the duty to which it is to be put. It should be designed and constructed so that it will continue to operate for periods of years with the minimum repairs and attention, particularly if the major part of the unit is to be submerged in liquid and out of sight. Mechanical equipment for this type of work should have the fewest possible wearing parts in contact with abrasive or corrosive materials, and if parts must be exposed to such materials, they should be made of metals resistant to such attack. Adequate lubrication should be provided, with readily accessible lubrication points or with sealed lubrication devices to eliminate wear from lack of proper attention.

Different manufacturers of mechanical equipment use different shapes or forms for their units and their component elements. Sometimes these affect the efficiency of the unit, but usually they do not. Some manufacturers design and build mechanisms for stated purposes and use the best materials and most efficient mechanical principles. Others build their machines from stock parts of their main line of production and develop a unit around that stock line; the purpose for which the unit is to be used is a secondary consideration. There are adherents of both schools of thought, but in the author's opinion, the best machine for a given purpose is one designed with that purpose always in mind, regardless of what mechanical elements or parts may be contained in it.

Installation of Equipment

In considering the cost of mechanical equipment, not only must the actual sale price be taken into account, but also the cost of installation. Some units are so constructed as to have all elements subject to wear or abrasion located above the liquid level in the tank, so that no bearings, bearing supports, or wearing plates are required to be set in the tank walls or floors. Other units require the setting of a large number of anchor bolts in walls and floors for holding bearings, supports, cross beams, etc. The placement of these bolts is an expense which must be charged against this type of unit. It is definitely a part of the installation cost.

Most manufacturers of equipment can, and will, give the potential purchaser a fairly accurate idea of the cost of installing their units. This cost should always include the cost of setting all parts of the machine, especially those parts which require the setting of bolts or other parts in concrete.

Excavation Required for the Plant

In rocky or wet ground, excavation can be an item of extreme importance. Many industrial-waste plants must be placed in low ground, which is in most cases the worst possible place for construction purposes. Here, careful study should be given to a type of plant that requires the minimum of ground area and excavation. It may even pay, in heavy rock excavation, to construct the plant units as much aboveground as possible and pump the wastes to them. The extra cost of the pumping, capitalized, may not be so great as the cost of extra rock excavation.

Preparing the Ground at the Site

Frequently, no other site for a plant is available except one from which much rock or earth must be moved. If conditions are such as to require the cutting away of rock structure to prepare a flat area, the plant which occupies a small space may be the most economical. In some instances, units which have multiple settling areas, one above the other, or units which combine one or more operations, while not the least costly from an equipment standpoint, may result in a lower over-all plant cost. Units are available which combine sedimentation and flocculation in one tank and which combine clarification and digestion of sludge in one structure.

It is also possible to obtain digestion units which combine two-stage digestion in one tank. Naturally, by combining two operations in one structure, ground area is usually saved. In restricted sites or those with poor ground conditions, this may frequently be the economic solution. Also, where industrial plants are located in city areas, it is frequently possible, by utilizing these combination units, to put the entire plant within a single small building. Consideration has also been given in several cases, where no area was available on the industrial-plant site for the waste-treatment plant, to putting the necessary units in the basements or on the roofs of existing buildings.

Form Work

The cost of the containing structure is an important item in computing the cost of plants. A given type of mechanism may require a circular tank, which is the most economical form of construction. It usually requires less concrete than a tank of any other shape and less form work. Form work is an important item of cost in construction work as it involves careful carpentry work which, today, is one of the highest paid classes of labor. Tanks with involved or thin walls or baffles are much more expensive, as they are hard to form and require extra care and expense in the placement and compacting of the concrete. The tank bottoms are another item of expense, particularly if they must be comparatively flat or level. A mechanism has been developed which is set up and used as a screed to form the bottom, thus making a base which is a perfect fit for the unit and assures an efficient cleaning action.

Sometimes the site available for a plant makes it necessary to select a form of tank which may not be the cheapest to construct. This factor must be considered if site conditions are restricted.

Concrete for Construction

Tanks with thin walls may require a very high-grade concrete mixture with the use of much reinforcing steel, whereas tanks with heavier walls will require a lesser grade of concrete and a lesser amount of steel. Baffle walls and thin dividing walls which are not designed to sustain outside pressure may be made of expanded metal sheets, gunited on each side, the cost of which will be moderate compared with poured concrete walls. Architects are accustomed to designing buildings with very thin walls and floors which have a large percentage of steel in them. This same practice could be used in designing the structures for treatment plants, but a tank of relatively large size looks weak and out of proportion if its walls are very thin. It is common practice in designing plants of this type to make the main walls at least 10 inches and usually 12 inches thick; consequently less reinforcing steel is required and the yardage cost of the concrete in place is less.   The placement of steel in a thin wall requires time which must be charged against the concrete costs.   A 12-inch wall not only looks substantial, but a person can walk on it in safety.

Electric Wiring

The cost of electric wiring is another factor that must be considered. The unit requiring the greater horsepower and complexity of control will require larger supply cables, conduits, switches, etc., than the one with smaller power.   This item should be evaluated.

Some equipment is of such a nature that the electrical controls, motors, and other items are not built for outdoor all-weather service and must be protected by a building or some sort of housing.   If one type of unit requires this and another does not, the cost of this housing or protection should be added to the cost of the unit requiring it.

Land Occupied

It occasionally happens that industrial plants either have very small areas available for the treatment works or have reserved this space for further industrial construction, storage yards, etc.   In localities where industries are situated close together, it is frequently impossible to obtain extra land except at exorbitant cost.   In these cases, a type of plant should be considered which occupies a minimum of ground area, even though it may not be the most economical in first cost or in operation. The cost of extra land to provide a larger type of plant at a lower cost should be considered and charged against the initial cost of that plant.

In such cases it is also in order to discuss the possibility of combining the waste-treatment operations of several industries in a common plant.

Walks, Grading, Fencing, etc.

These items are not generally included in the preparation of industrial-waste-treatment plants, as these plants are commonly located on the grounds of the industry, but if they are outside these grounds, some attention should be given to the protection of the plant units and the protection of the public by proper fencing.   Open tanks are a temptation and also a source of danger to children.   They are also a temptation to thieves who may steal parts of the mechanisms or the electrical equipment and put the plant out of service.   A fence is an expense, but it is also relatively cheap insurance against accidents and damage.

If the plant is visible from public thoroughfares, a pleasing appearance should be maintained.   Neat walks encourage the operators and visitors to use them in going around the plant, and lawns and shrubbery cost little but greatly improve the appearance of a plant. The psychological effect of neat appearance on the public must not be disregarded.

Covering Tanks

While it is not usually necessary to cover the tanks in waste-treatment plants as the modern, mechanically operated units are usually free from the surface scums and unsightly masses of the older type, sometimes it is necessary to conceal the operation because of the proximity of residences. If such covers are required, they should be provided with sufficient man-holes, or other means of entrance, and ventilation ducts to prevent explosions if there is any possibility of gas being created within. It is preferable to put covers over tanks, the tops of which are sufficiently above the liquid level to permit a man to walk into the structure for observation and control.

Necessary Buildings

In many cases it is not necessary to provide new buildings for an industrial-waste plant. If modern units of equipment are used in the plant, the driving equipment is normally built for outdoor service requiring no housing, but it is frequently considered desirable to have a small structure in which the electrical controls are placed, which also provides facilities for storing tools and other accessories needed by the operator. If chemical feeders are employed, it is common practice to install these in a building, but in warm climates a complete building is not necessary; merely a roof on struts, which will keep out rain, is adequate. If buildings are deemed essential, they should be designed to conform to the general architecture of the main plant.

In some cases where municipal sewage-treatment plants were necessarily put in places used by the public, the entire plant has been constructed under the ground surface and roofed over with a flat concrete roof on which grass is planted, thus maintaining the public use of the ground as well as concealing the plant. An outstanding example of this type of plant is in operation at Spring Lake, N.J., a high-grade summer resort on the New Jersey coast. The logical place for the sewage-treatment plant was at the shore line, in front of one of the largest and finest hotels and immediately adjacent to the bathing pavilion. This plant has been in continuous operation since 1931, and few of the many thousands of people who visit this resort are aware of its existence, although they pass it and walk over it constantly. This same practice may be adopted for industrial-waste-treatment plants where land is restricted, or where there might be complaint about an uncovered plant. The tops of such plants may be used as tennis courts, bowling greens, etc.

OPERATING CHARGES

This is one of the most important factors in industrial-waste-treatment projects. The initial cost of a plant can be charged to capital investment and becomes an asset of the corporation. The operating expenses, however, are not an asset but a continuing expense item which are daily charged against the overhead of the plant and thus enter into the cost of production of the plant product. In highly competitive industries where the ratio of profit is small, any item which tends to increase the cost of production for one manufacturer and not another will meet with resistance as it will reduce the available profit.

As an example let us assume that the initial cost of one type of industrial plant is $25,000. The operating cost, covering chemicals, electricity, labor, maintenance, repairs, and supplies, amounts to $50 per day. Another type of plant which may have cost $35,000 to build but costs only $25 per day for operation will be the cheapest one for the industry to build. On the first plant the interest on the initial investment and amortization will amount to, say, 11 per cent per annum, or $2,750. Operation cost at $50 per day will amount to $18,250 per year, making a total over-all cost of $21,000 per year. The second plant has interest and amortization of $3,850 per year, but with operating costs at only $25 per day, the yearly cost being $9,125, the total book cost will be but $12,975 per year. Such savings are readily obtainable by a proper study of all the conditions involved in a problem and a knowledge of the various means of treatment that may be used.

Electric Power

This is an important item in plant-operating cost. The selection of a type of plant which may require a large usage of electric power for blowers or other units as against one which does not require the same amount of power can be brought out by an economic study before any decision is made. In some districts power is not plentiful, and large amounts are not available. In other localities where a type of plant is considered that uses large amounts of power, the feed lines to that section and the power house or transformer facilities may not be sufficient to carry the load. The result is heavy charges by the utility company for furnishing this additional capacity.

The horsepower of the driving elements of the units should be taken into consideration. In many instances, local utilities make a basic charge per month for stand-by service for motors of a given size. This charge is usually made, plus the actual charge for the current consumed, regardless of whether the motor is used or whether it uses all its rated power. This stand-by charge is normally based on the name-plate rating of the motor. Therefore, the power actually required for unit operations is important. The monthly bill for stand-by power and actual power consumption can amount to a respectable sum. Slow-running well-built units, running freely without drag on concrete floors or surfaces, will require less connected horsepower than other units and will, therefore, use smaller motors. This power element, in stand-by charges and power consumption, should be capitalized in every case and considered as an essential element in the calculation of the cost of operation.

Every equipment manufacturer can furnish accurate data on the actual power required to operate his units and will install motors which will furnish that power. Some manufacturers have redesigned their units to use modern gear-reduction units and methods which reduce the actual required power to a minimum. A machine which requires a 1½ horsepower motor in comparison to one which requires only a 1-horsepower motor may seem to offer little advantage, but this difference, capitalized, is important. On the assumption that the units run 24 hours per day, the 1½-horsepower unit will actually use 1 horsepower or 746 watts per hour, or 17.904 kilowatt-hours per day. In a year this unit will use 6,543.96 kilowatts. At a rate of 1 cent per kilowatt-hour, the power bill for current used will be $65.34 per year for that one unit. The unit with the 1-horsepower motor uses 0.75 horsepower, which in a year will equal 4,896.48 kilowatts, or a power bill of $48.96. The difference of $16.38 capitalized on a 5 per cent basis is equal to interest on an investment of $327.60. When multiplied by a number of machines, this difference can add greatly to the operating cost. This evaluation, therefore, is important in comparing equipment costs when an initial purchase is under consideration. Also, in many cases a monthly service charge is made by the local utility, based on the name-plate ratings of all motors. For the larger motor, this would be an additional item of expense.

Maintenance and Repairs

This item which, while not entering directly into the first cost, may have a strong bearing on the annual cost to the purchaser is frequently given too little consideration. If the unit has many wearing parts that are subject to gradual deterioration due to contact with other parts or to abrasion and that require periodic replacement, the cost of these repairs over a term of years may easily be equal to or greater than the original cost of the machine. One manufacturer of equipment for sewage and industrial-waste treatment determined by inquiries that the actual amount spent over periods of 10 to 15 years for repairs or replacements on his machines was considerably less than 1 per cent per year. It can be seen that, if a machine costing $5,000 has an annual repair cost of 5 per cent and one costing $7,500 has an annual repair cost of 1 per cent or less, in a term of 20 years the cheaper machine will have cost its owner a total of $10,000 as against a total of $9,000 for the more expensive unit.   But this is only part of the story.   It is not so much the actual cost of the repairs but the cost of the labor involved in making the replacements, and above this is the cost of the downtime, or the period in which the machine is out of service, which may subject the plant owner to fines or damage suits for failure to treat his wastes during that time.

If the equipment selected is such that certain parts may be expected to wear out and require periodic replacement, then repair parts should be included at the time of purchase.   This requires an outlay of capital funds which must be charged against that unit.   Manufacturers of equipment are well advised as to which parts of their units will require replacement and can readily provide a list of those which should be kept on hand.   Especially when the plant is in a foreign country or away from normal means of transportation, this should be a requirement when requesting prices.   The stocking of a few parts will save time and costly shutdown of the machine when the need occurs.   A standard rule of mining companies and many other industrial concerns when purchasing equipment for their distant plants is to require and pay for certain spare parts.   When a part is used, a replacement is immediately ordered so that at least one part is always on hand.   The capitalization of the maintenance item for various machines can frequently justify the purchase of an expensive unit if its maintenance cost is less than that for a cheaper unit.

Painting should not be considered, as all equipment should be kept painted to avoid destruction by rust.   If the machines are given a good shop coat of rust-resisting paint and are then painted in the field with some of the well-known corrosion- and wear-resisting coatings, further painting is a small item.   It is good plant-operating psychology to have a well-painted plant, as it receives better attention from its operators than one which is allowed to become rusty and unattractive.

Labor

With the present-day high cost of labor it is important to have a type of plant which requires the minimum of skilled help.   Modern mechanical units for every operation in industrial-waste treatment are available. These units are usually sturdily built and provided with automatic controls which maintain them in operation.   Many of them are also provided with automatic devices that sound an alarm when an overload occurs and with devices that shut down the machine if an operator does not respond to the alarm promptly. However, it is not good policy to expect any mechanical plant to operate without periodic attention.

When designing a plant, study should be given to a type which is not so complex that it requires the constant presence of chemists, engineers, mechanics, electricians, or other skilled workers. It is possible to design plants using modern available units which require the minimum of attention. In these plants, lubrication of the equipment is usually the main work of the attendant, with perhaps, in a chemical-precipitation type of plant, the periodic filling of the feeder hoppers. On a well-designed, average-sized plant, one man should be able to handle the operations, with perhaps an occasional call on other available workers in the factory.

A useful factor in reducing plant labor costs is to provide a chart, placed in a well-lighted place on the wall of a building accessible to every operator, which shows a complete diagram of the plants, its pipe lines, the location of all valves, controls, etc., with clear indications of their purpose. Alongside the chart should be placed a diagram showing what valves to open or close, what controls on the diagram must be operated to perform a certain duty, and which ones should be closed or opened in case of accident.

Supplies

Lubricants should be kept on hand in sufficient quantities to avoid depletion of supplies; these lubricants should be those recommended by the manufacturer of the equipment.

Every plant should be provided with a first-aid kit, which is kept constantly supplied with the needed medicaments. A proper toilet should be provided and, if the work around the plant is dusty or dirty, a proper washroom with shower bath. The telephone numbers of the local or plant physician, the local hospital, and the police and fire departments should be posted in a prominent place for immediate use in case of accident. If the plant is one that employs digestion of sludge a proper gas mask should be on hand in case it is necessary to enter a place into which gas may have leaked.

FIXED CHARGES

These are the items of expense which are set up by the business office of the industry to be charged off, annually or periodically as determined, against the initial cost of the plant and its eventual retirement or replacement. These charges fall into two categories.

1. The interest on the amount of money actually spent to build the plant and put it into operation is usually set at the rate at which the corporation could borrow the money to build the plant were that neces-

sary.   In other cases, where the funds are taken from reserves, the corporation may figure that if they used that amount of money for the production of goods a certain profit could be made from it.   In this case they
may decide that it is logical to charge as interest the amount of profit that
would have been earned had they used the capital in productive purposes.
However, as this interest charge becomes a charge against the business
operations, it is common practice to base it on the normal bank rate for
borrowed funds.   Therefore, it is usually placed at 5 to 6 per cent per
annum.

2. Amortization, or the writing off of the investment in a structure, is
based on charging against the operation a certain proportion of the capital
investment each year.   This is a matter for the judgment of the company
officers and may be 1 to 10 per cent.   It is customary, however, to set a
useful life of 20 years on the plant and its equipment and to set aside
each year 5 per cent of the original investment.   While 20 years is a
normal period, modern machinery units are built to operate for much
longer periods and with due care will do so.   When a corporation issues
bonds or other corporate obligations to cover the cost of such improvements as an industrial-waste plant, it is customary to set the term of
amortization coextensive with the term of the bonds.   An annual
write-off of amortization is only a bookkeeping item on the company
books, and no actual funds are required.   In the case of a bond or stock
issue, the amount of which must be refunded to the purchasers, it is
necessary to call in each year for payment a certain number of these
bonds and either pay cash for them or issue other obligations of the same
value.

The Federal Internal Revenue Bureau has set up amortization periods
for many items, and it may be of value to the corporation to make
their amortization program conform to that of the government for tax
purposes.

The total cost of operation of an industrial-waste-treatment plant then
consists of the fixed charges and the operating costs of the plant on an
annual basis.   The cost per unit of goods manufactured can be established at the end of any given period by dividing this total annual cost
by the number of units turned out in the same period.   In some industrial
plants where cost data are kept very accurately, it is the practice to charge
the cost of treatment against the individual department which produces
the wastes rather than to spread the cost over the entire factory production.   On the other hand, if the product of the department is a highly
competitive one, then the charging of waste treatment against the item
manufactured by that department might make a serious increase in price
necessary, whereas if the treatment cost is spread over the production of

the entire plant the unit cost to any one department would not be a matter of importance.

Bibliography

1. Ryan, W. A., Economic Methods for Treatment of Industrial Waste, Paper, Meeting, New York State Sewage Works Association, Kingston, N.Y., June 6–7, 1949.
2 Poole, B. A., Economies in Industrial Waste Treatment Plant Design, Proceedings, Second Industrial Waste Treatment Conference, Purdue University, Lafayette, Ind., pp. 114–120, 1946.
3. Check List for Reducing Industrial Waste Costs, *Sewage & Industrial Wastes*, vol. 22, No. 1, p. 86, January, 1950.
4. Report of Procedure for the Handling of Industrial Wastes, Committee on Industrial Wastes, California Sewage Works Association, 1945, *California Sewage Works Journal*, 1945. Abstracted at length, *Sewage Works Journal*, vol. 18, No. 3, pp. 503–526, May, 1946.

CHAPTER 17

REUSE OF WASTES AND POSSIBLE RECOVERY OF VALUES

The primary objective in the treatment of industrial wastes is to remove, eliminate, or abate the pollution of a stream or other body of water which renders it useless as a source of potable water or of water for industrial users, destroys its value as a recreational medium, or creates a menace to the public health.

With this primary objective in view at all times, the waste problem must be attacked and solved. It is not wise to be misled into the belief that the installation of a waste-treatment plant will make it possible to produce some by-product which may be marketed at a price that will pay the entire cost of operation, plus the fixed charges on the plant, and return a net profit to the plant owner.

All wastes contain by-products, the exhausted materials used in the process. These have a potential value as market commodities. As the basic materials were purchased it would seem practical to recover some of the by-products for reuse to cut down the need for purchasing a new supply at all times. It is also true that any by-product can be recovered from a waste or waste effluent, but no plant should be designed on the premise that this recovery can be made a profitable operation, or even pay part of the cost of the plant required to make the recovery.

The treatment plant must be designed to so treat the wastes of that particular industry that they will be rendered harmless and thus remove the cause of the complaint which has necessitated the building of the plant.

As, however, some wastes do contain elements which can be reclaimed or recovered, this field must be carefully studied with a full understanding of the cost of a reclaiming plant and the cost of its operation. If the recoverable element is in such form that it does not require a complex installation to separate it from the wastes and there is a market or use for it, then it may be possible to install such a plant and credit the prices received for the product recovered or reused against the operating cost of the plant. On the other hand, some wastes are very difficult to treat at low cost in any reasonable plant. In such cases, it may be well to study the possibility of building a recovery plant which will produce a marketable by-product which at the same time will completely destroy the waste or neutralize the polluting elements in it.

Many patents have been granted for, and much research has been done on, the recovery of by-products from wastes, as every one concerned with industrial-waste-treatment practice realizes that, if profitable recovery from such wastes can be shown, it will be much easier for the authorities to encourage the industrial groups to install plants which will clear up troublesome and dangerous pollution problems. But to date, very little hope has been offered.

There are, however, ways in which waste-treatment-plant by-products can be put to use with little expense for plant or operation. Our water famines of the past few years have made us realize our ever-increasing usage of water and the difficulties of obtaining greater and greater volumes for public consumption. It is a national demand, and yet there is one way of helping to solve it which has not been given the thought or attention it deserves. This is the reuse of plant effluents for nonpotable purposes, thus reserving the clear, pure waters of our unpolluted streams for household uses. The actual proportion of the daily average use of water for potable purposes alone and normal household purposes, such as cooking and bathing, is a small part of the general average of 147 gallons per capita per day used throughout the nation. On the other hand, the same water that has been kept pure for potable uses or that has been purified so that it may be used for that purpose is used for many other purposes which consume the greater part of the daily average but do not need pure or purified water.

Washing streets, fire demands, washing automobiles, cooling machinery, flushing toilets, watering lawns, irrigating lands, and filling boilers in household heating systems do not call for water of potable quality. In fact, a pure water for watering lawns and for irrigation is of less value than one which contains some organic matter which would help to stimulate plant growth.

Many industrial-waste-treatment plants, using conventional methods of treatment, turn out effluents which could perfectly well be used for many or even all the purposes mentioned above. By using the treated effluents for these purposes, the pure or treated water would be reserved for potable uses, and the supplies in our reservoirs would then be ample to carry us over the periods of drought without danger of shortage or deprivation. True, a separate piping system would be needed to convey two waters to the households and separate plumbing would be required to distribute them to the household or factory. But with the lower rate which could be charged for nonpotable water, it is possible that the cost of these extra pipe lines and fixtures could be written off in a normal term. Also, by using the treated effluents for the purposes which require the majority of the daily average usage, the cities would not be required to treat all the water, as is now the case, and very large sums would be saved by this elimination.

A great proportion of the daily average consumption of water is wasted by injudicious or careless use. Water is so cheap that we do not value it until there is a shortage. Because in an average city the householder buys about 20 barrels of water for which he pays 35 to 40 cents, or about 2 cents per barrel, the price is so low that little effort is made to cut down the usage. On the other hand, the gasoline with which we run our automobiles, which costs 20 to 30 cents per gallon, is never wasted, but all means are taken to get as many miles from each gallon as possible. If water were to be sold at the same price as gasoline, the demand for it would drop off so sharply that the authorities would begin to worry. Water is a necessity of life and cleanliness, and it should be obtainable at a price which all can pay, which is now possible; on the other hand, means should be taken to educate people to appreciate it as the cheapest of all commodities and to realize that wanton waste cannot continue.

It is a rare waste which costs more than 30 to 40 cents per 1,000 gallons, or four-thousandths of one cent per gallon, to treat to a high degree. If a waste-treatment plant could sell its effluent at cost or even less, the revenue derived would be a welcome offset to the expense of operation of the plant. Many plants would not have to go beyond the bounds of their own premises to make good and economic use of their treated waste effluents. For example, potable water is not essential for washing floors or cooling engines; the treated effluent could be used satisfactorily. The result would be an appreciable reduction in the water bill of the plant as well as a saving of potable water, which would then be available for the general use.

The outstanding study on this reclamation of industrial-waste effluents has been summarized in an excellent report published by the County Sanitation Districts of Los Angeles, California, in May, 1949.[19] The following factors are pointed out:

1. That the critical shortage of water in sections of Los Angeles County can in some measure be alleviated by reclaiming spent or waste waters.

2. That water which may be produced at spent water reclamation plants is of good quality, entirely acceptable, and better than some supplies obtained from underground storage or imported into the area.

3. That the reclamation of a satisfactory, limited supply of water from the spent and waste waters of the area may be accomplished safely and economically.

In reviewing the subject the report states:

1. The report deals with the reclamation of usable water supplies from sewage and industrial wastes.

2. Currently in excess of 95 per cent of all sewage and industrial wastes from the county is discharged at sea.

3. Public prejudice, lack of appropriate health and nuisance standards, and absence of clear, legal authorities are deterrents to such a reclamation program.

4. The scientific and engineering principles involved in the reclamation of water from sewage and industrial wastes are well established.

5. A modern, well-designed, well-operated sewage-treatment plant is capable of producing a better effluent than is available to many communities as a public raw-water supply.

6. Known sewage-treatment processes are able to remove practically all the matter from domestic sewage, rendering the water reasonably uncontaminated or unpolluted.

7. Acceptable water reclaimed from sewage may be used directly in agriculture, industry, and for recreational purposes.

8. Acceptable water reclaimed from sewage may be used for domestic purposes after percolation through sand beds acting as slow sand filters and blending with other acceptable underground supplies.

9. In general, the direct reuse in industry of acceptable water reclaimed from sewage is tolerated and encouraged in manufacturing processes which do not involve contact between the reclaimed water and human beings or foods to be consumed by humans.

10. The most obvious direct use for reclaimed sewage water is for cooling and condensing operations. There are a number of others.

11. Water reclaimed from sewage has been used in recreational areas for many years. The most notable example is Golden Gate Park (San Francisco, Calif.).

12. Reclaimed water used directly for lawn sprinkling or floriculture must, in general, meet agricultural-water standards.

13. In general, reclaimed water would serve as an excellent industrial cooling-water supply.

While this report was written primarily for the reclamation of water in the jurisdiction of the issuing authority, nevertheless the principles expounded are applicable to other sections of this and other countries.

It is interesting to note, in this respect, that in one of the newest countries of the world, Israel, the idea of sewage treatment for its communal developments and waste treatment for its industries is being predicated on the basis that such degrees of treatment will be given as will render the effluents suitable for irrigation purposes. It is indeed laudable when a new nation starts out on this sensible, economic basis, while our and other older nations still permit pollution of the streams and did not begin to consider the reuse of waste waters until recently when emergencies in public health and comfort arose.

Henry Kaiser realized the possibility of the reuse of plant effluents when he built his steel plant at Fontana, Calif., during World War II. Here, in a district where water was not plentiful and where large quantities were required in the rolling mills and elsewhere, the designing engineers were charged with the responsibility to design every plant which was to handle or treat a polluted water or waste on the basis of producing an effluent which would be of such quality that it could be used again in the mills.   This included the plant for removing the flue dust from the cooling waters, treating the sewage from the workers on the plant, and the effluent from the plant to treat the pickling liquors from the mill.

Sewage-treatment effluents have been used extensively for irrigation and other purposes and will be used even more in the future.   As many industrial wastes respond to the same types of treatment used in treating municipal sewage, the effluents from these plants are equally suitable for reuse.   Many industrial wastes which have been neutralized and contain no free acids or alkalies can be used for irrigation water.   Even a little residual color in the effluents will usually be no detriment to its use. Health officials may object to the use of effluent water on vegetables, etc., to be eaten uncooked, but it could well be used for the irrigation of fruit orchards and groves where the water does not touch the product.

When industrialists have a waste problem, they would be well advised to survey the nonpotable needs of the neighboring industries, with the idea that they might be able to dispose of their treated effluents at a price which would, to some extent, reimburse them for the cost of treatment. Where water is scarce or costly, an industrialist might well proceed even a little further with his waste treatment than the actual needs of the case required, with the idea, carefully based on a survey, that he could dispose of this more highly treated effluent at a moderate price.   In this he would be doing a public service of inestimable value.

The recovery of values from industrial wastes is a subject which requires careful thought.   Many wastes have constituents which have a theoretical value if they could be recovered and reused; but, as stated before, they usually require so much treatment to make them reusable that the cost is not warranted.   The actual cost of the plant to recover these waste constituents might be more than the cost of the waste-treatment plant itself, and unless a very large quantity of the materials could be recovered and sold or reused, the operating costs and fixed charges for the equipment required would probably outweigh any revenue received.

There is, however, much more research to be done in this regard—to work out means of recovering some of these waste materials at a reasonable cost.   Conservation is a subject currently very much in the public mind, and much more attention will be given in the future to the idea of recovering waste materials.

It has been said by one authority that the industrial wastes discharged into the streams of the United States are equivalent in polluting strength to the sewage of 60 million people. The same streams carry a load of sewage pollution from about the same number of people, which is a tremendous load to be imposed on the streams. This load, of course, includes all kinds of waste which are gradually being diminished as the effects of the many pollution-control programs of the Federal and state governments in the United States are put into evidence in the construction of treatment plants and conservancy works. In one state alone, Tennessee, it is said that the pollution effect of the industrial wastes discharged into the streams of that state are equivalent to 1.35 times the total population discharging sewage into these same streams.

Reducing industrial-waste loads to equivalent population, which is done on the basis of their strength in BOD and suspended solids, does not include all the objectionable compounds, mostly inorganic, in industrial wastes that may make some streams totally unfit for use as sources of domestic water supply or as a suitable environment for fish.

The following are examples of a few wastes from which values may be recovered.

Stockyard, Slaughterhouse, and Meat-packing-house Wastes

The wastes which come from the stockyards consist mainly of urine and manure. The killing floors contribute a load high in BOD from blood, paunch manure, bits of entrails, and gut washings. The removal of hair from hogs and other animals means a heavy load. The general cleanup of the killing and meat-preparation floors and tables adds a lot of dirt and other extraneous material. The pickling and cooking operations and the rendering of fats also contribute their share to the waste total.

About the only immediate source of revenue from these wastes, as a recovery item, and even this at times falls short of being a profitable operation, is the grease which may be skimmed from the settling basins, vats, etc. At the Racine Avenue, Chicago, Ill., pumping station, where stockyard drainage and waste are handled, hand skimming of basins in 1944 produced a total of over 1,100 tons of inedible grease, which at that time sold for a total of $24,730. No record is available of the expense involved in skimming and handling of this grease.

Table 17-1 shows the total poundage of animals killed in several years in all the packing houses of the United States, with the average amount of kill and the population equivalent of the waste discharged from the packing houses.[12]

If a steady market could be developed for the grease in these wastes, and an economical means of recovering it, refining it, and removing all the objectionable matter from it could be found, packing houses could consider installing joint recovery plants. This would reduce the capital cost to the individual plants as well as the operating charges, and the industries joining such a group would pay according to the volume or strength of the wastes contributed by them.

TABLE 17-1. DATA ON ANIMALS KILLED IN UNITED STATES PACKING HOUSES

Year	Annual kill, millions of lb	Average kill, tons per day	Population equivalent of wastes, millions of people
1930	30,164	50,300	8.70
1935	27,358	45,600	7.89
1940	35,669	59,500	10.29
1941	36,775	61,300	10.60
1942	40,676	67,800	11.73
1943	45,632	76,100	13.16
1944	47,395	79,000	13.67
1945	43,618	72,700	12.58

Wool-scouring Wastes

Grease from the wool of sheep is discharged in the waste wash waters of the wool-scouring process. The recovery of this grease is one of the few recovery operations which can show revenue worth considering. This grease, called lanolin, is used in paints, shoe dressings, leather dressings, hair-setting fluids, soap, etc.

There are several methods of recovering this grease from the waste wash waters, but perhaps the most common one is that of adding sulfuric acid to the waste to precipitate or crack the grease. The grease is then further acidified and separated from the liquid in filter presses. Bradford, England, is said to recover and sell over $800,000 worth of this recovered grease per year. The average grease content of the wastes from these washeries is about 890 ppm.

Brewery Wastes

The main potential recovery from brewery wastes is yeast. The potential amount of yeast that could be recovered from all the breweries in the United States is said to amount to 43 million pounds annually. This operation is, however, expensive, requiring an elaborate plant, which is costly to build and operate. Table 17-2 shows the losses of wastes from all United States breweries and the equivalent population of these wastes.

TABLE 17-2. LOSSES OF WASTES FROM UNITED STATES BREWERIES

Year	Quantity, bbl of beer	Population equivalent, millions of people
1936	56,055	3.47
1938	53,513	3.31
1940	53,675	3.33
1941	59,990	3.72
1942	67,700	4.20
1943	75,042	4.65
1944	85,469	5.30
1945	87,662	5.43

Distillery and Alcohol-manufacture Wastes

During World War II tremendous amounts of alcohol were required and used in the production of synthetic rubber. The residue of the stills employed in the distilling of liquor, without recovery, would have constituted the greatest single source of stream pollution in the country. It is estimated that, if these wastes had not been recovered, the population equivalent in 1944 alone would have been 27 million people. However, a substantial proportion of these still slops were recovered by a process of dewatering and drying in multiple-effect evaporators. In these plants the stillage is screened, the screened effluent put through centrifuges, and the cake from these is finally dried in multiple-effect vacuum pans. This produces a cattle feed which in 1943 had a value of from $30 to $35 per ton. It is estimated that approximately 1 million tons of this stillage was processed in the United States in 1945. This is probably the largest salvage operation undertaken by any industry and helps measureably in eliminating a serious pollution problem.

Corn-products Wastes

A great deal of pollution from the wastes has been eliminated by reducing losses in the plants themselves. Losses amounted to approximately an equivalent of 5.6 persons per bushel of corn processed. By settling the gluten wastes, the losses were reduced to 4.0 persons per bushel. Later, a system of concentration of the soluble elements was worked out by recirculation of the wastes, which were then dried. This reduced the population equivalent of the wastes to 1.0 person per bushel of corn processed. Still later, this process reduced the population equivalent to the low of 0.45 person per bushel of corn processed. The recovered solids from this process are mixed with gluten and hulls of corn, then dried and sold as cattle feed at $35 to $40 per ton.

Pulp- and Paper-mill Wastes

These wastes, especially from mills using the sulfite process of wood digestion, are very troublesome from a pollution standpoint. About one-half of the wood digested goes into the waste liquor. This liquor is largely composed of calcium salts of lignin, sulfonates, sulfites, wood sugars, and lime. The calcium salts are not recoverable. It is possible to change the process of digestion by using magnesium hydroxide as the base chemical, adding sulfur dioxide, and recovering the hydroxide by burning off the organic matter and calcining the magnesium sulfate to oxide. It is a costly process and requires extensive mill changes. It is doubtful if it is feasible for plants already operating on the basis of calcium salts to convert at a reasonable cost to the use of the magnesium salt. New plants, however, could be designed on this basis, and wastes problems would never originate.

For sulfite wastes of the calcium type, there is the possibility, which warrants investigation, of fermenting the wood sugars, amounting to about 12 per cent of the solids, to alcohol. Another possible recovery from the calcium process is that of fodder yeasts. The recovery of alcohol from this type of waste is reported to be in practice at pulp mills at Thorold, Ontario, Canada, and Bellingham, Wash. Figure 17-1 shows a flow sheet of the plant for the manufacture of alcohol from waste paper-pulp liquor as employed at Bellingham, Wash.

It has been estimated that, from the wastes in the northwestern section of the United States, about 70,000 tons of high protein food could be produced at a cost of less than $160 per ton, or 8 cents per pound.

Recent research work on the best methods of treating these sulfite wastes has been initiated by a joint program of the Sulfite Paper Manufacturers Committee on Waste Disposal with the Institute of Paper Chemistry at Appleton, Wis.

For recovery of waste fiber from paper-mill wastes, which not only will relieve the pollution element to a degree, but will reclaim fibers which may be returned profitably to the circuit, save-alls of various types are available and in wide use. These comprise the normal type of settling save-all, similar to the Adka type, which employs vacuum in a closed vessel to cause the light fibers to separate and rise to the surface of the tank, and the drum-filter vacuum type as made by Oliver United Filters, Inc., and others.

By-products Coke

Phenol in these wastes is a very severe pollutant of streams, especially if chlorine is present or is used in the treatment of the waste, as it has been estimated that 1 ppm of phenol will impart a taste to 20 million

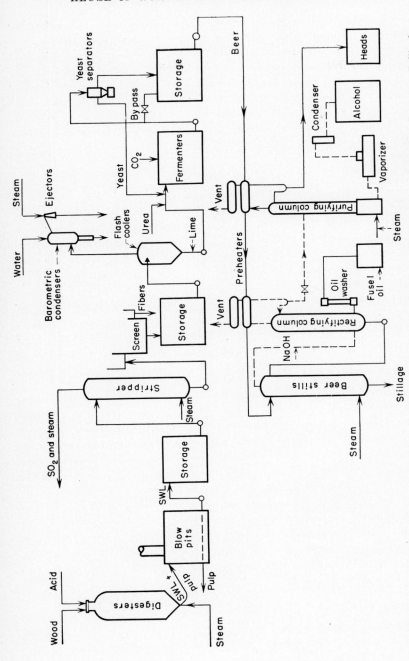

Fig. 17-1. Flow sheet for the manufacture of alcohol from waste liquor at Puget Sound Pulp and Timber Company, Bellingham, Wash.

parts of water. Recovery of phenol, which will remove this polluting element, may be made from the ammonia liquor from coke plants by a solvent-extraction process or a steaming-out process. It is estimated that, from the wastes of a coke plant producing 1,750 tons of coke per day, about 1,500 pounds of phenol can be recovered. This is roughly equivalent to a phenol recovery of 98 per cent. However, as the BOD of these wastes is also very high, and only about 77 per cent is reduced, the resultant wastes would still have a polluting population equivalent of 4,600 ppm in BOD.

Cannery Wastes

In canneries, a great deal of unnecessary waste not only becomes a pollution problem, but also results in a loss of valuable material. The possibility of drying these leaky residues before they become mixed with other materials and of selling them at a profit is now under investigation by cannery interests. Such a process, if successful, will relieve the cannery-waste problem materially, as otherwise the wastes are not suitable for profitable recovery.

Food-processing wastes do not seem to offer much opportunity for recovery.

Beet-sugar wastes offer little recovery value, except that betain may be recovered.

Candy-manufacturing Wastes

The main source of pollutional waste from these plants is lost sugar, due to careless plant operation. This waste is similar to that from sugar refineries and is a difficult problem, as the biological processes normally used do not affect the sugars, which pass through the system, and later, within a period of 3 to 4 days, the hydrocarbons begin to decompose. The process of predigestion, retaining the wastes in a digestion tank for anaerobic action for periods of 6 to 10 days, offers the best hope for the breakdown of these hydrocarbons and the treatment of the resultant digester effluent on high-rate trickling filters. Aeration periods of 24 hours and more have been tried on these wastes without noticeable effect, and longer periods than that seem impractical owing to the size and cost of plant and the cost of compressing the large volumes of air required to oxidize the organic matter.

Oil-refinery Wastes

The principal source of pollution from oil refineries is the waste oil which coats the surface of lakes and streams; it is obnoxious from the visual standpoint and is also a potential source of danger from fire. A great deal of the oil in suspension from this source may be recovered by skimming tanks, similar to those recommended by the American Petroleum Institute, which, however, do not recover oil in emulsion. Reports are extant to the effect that API basins at refineries in the vicinity of Chicago collect several thousand barrels of oil daily which is returned to the refinery for reprocessing and represents a considerable revenue.

In a recent case in Canada, a severe pollution problem from this source existed. After careful study, the consulting engineers[18] worked out an economical plant which not only recovers the oil in suspension in such

Fig. 17-2. Plant for the prevention of pollution by oil-refinery wastes at the British-American Oil Company, Clarkson, Ontario, Canada. (*Courtesy of The Dorr Company.*)

a condition that it may be directly returned to the stills without further treatment, but also has successfully been able to break down the oil emulsion, so that the resultant oil going to the lake was reduced to an average of 5 ppm in over 2 years of operation. The complaint was removed, upon completion of the plant.

This plant is used to treat the wastes from the plant of the British-American Oil Company, at Clarkson, Ontario, Canada, which has a capacity of 9,000 barrels of oil per day. All wastes containing emulsions or high turbidities are collected in a separate pipe line and treated by chemical precipitation, using 3 grains per gallon of hydrated lime and 3 grains per gallon of Ferrisul. The total daily flow of liquid treated is about 1 million gallons per day.

The plant (illustrated in Fig. 17-2) consists of an oil-flotation tank 40

feet in diameter and 9 feet deep; a pump house containing pumps, chemi-
cal-storage and chemical-feeding equipment; a flocculation tank 12 feet
wide by 28 feet long by 9 feet deep; a final sedimentation tank 60 feet
diameter by 8 feet depth; and glass-covered sludge-drying beds.   The oil-
flotation tank is equipped with a Dorr sludge-collection unit and also
has two adjustable decanting funnels connected by a neoprene hose to an
oil-discharge line.   Up to 200 barrels of oil per day is decanted from this

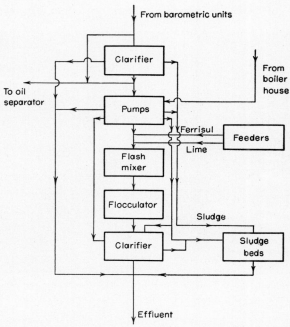

Fig. 17-3.   Flow sheet of plant for treating oil emulsions at the British-American Oil
Company.

tank.   This oil is clean and is sent to a storage tank and then put back
into the manufacturing circuit.   There is little visible oil in the overflow
from the decantation tank.   The effluent from this tank flows to a pump
well, with two vertical centrifugal pumps which lift the water to the Flash
Mixer.   The oil content of this water is about 275 ppm

In the Flash Mixer the effluent from the flotation tank is chemically
dosed and after the rapid mix passes into the flocculation tank in which
a very heavy floc is created.   After flocculation the flow passes into a
circular settling tank equipped with a Dorr sludge-collection mechanism.
The floc settles very rapidly, and the effluent passing into the lake is

clear and sparkling and has a residual oil content of usually less than 5 ppm.

The sludge from the final settling tank is lifted by a Dorr plunger pump and discharged to the glass-covered sludge-drying beds or into a tank truck. Sludge dries to spadeable consistency in about 1 week. Glass-covered beds are steam-heated to permit sludge drying even in freezing weather.

Before the construction of this plant, the oil in the discharge to the lake was 4 to 50 ppm. There is now no trace of oil in the lake at a point 50 feet from the plant outlet.

Figure 17-3 gives the flow sheet of this plant. Figure 17-4 shows the results in removal of oil before and after the plant went into operation.

Tannery Wastes

There is little of great recovery value in tannery wastes. Leather scraps, fleshings, and hair may be recovered from the liquid wastes by fine screens and treated with acid to produce a fertilizer. This has not been a particularly profitable operation, but it does relieve some of the polluting elements.

Rubber-plant Wastes

Reclamation of rubber particles in rubber-reclamation plants is practiced as a salvage operation in settling tanks, or save-alls, similar to those used in paper mills. This removal of waste rubber eliminates some of the pollutional elements which tend to form obstructions and sludge banks in the streams, but the final wastes are still a problem.

Textile Wastes

These wastes contain some fibers, particularly those from cotton and woolen mills. These fibers may be removed by fine screens, but offer practically no recovery value. The operation is mainly a means of eliminating this element of pollution. The wastes are usually colored and contain considerable acid or alkali, and these are not profitably recovered.

Laundry Wastes

There is no opportunity for recoverable values from these wastes.

Dairy and Creamery Wastes

These wastes offer little in the way of profitable recovery. Drippings from the various operations, whey, etc., can be recovered, but their low value in comparison to the raw material from which they emanate does not make their recovery attractive from a cost standpoint.

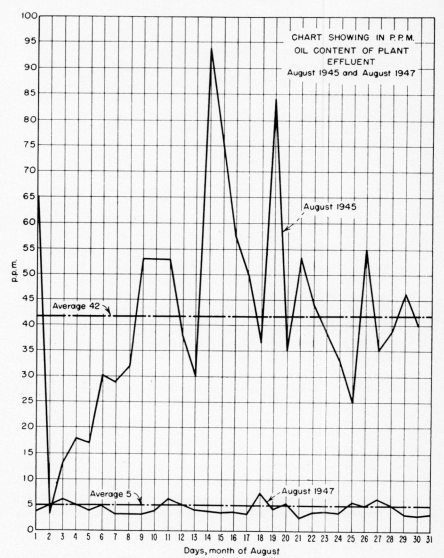

FIG. 17-4. Chart showing results of treatment at the British-American Oil Company before and after construction of the new plant.

Chemical-plant Wastes

While it is possible to recover various elements in these wastes, it is not ordinarily attractive from an economic standpoint. The acids and alkalies in the wastes are usually very dilute and do not warrant concentration. The organic residues are usually too dilute or unstable to be economically recovered.

From dye-manufacturing wastes which contain sodium thiosulfate 5 to 10 tons of sulfur are being recovered daily. In other cases anilin, phthalic acid, and solvents are being recovered.

Plating Wastes

Wastes from the electroplating processes offer some recovery possibilities. Tin, nickel, chromium, silver, and gold are usually recovered as their value is high; but lead, zinc, and aluminum are not usually recovered as their value does not warrant the expense.

Pickling Liquors

The ferrous sulfate which may be recovered from these wastes has potential value as a precipitant in sewage, water, and industrial-waste-treatment problems. The wastes of plating plants which pickle copper and brass contain cuprous solutions which may be treated with iron filings, mill turnings, or scrap iron to produce ferrous sulfate. This is not an expensive process, and if ferrous sulfate is in local demand it may be a source of profit. The plant necessary to recover the ferrous sulfate is not expensive and is frequently installed to eliminate the pollutional factor in these wastes, the recovery of ferrous sulfate being a secondary consideration, with its sale used as an offset to a portion of the operating expense of the plant.

It has been suggested that treatment by synthetic resins in the modern demineralization processes could be used for the recovery of copper, but at the present low price of this metal, and the expense of the installation and regeneration required in the demineralization processes, the cost may not be warranted. This method has been explored, however, and means may be developed whereby it could be used on a better economic plane. In this process, pretreatment is usually required as the liquids going to the cells must be practically free from solids in suspension, 10 ppm being the upper limit specified.

Use of Gas for Power and Heat

One of the by-products of waste treatment, particularly from those of an organic nature which respond to the anaerobic digestion process, similar to that employed in handling municipal sewage sludge, is a considerable quantity of gas, which is potentially valuable as fuel.

In the modern, heated, and conditioned digestion operation, where digestion in the alkaline phase is maintained, the principal product is a methane type of gas. This gas usually has a value of 600 to 700 BTU per cubic foot and can be immediately used for the production of heat and power. It is common practice now, in municipal sewage-treatment plants, to utilize this gas to produce the heat required to maintain the digestion tanks at a temperature conducive to rapid bacterial activity, which is usually between 85 and 95°F. To accomplish this, the gas is piped to boilers of the type commonly used in the home. The heated water from these boilers is circulated through coils in the digestion tank, in the form of circular coils laid on the inside of the tank walls, or in vertical heat-exchanger units suspended in the tank, or by means of external heat exchangers in which the liquid to be heated is passed through an exchange unit, with the hot water in the adjacent coils.

In many plants, particularly of the larger size, it is now becoming popular to utilize the gas directly as a power-producing element and use the by-product heat created in the power-generation phase to supply the heat for the digesters. This is by far the most economical use of the gas, as the two elements of heat and power are obtained from the same volume of gas.

In this power-generation operation, the gas is piped directly to the intake manifold of a gas engine of the internal-combustion type. The engine utilizes the gas as fuel and in its operation, similar to the action in the automobile, produces heat which requires a circulating flow of water to maintain a definite temperature in the cylinders and jackets of the engine. Instead of wasting this heat through a radiator, it is used to heat the digester, by sending the cooling water through an exhaust gas heater supplied with heat from the engine exhaust. This is a direct operation, requiring no additional fuel. The heat is transmitted directly to the digester, and the return flow from the digester coils is sufficiently lowered in temperature by its passage through the digester to be returned directly to the engine-cooling system.

This use of gas has gained such headway that several manufacturers of engines are making ones especially adapted to the use of this gas. The most modern type is that known as the "supercharged dual-fuel" type, in which the gas forms the basic fuel, but a small proportion of diesel fuel oil, usually representing about 5 per cent of the total fuel value, is added to act as a flame propagant to maintain proper engine operation. These engines are entirely automatic in operation, and in the latest models the maintenance of a proper fuel ratio is automatic. In case the supply of gas falls off, the engine automatically compensates for this by increasing the flow of diesel oil in sufficient amount to maintain the BTU balance required to run the engine efficiently. As the gas supply again builds up, the engine automatically cuts down the oil supply until the proper ratio of about 95 per cent gas and 5 per cent oil is again reached. These engines will now uniformly produce 1 kilowatt of power for a total BTU input of about 9,000.

Fig. 17-5. Installation of a 465-horsepower Worthington gas-engine driving blower at Fort Wayne, Ind., sewage-treatment plant. (*Courtesy of Worthington Pump & Machinery Company.*)

The gas may also be used directly as fuel in boilers, to heat the plant buildings, etc., if the power possibilities do not seem attractive.

Figure 17-5 illustrates a modern gas-engine generator set of this type.

The digestion method may be used on any organic waste. Tannery, packing-house, cannery, and other wastes respond to this production of gas. In the predigestion of hydrocarbon wastes, such as those from distilleries or cane-sugar refineries, a considerable amount of power may thus be developed. As the fuel for these engines is a waste product in itself, it is had at low cost. The charges against power production from digester gas are normally only the fixed charges and amortization on the operation and the operating costs for lubrication and attention. There is no fuel cost; therefore, the cost of power produced from this gas is usually less than one-quarter of one cent per kilowatt-hour.

Practically all cities of any size, both in the United States and in many other countries, now develop power from their sewage-plant gas. New York City alone has over 40,000 horsepower of engines in operation at a number of the presently constructed plants and more installations are contemplated for future plants.

Industrial plants which consume large amounts of power and produce wastes containing large amounts of organic matter will be well advised to investigate the possibility of recovering a low-cost fuel and developing valuable power which will lighten their monthly power bills.

Bibliography

1. Dickerson, W. H., Economic Importance of Waste Products Utilization, *Chemical Age*, vol. 29, No. 9, pp. 339–342, September, 1931.
2. Sulfuric Acid from Refinery Sludge, *Chemical & Metallurgical Engineering*, vol. 48, pp. 144–145, May, 1941.
3. Gehm, H. W., Recovery of Chemicals from Pickling Liquor and Copperas Waste, *Industrial & Engineering Chemistry*, vol. 34, p. 382, March, 1942.
4. Nolte, A. J., H. W. Von Loesche, and G. W. Pulley, Feed Yeast and Industrial Alcohol from Citrus Waste Press Juice, *Industrial & Engineering Chemistry*, vol. 34, p. 670, 1942.
5. Weber, G. L., Plastics from Citrus Waste, *Pacific Plastics*, p. 5, October, 1943.
6. Butyl Alcohol by Fermentation of Waste Sulfite Liquor, *Chemical & Metallurgical Engineering*, vol. 52, No. 6, p. 101, June, 1948.
7. Halperin, Z., Tartrates Recovered from Winery Wastes, *Chemical & Metallurgical Engineering*, vol. 52, No. 9, pp. 116–119, September, 1945.
8. Boruff, C. S., and L. P. Weiner, Feed By-products from Grain Alcohol and Whiskey Stillage, Proceedings, First Industrial Waste Utilization Conference, Purdue University, Lafayette, Ind., 1944.
9. Nolan, W. J., Profit Realized from Industrial Waste Treatment, *Water & Sewage*, vol. 87, No. 6, pp. 22–25, 1949.
10. Sawyer, F. G., M. F. Ohman, and F. E. Lusk, Iodine from Oil Well Brines, *Industrial & Engineering Chemistry*, p. 1547, August, 1949.
11. Gas Production from Waste Disposal, Bulletin 32, Illinois State Water Survey, Urbana, Ill., 1939.
12. Mohlman, F. W., Possibilities of Recovery and Utilization, *Proceedings, American Society of Civil Engineers*, vol. 74, pp 1052–1061, September, 1948.
13. Converting Pickling Liquor into Paint Pigment, *Sewage Works Engineering and Municipal Sanitation*, vol. 19, p. 297, June, 1948.
14. Mortenson, E. N., Grease Recovery in the Meat Packing Industry, Proceedings, Second Industrial Waste Conference, Purdue University, Lafayette, Ind., pp. 28–29, 1946.
15. Morris, H. H., III, Vegetable Wastes, Their Availability and Utilization, Proceedings, Second Industrial Waste Utilization Conference, Purdue University, Lafayette, Ind., pp. 54–69, 1946.
16. Murdock, H. R., Current Developments in Waste Utilization, *Industrial & Engineering Chemistry*, vol. 37, pp. 97–98, September, 1945.

17. Stringer, W. E., Whey Once Discarded Now Provides Useful Products, *Food Industries*, vol. 21, No. 7, pp. 54–57, July, 1949.
18. Proctor, E. M., Oil Refinery Waste Treatment, Paper, Annual Meeting American Society of Mechanical Engineers, New York City, Nov. 27–Dec. 2, 1949.
19. Report upon the Reclamation of Water from Sewage and Industrial Wastes in Los Angeles County, California, Board of Engineers, County Sanitation Districts of Los Angeles County, 1949.
20. Veatch, N. T., Industrial Uses of Reclaimed Sewage Effluents, *Sewage Works Journal*, vol. 20, No. 1, January, 1948.
21. Koebig, A. H., Jr., Covina Sewage Treatment Plant, *California Sewage Works Journal*, vol. 12, No. 2, 1940.
22. Rawn, A. M., C. G. Hyde, and F. Thomas, Report upon the Collection, Treatment and Disposal of Sewage and Industrial Wastes of Orange County, California, June 30, 1947.
23. Marshall, H. B., and A. Margaret Johnson. Utilization of Waste Sulphite Liquor, Report 4-4 50, Research Council of Ontario, Toronto, Ontario, June, 1950. A bibliography of the literature from July, 1943, to December, 1949.

APPENDIX I

FEDERAL AND STATE LAWS CONCERNING THE TREATMENT OF INDUSTRIAL WASTES

The United States has been tardy in enacting legislation to control stream pollution by industrial wastes. In England and Germany, which are highly industrialized countries with small streams, regulations limiting the indiscriminate discharge of industrial wastes have been in force for many years. The United States, a younger nation, with many large streams and bodies of water, has been more lax in permitting the discharge of industrial effluents into them.

Public consciousness has at last been awakened to the fact that this indiscriminate pollution has done a great deal of damage and that something must be done about it. After years of discussion and after numerous bills had been presented to Congress and either defeated or killed in committee, public sentiment became so strong that in 1947 the Congress considered and finally passed a bill, known as Public Law 845, which made the pollution of streams by industrial wastes a Federal responsibility. When and if the several states fail to discharge their responsibility, provision was made for stream-pollution agencies in various sections of the country to enact this law. It also provided for funds to be granted to the several states to assist them in their work of enforcement and for the loaning of funds to individual industries to enable them to comply with the provisions of the law. As this was a tremendous step forward it is considered well worth while to give the full text of this basic law.

An Act to Provide for Water Pollution Control Activities in the Public Health Service of the Federal Security Agency and in the Federal Works Agency, and for Other Purposes

Passed by the 80th Congress and signed by the President of the United States, June 30, 1948

Be It Enacted by the Senate and House of Representatives of the United States of America in Congress Assembled:

That in connection with the exercise of the jurisdiction over the waterways of the Nation and in consequence of the benefits resulting to the public health and welfare by the abatement of stream pollution, it is hereby declared to be the policy of Congress to recognize, preserve and protect the primary responsibilities and rights of the States in controlling water pollution; to support and aid technical

325

research to devise and perfect methods of treatment of industrial wastes which are not susceptible to known effective methods of treatment; and to provide Federal technical services to State and interstate agencies and *to industries,** and financial aid to State and interstate agencies and to municipalities, in the formulation and execution of their stream pollution abatement programs.   To this end, the Surgeon General of the Public Health Service (under the supervision and direction of the Federal Security Administrator) and the Federal Works Administrator shall have the responsibilities and authority relating to water pollution vested in them respectively by this Act.

Section 2.   (a). The Surgeon General, shall, after careful investigation, and in cooperation with other Federal agencies, with State water pollution agencies and interstate agencies, and with the municipalities and *industries* involved, prepare or adopt comprehensive programs for eliminating or reducing the pollution of interstate waters or tributaries thereof hereinafter declared to be a public nuisance and improving the sanitary condition of such interstate waters and tributaries thereof.   In the development of such comprehensive programs due regard shall be given to the improvements which are necessary to conserve such waters for public water supplies, propagation of fish and aquatic life, recreational purposes, and agricultural, *industrial* and other legitimate uses.   For the purpose of this subsection the Surgeon General is authorized to make joint investigations with any such agencies of the condition of any waters in any State or States, and of the discharges of any sewage, *industrial wastes*, or substance which may deleteriously affect such waters.

(b). The Surgeon General shall encourage cooperative activities by the States for the prevention and abatement of water pollution; encourage the enactment of uniform State laws relating to water pollution; encourage compacts between States for the prevention and abatement of water pollution; collect and disseminate information relating to water pollution and the prevention and abatement thereof; support and aid technical research to devise and perfect methods of treatment of *industrial wastes* which are not susceptible to known effective methods of treatment; make available to State and interstate agencies, municipalities, *industries* and individuals the results of surveys, studies, investigations, research and experiments relating to water pollution and the prevention and abatement thereof conducted by the Surgeon General and by authorized cooperating agencies; and to furnish such assistance to State agencies as may be authorized by law.

(c). The consent of the Congress is hereby given to two or more States to negotiate and enter into agreements or compacts, not in conflict with any law or treaty of the United States for (1) cooperative effort and mutual assistance for the prevention and abatement of water pollution and the enforcement of their respective laws relating thereto, and (2) the establishment of such agencies, joint or otherwise, as they may deem desirable for making effective such agreements and compacts.   No such agreement or compact shall be binding or obligatory upon any State a party thereto unless and until it has been approved by the Congress.

* Italics added for emphasis.

(d). (1). The pollution of interstate waters in or adjacent to any State or States (whether the matter causing or contributing to such pollution is discharged directly into such waters or reaches such waters after discharge into a tributary of such waters), which endangers the health or welfare of persons in a State other than that in which the discharge originates, is hereby declared to be a public nuisance and subject to abatement as herein provided.

(2). Whenever the Surgeon General, on the basis of reports, surveys, and studies, finds that any pollution declared to be a public nuisance by paragraph (1) of this subsection is occurring, he shall give formal notification thereof to the person or persons discharging any matter causing or contributing to such pollution and shall advise the water pollution agency or interstate agency of the State or States where such discharge or discharges originate of such notification. This notification may outline recommended remedial measures which are reasonable and equitable in that case and shall specify a reasonable time to secure abatement of the pollution. If action calculated to secure abatement of the pollution within the time specified is not commenced, this failure shall again be brought to the attention of the person or persons discharging the matter and of the water pollution agency or interstate agency of the State or States where such discharge or discharges originate. The notification to such agency may be accompanied by a recommendation that it initiate a suit to abate the pollution in a court of proper jurisdiction.

(3). If, within a reasonable time after the second notification by the Surgeon General, the person or persons discharging the matter fail to initiate action to abate the pollution, or the State water pollution agency or interstate agency fails to initiate a suit to secure abatement, the Federal Security Administrator is authorized to call a public hearing, to be held in or near one or more of the places where the discharge or discharges causing or contributing to such pollution originate, before a board of five or more persons appointed by the Administrator, who may be officers or employees of the Federal Security Agency or of the water pollution agency or interstate agency of the State or States where such discharge or discharges originate (except that at least one of the members of the board shall be representative of the water pollution agency of the State or States where such discharge or discharges originate and at least one shall be a representative of the Department of Commerce, and not less than a majority of the board shall be persons other than officers or employees of the Federal Security Agency). On the basis of the evidence presented at such hearing the board shall make its recommendations to the Federal Security Administrator concerning the measures, if any, which it finds to be reasonable and equitable to secure abatement of such pollution.

(4). After affording the person or persons discharging the matter causing or contributing to the pollution reasonable opportunity to comply with the recommendations of the board, the Federal Security Administrator may, with the consent of the water pollution agency (or of any officer or agency authorized to give such consent) of the State or States in which the matter causing or contributing to the pollution is discharged, request the Attorney General to bring a suit on behalf of the United States to secure abatement of the pollution.

(5). Before or after any suit authorized by paragraph (4) is commenced, any person who is alleged to be discharging matter contributing to the pollution, abatement of which is sought, may, with the consent of the water pollution agency (or of any officer or agency authorized to give such consent) of the State in which such matter is discharged, be joined as a defendant. The court shall have power to enforce its judgment against any such defendant.

(6). In any suit brought pursuant to paragraph (4) in which two or more persons in different judicial districts are originally joined as defendants, the suit may be commenced in the judicial district in which any discharge caused by any of the defendants occurs.

(7). The court shall receive in evidence in any such suit a transcript of the proceedings before the board and a copy of the board's recommendation; and may receive such further evidence as the court in its discretion deems proper. The court, giving due consideration to the practicability and to the physical and economic feasibility of securing abatement of any pollution proved, shall have jurisdiction to enter such judgment, and orders enforcing such judgment, as the public interest and the equities of the case may require. The jurisdiction of the Surgeon General, or any other agency which has jurisdiction pursuant to the provisions of this Act, shall not extend to any region or areas nor shall it affect the rights or jurisdiction of any public body where there are in effect provisions for sewage disposal pursuant to agreement between the United States of America and any such public body by stipulation entered in the Supreme Court of the United States. While any such stipulation or modification thereof is in force and effect no proceedings of any kind may be maintained by virtue of this Act against such public body or any public agency, corporation or individual within its jurisdiction. Neither this provision nor any provision of this Act shall be construed to give to the Surgeon General or any other person or agency the right to intervene in the said proceedings wherein such stipulation was entered.

(8). As used in this subsection, the term "person" includes an individual, corporation, partnership, association, a State, Municipality and a political subdivision of a State.

Section 3. The Surgeon General may, upon request of any State water pollution agency or interstate agency, conduct investigations and research and make surveys concerning any specific problem of water pollution confronting any State, interstate agency, community, municipality or *industrial plant* with a view to recommending a solution of such problem.

Section 4. The Surgeon General shall prepare and publish, from time to time, reports of such surveys, studies, investigations, research and experiments made under the authority of this Act as he may consider desirable, together with appropriate recommendations with regard to the control of water pollution.

Section 5. The Federal Works Administrator is authorized, subject to the provisions of section 9(c), to make loans to any State, municipality or interstate agency for the construction of necessary treatment works to preserve the discharge by such State or municipality of untreated or inadequately treated sewage or other waste into interstate waters or into a tributary of such waters, and for the preparation (either by its engineering staff or by practicing engineers employed for the purpose) of engineering reports, plans and specifications in connection therewith. Such loans shall be subject, however, to the following limitations: (a) No loan shall be made for any project unless such project shall have been approved by the appropriate State water pollution agency or agencies and by the Surgeon General, and unless such project is included in a comprehensive program developed pursuant to this Act; (b) no loan shall be made for any project in an amount exceeding $33\frac{1}{3}$ per centum of the estimated reasonable cost thereof, as determined by the Federal Works Administrator, or in an amount exceeding $200,000, whichever is the smaller; (c) every such loan shall bear interest at the rate of 2 per centum per annum, payable semiannually; and (d) the bonds or other obligations evidencing any such loan (1) must be duly authorized and issued pursuant to State and local law, and (2) may, as to the security thereof, and the payment of principal thereof and interest thereon, be subordinated (to the extent deemed feasible and desirable by the Federal Works Administrator for facilitating the financing of such projects) to other bonds or obligations of the obligor issued to finance such project or that may then be outstanding.

Section 6. (a). The Surgeon General and the Federal Works Administrator, in carrying out their respective functions under this Act, shall provide for the review of all reports of examinations, research, investigations, plans, studies and surveys made pursuant to the provisions of this Act and all applications for loans under section 5, in determining the desirability of projects for treatment works and of approving loans in connection therewith, consideration shall be given to the public benefits to be derived by the construction thereof, the propriety of Federal aid in such construction, the relation of the ultimate cost of constructing and maintaining the works to the public interest and to the public necessity for the works, and the adequacy of the provisions made or proposed by the applicant for the loan for assuring proper and efficient operation and maintenance of the works after completion of the construction thereof.

(b). There is hereby established in the Public Health Service a Water Pollution Control Advisory Board to be composed as follows: The Surgeon General or a sanitary engineer officer designated by him, who shall be Chairman of the Board; a representative of the Department of the Army, a representative of the Department of the Interior, a representative of the Federal Works Agency and a representative of the Department of Agriculture, designated by the Secretary of the Army, the Secretary of the Interior, the Federal Works Administrator and the Secretary of Agriculture, respectively; and six persons (not officers or employees of the Federal Government) to be appointed annually by the President. One of the persons appointed by the President shall be an engineer who is expert in sewage and *industrial waste disposal*, one shall be a person who shall have shown an active interest in the field of wildlife conservation, and, except as the President may determine that the purposes of this Act will be better furthered by different representation, one shall be a person representative of municipal government, one shall be a person representative of State Government, and one shall be a person representative of affected industry. The members of the Board who are not officers or employees of the United States shall be entitled to receive compensation at a per diem rate to be fixed by the Federal Security Administrator, together with an allowance for actual and necessary traveling and subsistence expenses while engaged on the business of the Board. It shall be the duty of the Board to review the policies and program of the Public Health Service as undertaken under authority of this Act and to make recommendations thereon in reports to the Surgeon General. Such clerical and technical assistance as may be necessary to discharge the duties of the Board shall be provided from the personnel of the Public Health Service.

Section 7. There is hereby authorized to be appropriated to the Federal Security Agency for each of the five fiscal years during the period beginning July 1, 1948 and ending June 30, 1953, a sum not to exceed the sum of $20,000,000 for the purpose of making loans under section 5 of this Act. Sums so appropriated shall remain available until expended.

Section 8. (a). There is hereby authorized to be appropriated to the Federal Security Agency for each of the five fiscal years during the period beginning July 1, 1948 and ending June 30, 1953, the sum of $1,000,000, to be allotted equitably and paid to the States for expenditure by or under the direction of their respective State water pollution agencies, and to interstate agencies for expenditure by them, for the conduct of investigations, research, surveys and studies related to the prevention and control of water pollution caused by *industrial wastes*. Sums appropriated pursuant to this subsection shall remain available until expended, shall be allotted by the Surgeon General in accordance with regulations prescribed by the Federal Security Administrator and shall be paid prior to audit or settlement by the General Accounting Office.

(b). There is hereby authorized to be appropriated to the Federal Works Agency for each of the five fiscal years during the period beginning July 1, 1948 and ending June 30, 1953, a sum not to exceed $800,000 to enable the Federal Works Administrator to erect and to furnish and equip such buildings and facilities at Cincinnati, Ohio, as may be necessary for the use of the Public Health Service in connection with the research and study of pollution of interstate waters and the training of personnel in work related to the control of pollution of interstate waters. The amount authorized for this purpose shall include the cost of preparation of drawings and specifications, supervision of construction and other administrative expenses incident to the work; Provided, That the Federal Works Agency shall prepare the plans and Specifications, make all necessary contracts and supervise construction. Sums appropriated pursuant to this authorization shall remain available until expended.

(c). There is hereby authorized to be appropriated to the Federal Works Agency for each of the five fiscal years during the period beginning July 1, 1948 and ending June 30, 1953, a sum not to exceed the sum of $1,000,000 to enable the Federal Works Administrator to make grants to States, municipalities or interstate agencies to aid in financing the cost of engineering, architectural and economic investigations and studies, surveys, designs, plans, working drawings, specifications, procedures and other action preliminary to the construction of projects approved by the appropriate State water pollution agency or agencies and by the Surgeon General. Grants made under this subsection with respect to any project shall not exceed whichever of the following amounts is the smaller; (1) $20,000, or (2) $33\frac{1}{3}$ per centum of the estimated reasonable cost (as determined by the Federal Works Administrator) of the action preliminary to the construction of such projects. Sums appropriated pursuant to this subsection shall remain available until expended.

(d). There is hereby authorized to be appropriated to the Federal Security Agency for each of the five fiscal years, during the period beginning July 1, 1948 and ending June 30, 1953, such sum (not to exceed the sum of $2,000,000) as may be necessary to enable it to carry out its functions under this Act.

(e). There is hereby authorized to be appropriated to the Federal Works Agency for each of the five fiscal years during the period beginning July 1, 1948 and ending June 30, 1953, such sum (not to exceed the sum of $500,000) as may be necessary to enable it to carry out its functions under this Act.

Section 9. (a). To assist in carrying out the purposes of this Act, the appointment of engineer and scientist officers may be made under the provisions of section 208 (b) (1) of the Public Health Service Act, in addition to the appointments authorized by such section 208 (b) (1); but not more than five such additional officers shall hold office at the same time.

(b). The Federal Security Administrator, with the consent of the head of any other agency of the Federal Government, may utilize such officers and employees of such agency as may be found necessary to assist in carrying out the purposes of this Act.

(c). (1). Upon written request of the Federal Works Administrator, from time to time submitted to the Federal Security Administrator, specifying (a) particular projects approved by the Surgeon General, (b) the total estimated costs of such projects and (c) the total sum requested for loans which the Federal Works Administrator proposes to make for such projects, the Federal Security Administrator shall transfer such total sum (within the amount appropriated therefor) to the Federal Works Administrator for the making of loans for such projects pursuant to section 5 hereof. In making such loans, the Federal Works Administrator shall adhere to the order or sequence of priority for projects established by the Surgeon General and shall take such measures as, in his judgment, will assume that the engineering plans and specifications, the details of construction and the completed treatment works conform to the project as approved by the Surgeon General; and the Federal Works Administrator shall furnish written reports to the Federal Security Administrator on the progress of the work.

(2). The Federal Works Administrator is hereby authorized (a) to hold, administer, exchange, refund or sell at public or private sale any bonds or other obligations evidencing loans made under this Act; and (b) to collect or provide for the collection of interest on and principal of such bonds or other obligations. All moneys received as proceeds from such sales, and all moneys so collected, shall be covered into the Treasury as miscellaneous receipts.

(d). The Surgeon General and the Federal Works Administrator are each authorized to prescribe such regulations as are necessary to carry out their respective functions under this Act.

Section 10. When used in this Act;

(a). The term "State water pollution agency" means the State health authority, except that, in the case of any State in which there is a single State agency, other than the State health authority, charged with responsibility for enforcing

State laws relating to the abatement of water pollution, it means such other State agency;

(b). The term "interstate agency" means an agency of two or more States having powers or duties pertaining to the abatement of pollution of waters;

(c). The term "treatment works" means the various devices used in the treatment of sewage or industrial waste of a liquid nature, including the necessary intercepting sewers, outfall sewers, pumping, power and other equipment, and their appurtenances, and includes any extensions, improvements, remodeling, additions and alterations thereof;

(d). The term "State" means a State, the District of Columbia, Hawaii, Alaska, Puerto Rico or the Virgin Islands;

(e). The term "interstate waters" means all rivers, lakes and other waters that flow across, or form a part of, State boundaries; and

(f). The term "municipality" means a city, town, district or other public body created by or pursuant to State law and having jurisdiction over disposal of sewage, industrial wastes or other wastes.

Section 11.   This Act shall not be construed as (1) superseding or limiting the functions, under any other law, of the Surgeon General or of the Public Health Service, or of any other officer or agency of the United States, relating to water pollution, or (2) affecting or impairing the provisions of the Oil Pollution Act, 1924, or sections 13 through 17 of the Act entitled "An Act making appropriations for the construction, repair and preservation of certain public works on rivers and harbors and for other purposes," approved March 3, 1899, as amended, or (3) affecting or impairing the provisions of any treaty of the United States.

Section 12.   If any provision of this Act, or the application of any provision of this Act to any person or circumstance, is held invalid, the application of such provision to other persons or circumstances, and the remainder of this Act, shall not be affected thereby.

Section 13.   This Act may be cited as the "Water Pollution Control Act."

THE EXTENT OF STATE REGULATION

The individual states have made sporadic attempts to control industrial pollution by enacting various laws and regulations.   Unfortunately, many of the streams concerned were interstate boundaries, and unless the state on the opposite side enacted a similar law, with the same objectives and penalties, it was difficult for the one state to enforce its own provisions.   Many of these early state laws failed to provide penalties for infringement of the law; if they did provide penalties, the legal action and policing of all the industries was too great a task for their limited forces and budgets, and in many cases infractions continued for years. In other states, where large industrial groups contributed heavily in taxes, payrolls, and donations to public interest, the laws specifically exempted these industries from any treatment.

It is interesting in this regard to consider the situation that existed in the several states in 1925 and today.   In 1925, the author prepared an article,[10] which was delivered before a prominent technical group, in which he presented data assembled from a questionnaire sent to all the states as to the existence of a law against industrial pollution and its general provisions.   An inspection of these data shows that 47 of the states, four provinces of Canada, Hawaii, and Puerto Rico, the Philippine Islands and the District of Columbia had general health laws which covered pollution of waters by industrial wastes.   Thirty-five of the states listed certain wastes which must be excluded from streams; 12 states made no mention of specific wastes, but had general clauses referring to wastes from "any manufacturing plant" or "wastes containing any harmful or deleterious substance."   In 13 states certain industries were exempted from treatment; in the majority of cases, these were in heavily industrialized states where there were large concentrations of these particular industries.   In all states except two, penalties were provided for infraction of the law, ranging from fines of $10 to $5,000 or imprisonment for 10 days to 1 year or both.

Now let us look at the record as it existed in 1948.   At this time a Committee on Industrial Waste Disposal of the American Institute of Chemical Engineers endeavored to evaluate the situation and issued a 15-point questionnaire to the responsible heads of all the states, the territorial divisions of the United States, and the provinces of the Dominion of Canada.   Fifty-seven replies were received from the 59 jurisdictional bodies approached, and the results were summarized in an admirable paper[18] given before a meeting of the institute.   It is interesting to scan these data.   The questions asked and the nature of the replies follow.

1. *Do you have a state (or provincial) law regulating the discharge of industrial wastes into streams?*

Affirmative replies to this came from 37 states, four Canadian provinces, and Hawaii and Alaska.   Modified replies came from seven states and two provinces.   Negative replies were received from four states and the District of Columbia.

2. *When was this law put into effect?*

The earliest date given was 1903 in New York.   The replies indicated that the greatest legislative activity was in two general periods: 1921 to 1930 and 1941 to 1948.

3. *Does it specify definite types of waste which must be treated before discharge?*

Negative replies were received from 30 states.   Affirmative replies came from only five states, and seven states gave modified replies. All territories and provinces gave negative replies.

4. *Does it require pretreatment of all wastes before discharge into streams?*

This was required in only five states and Alaska.   Twenty-five states replied that they did not require pretreatment.

5. *Does it require presentation to and approval of plans for waste-treatment plants by your organization?*

Presentation and approval of plans were required by 35 states, Hawaii and Alaska, and all six provinces of Canada.   Four states advised that they did not require approval.

6. *Does it provide penalties for noncompliance?*

Practically all state laws had "teeth" and provided penalties for noncompliance.   Two states answered negatively.   The penalties, however, varied widely, ranging from $50 to $3,000.   Added to most were the costs.   Jail terms of 90 days to 6 months were provided in some cases in addition to the fines.

7. *Does it specifically exempt any given industries?*
8. *If so, which ones?*

These two questions are in reality one.   Pennsylvania, Virginia, West Virginia, Ohio, and Nevada make exemptions with regard to mines and concentrators.   Vermont excepts war industries.   Maine exempts industries on major rivers and those established prior to the 1945 law. Forty-one states either made no exception or failed to answer the question.   No exceptions were made in the territories and provinces.

9. *Does it classify the state or provincial streams as to degrees of treatment required?*

Nine states classify their state streams.   Three states qualified their replies.   Thirty-six remaining states either made no classification or failed to reply.   The territories and six provinces replied in the negative.

10. *Does it provide for cooperation between your agency and industrial concerns?*

Twenty-eight affirmative and 11 negative answers were received to this question.   Three provinces of Canada replied in the negative, and two stated that provision for cooperation was made indirectly.   Hawaii answered in the affirmative; Alaska, in the negative.

11. *Does your organization have any part in designing waste-treatment plants for industries?*

Twenty-one states replied in the negative. Twelve had such a part. Twelve qualified their replies. Two provinces of Canada had such arrangements; the others did not. Hawaii replied in the negative. Alaska qualified her answer.

12. *Does the law or your present regulation permit formation of group plants or the creation of sanitary districts?*

Thirty-seven replied in the affirmative. Six gave negative replies, and three qualified their replies. Hawaii answered in the negative; Alaska, in the affirmative. Two provinces of Canada answered yes; the others, no.

13. *Does the law provide any formula for establishing charges to be paid by industry for treatment of their wastes in municipal plants?*

Forty states, Hawaii and Alaska, and all Canadian provinces except one answered in the negative. Four states answered in the affirmative.

14. *How does your department decide on the degree of treatment that will be required in any given industry?*

15. *List, in the relative order of the seriousness of their pollutional effect, the wastes which are causing the greatest difficulty within your jurisdiction.*

As these last two questions do not throw any light on the subject of this chapter, the answers are not considered relevant to this discussion.

A comparison of these two surveys, made 23 years apart, shows that, while some progress has been made, there is still a wide gap in universal agreement on what should be done toward legislation aimed at the elimination or prevention of stream pollution by industrial wastes. The main points, *i.e.*, providing enforceable penalties for infraction of the law, exempting certain large industries, and providing for cooperation of the jurisdictional bodies with industries to obtain compliance on a friendly basis, still leave much to be desired. The organization of state sanitary engineers would do well to consider these points and endeavor to work out a comprehensive law to which all states could agree. An attempt was made in this direction at a recent meeting of the engineers and state health authorities of the states of Illinois, Indiana, Iowa, Michigan, Minnesota, Mississippi, New York, Ohio, Pennsylvania, Wisconsin, which make up the Upper Mississippi River Board of Public Health Engineers and the Great Lakes Board of Public Health Engineers. These men combined their knowledge of the requirements of their respective jurisdictions and their ideas of the needs of a perfect, operable set of rules and regulations and drafted a tentative setup. It is interesting to note some of the proposed provisions of this code as they affect the industrial-plant owner.

Submission of Plans.

It is suggested that preliminary plans be submitted with the Engineers Report for review *prior* to the preparation of final plans. However, no approval can be issued until final, complete, detailed plans and specifications have been submitted to the approving authority and found to be satisfactory.

New Processes, Methods, and Equipment

The policy of the reviewing authority is to encourage rather than obstruct the development of new methods and equipment for the treatment of sewage and wastes, but under no circumstances will experimental installations be permitted at the expense of any municipality. Any new development must have been thoroughly tested in full-scale installation under competent supervision before approval of a plant utilizing this process or equipment can be issued, unless a municipality is amply protected by a performance bond so that in case of failure any expenditure of public money will be refunded. Where it is necessary to revise or rebuild permanent plant structures in order to accommodate other mechanical equipment after the original installation has been rejected, the performance bond shall include provisions to cover the cost of the installation.

Industrial Wastes

Where appreciable amounts of industrial wastes are involved, consideration shall be given to the character of the wastes in the design of the plant.

Where it is necessary to provide preliminary treatment of industrial wastes or where they are of such character that they should be excluded from the sewers, the municipality should be so advised at the time the plans are submitted so that the industry may be properly notified.

Other sections of this admirable code establish the norms for design which are in general accord with modern and current practice, and it indicates a desire and willingness to cooperate and assist the industries to solve their problems in an efficient and satifsactory manner. Once this code is adopted by such a representative group of the principal industrial states of the union, it is likely that the other states will gradually fall into line and eventually make it the standard code for the entire nation.

The modern trend is to recognize that industry should not be arbitrarily penalized in the elimination of pollution, but that it must be educated to accept its responsibility toward the general health and welfare of the population and to cooperate with the health authorities in carrying out sensible and practical plans.

Another outstanding group endeavor to prepare workable codes for handling industrial wastes has been drafted by a Committee of the Water Pollution Control Council, Pacific Northwest Area, which includes the states of Montana, Idaho, Oregon, Washington, the Territory of Alaska, and the province of British Columbia in Canada. This code, adopted by the Washington State Pollution Control Commission, is believed to be the first set of rules and regulations developed under Public Law 845. For this reason and because of the statement of fundamental procedures for the prevention of industrial wastes inside plant premises and the reduction of industrial-plant-waste discharges, the entire code will be included here as an example and guide to other pollution-control agencies.[19]

FOREWORD

The Pollution Control Law of 1945 invested in the Pollution Control Commission the power to adopt, prescribe, and promulgate the rules, regulations, and standards necessary to carry out the purposes of the Act. It is the established policy of the Commission to employ judgment and reason in the enforcement of the provisions of this law and to apply cooperative measures in every case possible to obtain the necessary and desired results.

Pollution by wastes from industry exceeds by many times that resulting from domestic sewage. One of the reasons for this high pollution load is the lack of understanding on the part of certain industrial management of the effects of industrial pollution. Much of the load contributed by industry can be eliminated by careful operations and comparatively inexpensive waste prevention measures. Waste saving measures have been known to result in profit to certain industries. The true value of these measures, however, is in the reduction of the pollution load on public waters or on the operation load applied to municipal sewage treatment facilities in case the industry has access to the municipal system.

The minimum requirements listed below are designed to bring about more careful industrial operation and to promote waste prevention. To be of most value they must be, and are, applied on an industry-wide basis and as such will constitute a fair and reasonable means of reducing industrial pollution. It is expected that in some cases these measures will not be sufficient to solve a pollution problem and that further reduction by waste treatment will be necessary. However, waste treatment will not be required until waste prevention has been given a fair trial.

The staff of the Commission is available to discuss the various problems created by these regulations. Plans for installations to be used to comply with them must be submitted to the Pollution Control Commission for approval before they are constructed. In this way the experience of the staff will be made use of in providing effective facilities.

Waste materials resulting from waste prevention measures as provided for by the minimum requirements below must be disposed of in such a manner as to insure that they will not, either directly or indirectly, enter any State waters.

The following definitions will apply to terms used herein:

Industrial Wastes are the water-borne wastes resulting from industrial processes or from the development of a natural resource.

Waters of the State includes all rivers, streams, ponds, lakes, inland waters, underground waters, salt waters, and other surface waters and water courses within the jurisdiction of the State of Washington.

Minimum Requirements

Slaughterhouses and Meat Packing Plants.

1. Yards and holding pens shall be dry cleaned before washing down.
2. All kill blood shall be separately collected and the blood thoroughly squee-geed from the floor into the collection tank. The disposal or utilization of the blood thus collected will depend on local facilities, but must be accomplished in a manner which conforms to sanitation regulations.
3. Paunch manure and hog stomach contents shall be collected separately and used as fertilizer, land-fill, or in any other satisfactory manner. A fine screen is recommended wherever its installation is feasible.
4. Fleshings, grease particles, and other solid material shall be collected by dry cleaning of floors and screening of wastes.
5. Adequate grease recovery basins shall be installed on drain lines from by-product processing rooms. These traps shall be skimmed and cleaned at least once each day. (Note: In the larger plants it is recommended that small basins be located wherever high grade greases can be recovered in significant quantity and that a main basin be installed on the main drain line. Wastes not containing grease should be by-passed around the basin.)

Poultry Killing and Packing Plants.

1. Provision shall be made for the collection of blood from the killing and bleeding and for the disposal of this blood in a satisfactory manner.
2. All manure, feathers, entrails, and other material removed from the carcass of the fowl shall be collected and the floor and equipment thoroughly dry cleaned before washing down. Provision shall be made for the proper disposal of this material.

Milk and Milk Products Plants.

1. Whole milk, skim milk, buttermilk, whey, condensed milk products, dried milk products, or spoiled milk or milk products shall not be dumped or otherwise allowed to enter a drain line which leads, either directly or indirectly, to a State water.
2. Mechanical can washers, both straight-line or rotary, shall be equipped with a drip collector and the drip milk collected and disposed of in a manner which conforms to sanitation regulations.
3. Milk or milk products left in sanitary lines, tanks, and equipment before washing shall be drained into suitable containers and disposed of in a satisfactory manner as directed above. It is recommended that these lines and equipment be installed to slope slightly to the point of collection.
4. Leaks in pumps, pipe lines, and other equipment handling milk or milk products shall be repaired as rapidly as possible.
5. Accidental spillage shall be reduced to a minimum by providing appropriate alarms or automatic equipment to prevent such accidents and by proper instruction to personnel.

Canneries, Vegetable and Fruit.

1. Vegetable and fruit canneries (unless other arrangements are made with this Commission) shall provide an efficient screen for the removal of skins, seeds, pomace, culls, discarded product, and other suspended material from the wastes from the washing, sorting, or other canning processes. This screen must be 40-mesh and may be of the vibrating, rotary, or any other effective type. It shall be located on the main outlet sewer line or lines from the cannery in such a way that all waste waters will pass through the screen except cooling condenser or other clean waters. The latter may be by-passed around the screen or discharged through a separate outlet. Prior to the installation of the screen a plan drawing of the facility shall be submitted to the Pollution Control Commission for approval, together with data as to capacity.
2. Screenings and other solid material removed from the product during the cannery operations shall be disposed of in a manner which will assure that it will not enter a State water.

Canneries, Fish and Shellfish.

1. Discarded portions of fish and shellfish products which result from cleaning, sorting, and other cannery or fish product operations shall be collected and disposed of in a manner which will prevent these materials from entering a State water. (It is suggested that arrangements be made with rendering plants for collection of this material at regular intervals. This will necessitate the installation of a hopper or other suitable containers as well as screens over floor drains to retain the solids.)

Wineries.

Wastes from dry wine production consist of pomace, lees and wash waters. In addition, the manufacture of wine or brandy will produce still slops from the distillation process.

1. Pomace, which is a garbage-like material, shall not be allowed to enter the liquid waste waters. If disposed of on land, the location of the disposal field shall be such that seepage water from the pile will not enter a surface water and the flood waters will not carry the material into public waters. Prevention of ground-water contamination in the area must be also considered in the location of the field.
2. The major portion of the lees shall be separated and disposed of along with the pomace, unless arrangements are made by agreement with the Commission and the respective municipal officials for disposal in a municipal sewage system and treatment plant. If discharge to a municipal system is approved, facilities to spread the discharge over a period of time, rather than in batches, must be provided.
3. Still slops shall not be disposed of in the sewer system. This waste product disposal is a locality problem and is subject to the same requirements given for pomace if land disposal is used.

Breweries.

1. Under no condition will brewery grains be discharged to the sewer system. (Note: Grains have a definite market value and are almost always recovered and sold for cattle feed; however, provision must be made for holding or storage in case of breakdown or delay in transportation.)

2. Because of high concentration of grain liquor, grain should be sold in a wet condition. In case the grain is dehydrated, special arrangements must be made for the disposal of the liquor by agreement with the Pollution Commission.

3. Spent hops shall be collected and disposed of as fertilizer, dumping on land, incineration or in some manner as to prevent this material from entering State waters.

4. Methods shall be devised for the separation and recovery of the yeast to prevent its entrance to the liquid waste drains.

Sawmills, Veneer Mills, and Other Wood Handling.

1. Sawmills and veneer plants located in close proximity to any waterway should take the following precautions in the disposal of waste sawdust, bark, slabs and trimmings:

    A. At the mill site, wastes should be kept out of any adjacent waterway and should be kept above the high-water mark and not in such a place that they will later be washed to the water. (Note: Underwater cutting is the cause of a considerable water pollution problem due to the formation of banks and piles of sawdust in the water. It is strongly urged that this practice be discontinued on an industry-wide basis, or that the area where the cutting is done be confined and the accumulated material disposed of on land.)

    B. If debris is to be burned, a properly constructed burner is to be used and consideration given to the following:

    (*a*). The burner shall be well enough away from the water or other provisions be made, so that unburned wastes will not escape from the burner, either on the ground or through air to the waterway.

    (*b*). Chutes which cross a waterway when leading from the mill to the burner should be constructed in such a manner that wastes will not fall from the chute to the waterway.

    (*c*). Burned-out screens and sections should be patched or replaced.

    (*d*). Chutes carrying wastes to a burner under forced draft should be deflected downward or passed through a hopper or a series of baffles so that fine sawdust will tend to settle to the fire and not be carried out the screen.

    C. Sawmills which truck sawdust and slabs away from a mill site should have these wastes dumped away from waterways, and in no case should sawdust and slabs be dumped below the high-water mark of the waterway or in such a position that they be later washed or leached to the waterway.

2. When log ponds are located near water courses, the following precautions should be observed:
   A. No log pond should be located in such a manner that the entire stream flows through the log pond.
   B. The overflow should be regulated in such a way that the amount of sawdust, chips, and suspended material that reach the waterway is reduced to a minimum.
   C. Log ponds should be cleaned by dragging and dredging rather than by flushing into a stream or river.
3. The sanitary and other provisions of the State and County Health Departments regarding logging and milling in watersheds above sources of drinking water supplies are to be carefully followed:
   A. Permanent and semi-permanent camps should provide sanitary facilities, including septic tanks and chlorination where necessary.
   B. Septic tanks are to be cleaned by pumping and dry land disposal of sludge rather than flushing these tanks to the waterway.
   C. Yarding logs across small streams should be carried out with due consideration to the damage caused to down-stream water users.

Oils and Like Material.

1. "Oil" refers to the following: (*a*) oils used for heating or power production; (*b*) oils used for lubrication; (*c*) oil emulsions used for cutting or cooling purposes; (*d*) petroleum cleaning fluids; (*e*) any other petroleum or asphaltic base compounds.
2. Ships, Cargo and Passenger.
   A. Bilge or ballast water, waste or other material containing oil in any amount whatever shall not be dumped or otherwise allowed to discharge from cargo or passenger ships into the waters of the State.
   B. When loading oil, ship-to-wharf connections shall be such as to prevent leakage and the discharge of oil into the waters. Every precaution shall be taken to prevent accidental spills from either ship or shore facilities, and to hold and recover such spills as may occur.
3. Oil Transportation Equipment.
   A. Tankers, railroad tank cars, tank trucks, or other facilities used for the loading, unloading, and transportation of oil shall be equipped for the collection of the drip from hose or other connections and the excess oil contained in hoses and pipe lines, wherever there is a possibility that this oil will find its way, either directly or indirectly, into a body of water. Provision shall be made, also, for catching accidental spills, and these facilities shall be of such capacity as to hold the maximum quantity of oil possible from any one spill.
   B. Roundhouses shall be provided for the collection of all oil and oil-and-water mixtures and an adequate separator shall be installed for the separation and recovery of both light and heavy oils from these mixtures. These separators shall be operated in such a manner as to assure their maximum efficiency.

4. Industry.
Wherever practical, all waste oils and lubricants from industrial operations should be collected in containers for proper disposal. Oil emulsions used for machine cutting and tool cutting should be collected, treated and reused wherever possible. In event that these emulsions are discarded, the emulsion must be broken down and the oil recovered for proper disposal. The general wastes from processes, if they contain oil, must be first passed through an adequate and well-operated oil separator before being discharged into the waters of the State.

5. Service Stations.
Service stations with direct outlets to a body of water shall not discard oil to that water or so dispose of it in such a manner that it will be washed into the waters by run-off.

6. Municipal Sewers.
Officials of cities, towns and sewer districts are directly responsible for the control of oil discharged from their respective sewerage systems. It is strongly urged that ordinances be passed which will make it unlawful to dump or otherwise discharge oil into these sewer systems.

7. Disposal of Oil.
Because it is usually desirable to dispose of waste or recovered oil by burning, this should be accomplished with due regard to local or other regulations and without the production of nuisances or hazards. The location of disposal points shall be such as to eliminate any possible pollution of either surface or underground waters.

8. Immediate Action.
Immediate steps shall be taken in case of an accidental spill to prevent the spread of the oil and to remove it from the water surface as completely as possible. (For large spills, booms of logs have been used to keep the oil from spreading. The oil may then be pumped from the water surface. Oil resulting from small spills and that remaining after pumping the larger spill can be removed by the use of old burlap, matting, or sawdust. These materials are then burned.)

9. Reports.
In case of an accidental oil spill of an appreciable magnitude the party responsible shall make a full and complete written report within 3 days to the Pollution Control Commission. This report shall include the reasons for the accident and the provisions to be taken to prevent its recurrence.

Tanneries.

1. A screen will be provided for the wastes from the beamhouse and all hair and fleshing will be removed and disposed of in a satisfactory manner. As a rule $\frac{1}{8}''$ round openings will be satisfactory for the screen for this purpose.
2. Lime sludge will be removed in as dry a manner as possible. If the lime is flushed out of the vats, ponds or settling tanks will be provided for the removal of the major portion of the lime from the wastes before it is discharged. In some cases, the water which collects above the lime sludge in

the vats can be removed and the lime either shovelled or pumped to land or to ponds.

3. If the tannery uses vegetable tan liquors, this liquor should be mixed with the beamhouse wastes and settled in a pond or tank before the waste is discharged. Under some conditions it may be allowable to store the liquor in a tank and discharge it over a long period of time. It should never be discharged in a batch.

4. It is desirable under most conditions where chrome liquors are used for tanning to also mix these liquors with beamhouse waste and settle either in a pond or tank before discharging to a waterway.

Beet Sugar Factories.

1. An effective screen shall be provided for the factory and process wastes from the manufacture of beet sugar. The screenings will be removed and disposed of on land or in any other satisfactory manner. It is suggested that the slot openings of the screen be ⅛″ by ¾″.

2. Steffens waste shall never be discharged to a State waterway. This waste must either be evaporated or ponded. In the latter case, it will be necessary to make arrangements with the Pollution Control Commission for the discharge of the ponded waste under controlled conditions, and during highwater periods.

3. Settling ponds shall be used for the removal of settleable material from factory and process waste. It is suggested that short-period ponds, constructed to operate in parallel, are more effective than large ponds operated in series. Certain of these ponds will be used until the material which settles starts to decompose. The waste will then be directed to other ponds.

Coal Washeries.

1. Effective ponds will be provided for the removal of fine coal and dust before the wash waters are discharged to a stream. The detention period in the ponds will be as long as is possible, and will be established by agreement with the Pollution Control Commission.

Gravel Washeries.

1. Effective ponds will be provided for the removal of sand and silt from gravel washings before the wash water is discharged to a waterway. The detention period will be as long as is possible and will be established by agreement with the Pollution Control Commission.

Flax Processing.

1. The waste from the processing of flax will be impounded and discharged at high stream flows and under conditions controlled by the Pollution Control Commission.

Dehydration, Potatoes and Fruits.

1. In cases where the skins of the potatoes or fruits are removed by means of abrasive equipment, a screen will be provided for the collection of this material and its removal from the water before discharge.

2. In case lime is used for the removal of skins, the waste from the process shall be ponded and discharged under controlled conditions by agreement with the Pollution Control Commission.

3. Peelings, cores, and rejects shall be removed in as dry a condition as possible and disposed of in such a manner as not to enter a waterway.

Metal Industry.

1. The wastes from metal industries shall be corrected to a pH value within the limits of 6.0 and 9.0.

2. A concentration of toxic material will be regulated to come below the tolerance of aquatic life to those materials. For instance, in the case of cyanides, the concentration shall not be above 0.5 p.p.m. as KCN. In the case of chlorine, the concentrations shall not be above 1.0 p.p.m. Other tolerance limits for the metals, fluorides, etc., will be established at a later date.

Pulp and Paper Mills.

Because of the size and the seriousness of the sulfite waste liquor problem, regulation concerning the disposal of this waste will be handled in a separate item and will not be included in this statement of minimum requirements. The following minimum regulations apply to the formation of the pulp sheet and to paper and board production:

1. Provision shall be made either by the installation of effective save-alls and/or by closing, or partially closing, the white-water system to reduce the fiber loss from beater and machine operations to 1 per cent of production.

2. Bark and knotty rejects shall be kept entirely out of State waters.

To indicate also that other countries are cognizant of the need for intelligent regulations, the regulations set up by the government of Cuba[19] relating to polluting discharges into streams may be cited. A few of the salient features of this code are:

1. No liquid may be discharged into a stream which, after 6 hours subsidence, contains more than 10 ppm of dry organic matter in suspension.

2. Not having been settled for 6 hours must not contain more than 10 ppm of dry organic matter or more than 30 ppm mineral matter in suspension.

3. Organic carbon must not exceed 20 ppm.

4. Organic nitrogen must not exceed 3 ppm.

5. Not more than 20 ppm of any metal except Ca, Mg, K, and Na.

6. Not more than 0.5 ppm of arsenic in any form.

7. No film of hydrocarbon oil or more than 0.5 ppm of such oil in suspension.

Bibliography

1. Hazelhurst, G. H., Proposed Legislation in Connection with Stream Pollution and the Formation of a Stream Conservation Board, Paper, Conference of State Sanitary Engineers, 1936.

2. The National Water Pollution Control Program, Federal Security Agency, Public Health Service and Federal Works Agency, Bureau of Community Facilities, Washington, D.C., Mimeographed, Sept. 20, 1948.
3. Bloodgood, D. E., Effect of Stream Pollution Legislation and Control, *Proceedings, American Society of Civil Engineers*, vol. 74, pp. 1048–1051, September, 1948.
4. Parker, L. T., Pollution Lawsuits, *Sewage Works Engineering and Municipal Sanitation*, vol. 19, pp. 138, 179–180, March, 1948.
5. Parker, L. T., The Right to Pollute Streams, *Sewage Works Engineering and Municipal Sanitation*, vol. 16, pp. 23–24, January, 1945.
6. Trelles, R. A., Condiciones Fisicas, Quimicas y Microbiologicas a Que Deben Ajustarse las Descargas de Liquidos Residuales, Cloacales, etc. Sobre El Problema de la Contaminacion de las Cursos de Agua en El Pais (Argentina), *Revista de Obras Sanitarias de la Nacion*, Ano XII, No. 127, pp. 9–29, July, 1948.
7. Weston, A. D., Classification of Streams under Consideration for Compacts in New England, Paper, Annual Meeting American Society of Civil Engineers, New York, Jan. 21–23, 1948.
8. Anable, A., and R. P. Kite, A Current Appraisal of the Regulations of Pollution Abatement, *Chemical Engineering Progress*, Jan. 1, 1948, p. 3.
9. Bauman, J. B., The Fundamentals of Public Health Law, Reprint 1460, U.S. Public Health Reports, U.S. Public Health Service, Washington, D.C.
10. Besselievre, E. B., Statutory Regulation of Stream Pollution and the Common Law, *Transactions, American Institute of Chemical Engineers*, vol. 16, Part 2, p. 217, 1924.
11. Industrial Waste Limits, *The American City*, vol. 65, No. 1, p. 15, January, 1950.
12. Scott, W. J., Federal and State Legislation for Stream Pollution Control, *Sewage Works Journal*, vol. 19, No. 5, pp. 883–889, September, 1947.
13. Palmer, C. L., Municipal Regulations for Control of Sewer Usage by Industry, Paper, Twenty-second Annual Conference Michigan Sewage Works Association, Jackson, Mich., May 14–16, 1947.
14. Summary of State Laws and Regulations Affecting Pollution of Waters, Appendix 1, Third Report of Special Advisory Committee on Water Pollution, National Resources Committee, Washington, D.C. Revised as of November, 1938.
15. Doll, B. E., Formulating Legislation to Protect Ground Water from Pollution, Paper, Twentieth Annual Meeting Federation of Sewage Works Association, San Francisco, Calif., July 21–24, 1947.
16. National Round-up of Pollution Abatement Progress—Status of Legislation and Controls by Individual States, *Sewage Works Engineering and Municipal Sanitation*, vol. 17, No. 10, p. 518; and No. 11, p. 587, 1946.
17. Scott, W. J., A. D. Weston, S. Hess, J. H. Allen, and R. N. Clark, Operations of Authorities Concerned with the Sanitation of Rivers and Harbors, Symposium, American Society of Civil Engineers, Annual Meeting, New York, January, 1948.
18. Minimum Requirements for the Control of Industrial Wastes, Washington State Pollution Control Commission, *Sewage and Industrial Wastes*, vol. 22, No. 4, pp. 514–520, April, 1950.
19. Black, A. P., Sewage Treatment in Cuba, *Municipal Sanitation*, vol. 10, No. 8, pp. 397–398, August, 1939.

APPENDIX II

MISCELLANEOUS DATA

As the field of industrial-waste treatment is becoming one of universal importance and different nations use different units of measurement, it is essential that investigators be able to convert readily from the units used in one country to those used in their own, in order to understand books, articles, and reports available on waste projects. To assist the reader in this there is appended a table of some useful factors which transpose the various common units of measurement from one system to another by means of a simple multiplication.

In the majority of countries outside the United States and the British Empire, the metric system is used and analyses and studies are reported in metric units. It is important for one trained in the use of English units of measurement to be able to convert the metric units into those with which he is acquainted and equally important for the one accustomed to the metric system to be able to convert the English units into those with which he is familiar.*

---

* If a more complete list is desired, a useful booklet entitled "Conversion Factors for Engineers," published by The Dorr Company, may be had free from any of its offices.

Unit	Multiply by	To get
Grams per cubic meter...........	0.436998	Grains per cubic foot. This divided by 7.48 gives grains per U.S. gallon
Grams per cubic meter...........	0.0584	Grains per U.S. gallon
Grams per liter.................	58.417	Grains per U.S. gallon
Grams per liter.................	1,000.0	Parts per million
Kilograms per square centimeter..	14.2233	Pounds per square inch
Kilograms per square meter......	0.2048155	Pounds per square foot
Meters.........................	3.281	Feet
Kilometers.....................	0.6214	Miles
Kilogram-calories...............	3.96832	BTU
Kilogram-calories...............	0.00155932	Horsepower per hour
Cheval-vapeur (French)..........	0.986317	Horsepower
Cheval-vapeur (French)..........	0.735352	Kilowatts
Grains per gallon (British)........	14.25417	Parts per million
Pounds per million gallons (U.S.)..	0.0007	Grains per gallon (U.S.)
Tons (metric)..................	2,205.0	Pounds
Gallons (imperial)..............	1.20095	Gallons (U.S.)
Second-feet (cubic feet per second).	2,446.59	Cubic meters per day
Second-feet (cubic feet per second).	101.941	Cubic meters per hour
Second-feet (cubic feet per second).	646,316.9	Gallons per day (U.S.)
Temperature (centigrade) plus 17.78......................	1.8	Temperature (Fahrenheit)
Temperature (Fahrenheit) minus 32..........................	$\frac{5}{9}$	Temperature (centigrade)

PIPE FLOW CHART*

By simply laying a straightedge across the chart on page 348 any one of these questions may be answered:

1. How many cubic feet will flow through a pipe of given diameter at a given velocity?

2. How many gallons, other conditions being the same as in No. 1?

3. What will be the velocity in feet per second, knowing the diameter and cubic feet per minute?

4. Same as (3) except that the flow is given in gallons per minute.

5. What diameter of pipe must be used to carry a given number of cubic feet per minute at a given velocity?

6. Same as (5) except that quantity is in gallons per minute.

* Contributed by W. F. Schaphorst, M.E., Newark, N.J.

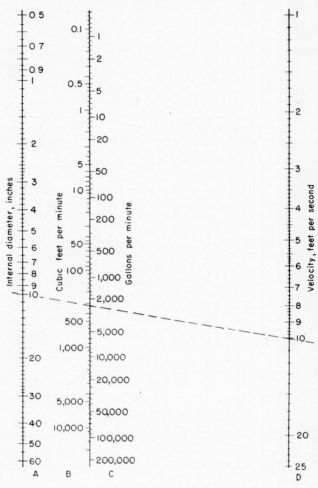

Pipe flow chart.

For example, how many gallons of water per minute will flow from a 10-inch pipe line if the velocity reaches 10 ft. per second?

The dash line drawn across the chart shows that if the internal diameter of the pipe is 10 inches (col. A), and the water is flowing at a velocity of 10 feet per second (col. D), the amount of water flowing is a hair less than 2,500 gallons per minute (col. C), which is equivalent to about 325 cubic feet per minute (col. B).

Naturally the chart may be used to obtain the pipe diameter needed to avoid exceeding a given velocity at a given rate of flow. It may also be used for converting gallons to cubic feet and the reverse.

CHART FOR CONVERTING GRAINS PER GALLON TO POUNDS PER MILLION AND THE REVERSE*

Pumpage		Dose, grains per gal														
Million gal per 24 hr	Thousand gal per hr	10	20	30	40	50	60	70	80	90	100	110	120	130	140	150	160
		Dose, lb per million gal															
		0.07	0.14	0.21	0.28	0.35	0.42	0.49	0.56	0.63	0.70	0.77	0.84	0.91	0.98	1.05	1.12
		Amount of chemical required for various pumpages and doses, lb per hr															
1.0	41.7	0.417	0.833	1.25	1.67	2.08	2.50	2.92	3.33	3.75	4.17	4.58	5.00	5.42	5.83	6.25	6.67
1.5	62.5*	0.625	1.25	1.88	2.50	3.13	3.75	4.38	5.00	5.63	6.25	6.88	7.50	8.13	8.75	9.38	10.0
2.0	83.3	0.833	1.67	2.50	3.33	4.17	5.00	5.83	6.67	7.50	8.33	9.17	10.0	10.8	11.7	12.5	13.3
2.5	104	1.04	2.08	3.13	4.17	5.21	6.25	7.29	8.33	9.38	10.4	11.5	12.5	13.5	14.6	15.6	16.7
3.0	125†	1.25	2.50	3.75	5.00	6.25	7.50	8.75	10.0	11.3	12.5	13.8	15.0	16.3	17.5	18.8	20.0
3.5	146	1.46	2.92	4.38	5.83	7.29	8.75	10.2	11.7	13.1	14.6	16.0	17.5	19.0	20.4	21.9	23.3
4.0	167	1.67	3.33	5.00	6.67	8.33	10.0	11.7	13.3	15.0	16.7	18.3	20.0	21.7	23.3	25.0	26.7
4.5	187	1.88	3.75	5.63	7.50	9.38	11.3	13.1	15.0	16.9	18.8	20.6	22.5	24.4	26.3	28.1	30.0
5.0	208	2.08	4.17	6.25	8.33	10.4	12.5	14.6	16.7	18.8	20.8	22.9	25.0	27.1	29.2	31.3	33.3
5.5	229	2.29	4.58	6.88	9.17	11.5	13.8	16.0	18.3	20.6	22.9	25.2	27.5	29.8	32.1	34.4	36.7
6.0	250†	2.50	5.00	7.50	10.0	12.5	15.0	17.5	20.0	22.5	25.0	27.5	30.0	32.5	35.0	37.5	40.0
6.5	271	2.71	5.42	8.13	10.8	13.5	16.3	19.0	21.7	24.4	27.1	29.8	32.5	35.2	37.9	40.6	43.3
7.0	292	2.92	5.83	8.75	11.7	14.6	17.5	20.4	23.3	26.3	29.2	32.1	35.0	37.9	40.8	43.8	46.7
7.5	312	3.13	6.25	9.38	12.5	15.6	18.8	21.9	25.0	28.1	31.3	34.4	37.5	40.6	43.8	46.9	50.0
8.0	333	3.33	6.68	10.0	13.3	16.7	20.0	23.3	26.7	30.0	33.3	36.7	40.0	43.3	46.7	50.0	53.3
8.5	354	3.54	7.08	10.6	14.2	17.7	21.3	24.8	28.3	31.9	35.4	39.0	42.5	46.0	49.6	53.1	56.7
9.0	375†	3.75	7.50	11.3	15.0	18.8	22.5	26.3	30.0	33.8	37.5	41.3	45.0	48.8	52.5	56.3	60.0
9.5	396	3.96	7.92	11.9	15.8	19.8	23.8	27.7	31.7	35.6	39.6	43.5	47.5	51.5	55.4	59.4	63.3
10.0	417	4.17	8.33	12.5	16.7	20.8	25.0	29.2	33.3	37.5	41.7	45.8	50.0	54.2	58.3	62.5	66.7
10.5	437	4.38	8.75	13.1	17.5	21.9	26.3	30.6	35.0	39.4	43.8	48.1	52.5	56.9	61.3	65.6	70.0
11.0	458	4.58	9.17	13.8	18.3	22.9	27.5	32.1	36.7	41.3	45.8	50.4	55.0	59.6	64.2	68.8	73.3
11.5	479	4.79	9.58	14.4	19.2	24.0	28.8	33.5	38.3	43.1	47.9	52.7	57.5	62.3	67.1	71.9	76.7
12.0	500†	5.00	10.0	15.0	20.0	25.0	30.0	35.0	40.0	45.0	50.0	55.0	60.0	65.0	70.0	75.0	80.0
12.5	521	5.21	10.4	15.6	20.8	26.0	31.3	36.5	41.7	46.9	52.1	57.3	62.5	67.7	72.9	78.1	83.3
13.0	542	5.42	10.8	16.3	21.7	27.1	32.5	37.9	43.3	48.8	54.2	59.6	65.0	70.4	75.8	81.3	86.7
13.5	562	5.63	11.3	16.9	22.5	28.1	33.8	39.4	45.0	50.6	56.3	61.9	67.5	73.1	78.8	84.4	90.0
14.0	583	5.83	11.7	17.5	23.3	29.2	35.0	40.8	46.7	52.5	58.3	64.2	70.0	75.8	81.7	87.5	93.3
14.5	604	6.04	12.1	18.1	24.2	30.2	36.3	42.3	48.3	54.4	60.4	66.5	72.5	78.5	84.6	90.6	96.7
15.0	625†	6.25	12.5	18.8	25.0	31.3	37.5	43.8	50.0	56.3	62.5	68.8	75.0	81.3	87.5	93.8	100.0

* Courtesy W. Donaldson and Fuller & McClintock, Engineers.

Note: It is now becoming modern practice to record and report all chemical dosages in pounds per million (P.M.G.) and thereby have simplification in reporting and recording, rather than using the older scheme involving grains per gallon, parts per million, etc.

† Exact values.

Example: 1 grain per gal = 142 lb per million gal = 5.95 lb per hr for each million gal
0.70 grain per gal = 100 lb per million gal = 4.17 lb per hr for each million gal
What weight of chemical must be fed each hour to give a 70 lb. dose for a pumpage of 8.0 mgd?
Opposite 8.0 mgd and under 70 find 23.3, which is the correct weight.

INTERCONVERSION TABLES FOR UNITS OF VOLUME AND WEIGHT AND ENERGY

To convert from	Multiply by														
	To cu in	To cu ft	To cu yd	To fl oz	To pt	To qt	To gal	To grain	To oz troy	To oz av	To lb troy	To lb av	To cc or grams	To liter or kg	To cu m
Cu in	1.00000	.0$_3$5787	.0$_4$2143	.554112	.034632	.017316	.004329	252.891	.526857	.578037	.043905	.036127	16.3871	.016387	.0$_4$1639
Cu ft	1,728.00	1.00000	.037037	957.505	59.8442	29.9221	7.48052	436.996	910.408	998.848	75.8674	62.4280	28,316.9	28.3169	.028317
Cu yd	46,656.0	27.0000	1.00000	25,852.6	1,615.79	807.896	201.974	117,990$_3$	24,581.0	26,968.9	2,048.42	1685.56	764,556	764.556	.764556
Fl oz	1.80469	.001044	.0$_4$3868	1.00000	.062500	.031250	.007813	456.390	.950813	1.04318	.079234	.065199	29.5736	.029573	.0$_4$2957
Pt	28.8750	.016710	.0$_4$6189	16.0000	1.00000	.500000	.125000	7,302.23	15.2130	16.6908	1.26775	1.04318	473.177	.473177	.0$_4$4732
Qt	57.7500	.033420	.001238	32.0000	2.00000	1.00000	.250000	1,460.45	30.4260	33.3816	2.53550	2.08635	946.354	.946354	.0$_3$9463
Gal	231.000	.133681	.004951	128.000	8.00000	4.00000	1.00000	58,417.9	121.704	133.527	10.1420	8.34541	3,785.42	3.78542	.003785
Grain	.003954	.0$_5$2288	.0$_8$8475	.002191	.0$_3$1369	.0$_4$6850	.0$_4$1712	1.00000	.002083	.002286	.0$_3$1736	.0$_3$1428	.064799	.0$_3$6479	.0$_6$6479
Oz troy	1.89805	.001098	.0$_4$4068	1.05173	.065733	.032867	.008217	480.000	1.00000	1.09714	.083333	.068571	31.1035	.031104	.0$_4$3110
Oz av	1.72999	.001001	.0$_4$3708	.958608	.059913	.029957	.007489	437.500	.911457	1.00000	.075955	.062500	28.3495	.028350	.0$_4$2835
Lb troy	22.7766	.013181	.0$_4$4882	12.6208	.788800	.394400	.098600	5,760.00	12.0000	13.1657	1.00000	.822857	373.242	.373242	.0$_3$3732
Lb av	27.6799	.016018	.0$_5$5933	15.3378	.958611	.479306	.119826	7,000.00	14.5833	16.0000	1.21528	1.00000	453.593	.453593	.0$_4$4536
Cc or gram	.061024	.0$_4$3531	.0$_5$1308	.033814	.002113	.001057	.0$_2$2642	15.4323	.032151	.035274	.002679	.002205	1.00000	.001000	.000001
Liter or kilogram	61.0237	.035315	.001308	33.8140	2.11337	1.05669	.264172	15,432.3	32.1507	35.2739	2.67923	2.20462	1,000.00	1.00000	.001000
Cu m	61,023.7	35.3146	1.30795	33,814.0	2,113.37	1,056.69	264.172	154,320$_3$	32,150.7	35,273.9	2,679.23	2,204.62	1,000,000	1,000.00	1.00000

Note. The small subnumeral following a zero indicates that the zero is to be taken that number of times; thus, .0$_4$1428 is equivalent to .0001428.

Values used in constructing table:

1 in. = 2.540001 cm   1 lb av = 453.5926 g   1 lb av = 7000 grains

∴ 1 cu in. = 16.387083 cc = 16.387083 g H$_2$O at   1 gal = 8.34541 lb   ∴ 1 gal = 58417.87 grains

4°C = 39°F   ∴ 1 lb av = 27.679886 cu in. H$_2$O at 4°C   231 cu in. = 1 gal = 3785.4162 g

Multiply by

To convert from	BTU	PCU	Calories	Ft-lb	Ft-tons	Kg-m	Hp-hr	Kwhr	Joules	Lb C	Lb H₂O
BTU	1.00000	.555556	.251996	778.000	.389001	107.563	$.0_3929$	$.0_32931$	1,055.20	$.0_46876$	.001031
PCU*	1.80000	1.00000	45.3$_5$93	1,400.40	.700202	193.613	$.0_7072$	$.0_5276$	1,899.36	$.0_11238$	.001855
Calories	3.96832	2.20462	1.00000	3,091.36	1.54368	426.844	.001559	$.0_31163$	4,187.37	$.0_2729$	.004089
Ft-lb	.001285	$.0_7141$	$.0_3239$	1.00000	.000500	.138255	$.0_5050$	$.0_3767$	1.35625	$.0_8840$	$.0_1325$
Ft-ton†	2.57069	1.42816	.647804	2,000.00	1.00000	276.511	.001010	$.0_7535$	2,712.59	$.0_11768$	.002649
Kg-m	.009297	.005165	.002343	7.23301	.003617	1.00000	$.0_3653$	$.0_2725$	9.81009	$.0_6394$	$.0_9580$
Hp-hr	2,544.99	.141388	641.327	1,980,000	990.004	273.747	1.00000	.746000	2,685,473	.175044	2.62261
Kwhr	3,411.57	1,895.32	859.702	2,654,200	1,327.10	366,959	1.34041	1.00000	3,599,889	.234648	3.51562
Joules	$.0_39477$	$.0_5265$	$.0_2388$	.737311	$.0_3687$	.101937	$.0_3724$	$.0_2778$	1.00000	$.0_6518$	$.0_9766$
Lb C‡	14,544.0	8,080.00	3,665.03	113,150$_3$	5,657.63	1,564,396	5.71434	4.26285	153,470$_3$	1.00000	14.9876
Lb H₂O§	970.400	539.111	244.537	754.971	377.487	104,379	.381270	.284424	1,023,966	.066744	1.00000

* "PCU" refers to the "pound-centigrade unit."

† The ton used is 2,000 lb.

‡ "Lb C" refers to pounds of carbon oxidized, 100 % efficiency equivalent to the corresponding number of heat units.

§ "Lb H₂O" refers to pounds of water evaporated at 100°C = 212°F at 100 % efficiency.

By the use of the foregoing table (compiled by and published by the courtesy of the engineering staff of the du Pont Company) about 330 interconversions among 26 of the standard engineering units of measure can be directly estimated to three significant figures or calculated by simple multiplication to six figures. By the introduction of specific gravity factors the

When volume and weight interconversions are given, water is the medium the calculations are based upon.
medium can be changed, giving the weight of any volume of any material, etc.

COST OF COAGULANTS FOR VARIOUS DOSAGES

Ppm	Grains per gal	Price of chemical per 100 lb																			Lb per million gal
		$0.75	$0.80	$0.85	$0.90	$0.95	$1.00	$1.05	$1.10	$1.15	$1.20	$1.25	$1.30	$1.35	$1.40	$1.45	$1.50	$1.55	$1.60	$1.70	$1.75	
1	0.06	0.062	0.066	0.070	0.075	0.079	0.083	0.087	0.091	0.095	0.100	0.104	0.108	0.112	0.116	0.120	0.124	0.129	0.133	0.141	0.145	8.3
5	0.29	0.313	0.334	0.355	0.375	0.396	0.417	0.438	0.459	0.480	0.501	0.522	0.542	0.563	0.584	0.605	0.626	0.647	0.668	0.709	0.730	42.0
10	0.59	0.626	0.668	0.709	0.751	0.793	0.834	0.876	0.918	0.960	1.00	1.04	1.08	1.13	1.17	1.21	1.25	1.29	1.34	1.42	1.46	83.0
15	0.88	0.939	1.00	1.06	1.13	1.19	1.25	1.31	1.37	1.44	1.50	1.56	1.63	1.69	1.75	1.81	1.88	1.94	2.00	2.13	2.19	125.0
20	1.17	1.25	1.34	1.42	1.50	1.59	1.67	1.75	1.84	1.92	2.00	2.09	2.17	2.25	2.34	2.42	2.50	2.59	2.67	2.84	2.92	167.0
25	1.46	1.56	1.67	1.77	1.88	1.98	2.09	2.19	2.29	2.40	2.50	2.61	2.71	2.82	2.92	3.02	3.13	3.23	3.34	3.55	3.65	209.0
30	1.75	1.88	2.00	2.13	2.25	2.38	2.50	2.63	2.75	2.88	3.00	3.13	3.25	3.38	3.50	3.63	3.75	3.88	4.00	4.26	4.38	250.0
35	2.05	2.19	2.34	2.48	2.63	2.77	2.92	3.07	3.21	3.36	3.50	3.65	3.80	3.94	4.09	4.23	4.38	4.53	4.67	4.96	5.11	292.0
40	2.34	2.50	2.67	2.84	3.00	3.17	3.34	3.50	3.67	3.84	4.01	4.17	4.34	4.51	4.67	4.84	5.01	5.17	5.34	5.67	5.84	334.0
45	2.63	2.81	3.00	3.19	3.38	3.57	3.75	3.94	4.13	4.32	4.51	4.69	4.88	5.07	5.26	5.44	5.63	5.82	6.00	6.38	6.57	375.0
50	2.92	3.13	3.34	3.55	3.75	3.97	4.17	4.38	4.59	4.80	5.01	5.22	5.43	5.63	5.84	6.05	6.26	6.47	6.68	7.09	7.30	417.0
55	3.21	3.44	3.67	3.90	4.13	4.36	4.59	4.82	5.05	5.28	5.51	5.74	5.97	6.20	6.42	6.65	6.88	7.11	7.34	7.80	8.03	459.0
60	3.50	3.75	4.01	4.26	4.51	4.76	5.01	5.26	5.51	5.76	6.01	6.26	6.51	6.76	7.01	7.26	7.51	7.76	8.01	8.51	8.76	501.0
65	3.80	4.07	4.34	4.61	4.88	5.15	5.42	5.69	5.97	6.24	6.51	6.78	7.05	7.32	7.59	7.86	8.14	8.41	8.68	9.22	9.49	542.0
70	4.09	4.38	4.67	4.96	5.26	5.55	5.84	6.13	6.42	6.72	7.01	7.30	7.59	7.89	8.18	8.47	8.76	9.05	9.35	9.93	10.22	584.0
75	4.38	4.69	5.01	5.32	5.63	5.94	6.26	6.57	6.88	7.20	7.51	7.82	8.14	8.45	8.76	9.07	9.39	9.70	10.01	10.64	10.95	626.0
80	4.67	5.01	5.34	5.67	6.01	6.34	6.68	7.01	7.34	7.68	8.01	8.34	8.67	9.01	9.35	9.68	10.01	10.35	10.68	11.35	11.68	667.0
85	4.97	5.32	5.67	6.03	6.38	6.74	7.09	7.45	7.80	8.16	8.51	8.87	9.22	9.57	9.93	10.28	10.64	10.99	11.35	12.06	12.41	709.0
90	5.26	5.63	6.01	6.38	6.76	7.13	7.51	7.89	8.26	8.64	9.01	9.39	9.76	10.14	10.51	10.89	11.26	11.64	12.02	12.77	13.14	751.0
95	5.55	5.95	6.34	6.74	7.13	7.53	7.93	8.32	8.72	9.12	9.51	9.91	10.30	10.70	11.10	11.49	11.89	12.29	12.68	13.47	13.87	793.0
100	5.84	6.26	6.68	7.09	7.51	7.93	8.34	8.76	9.18	9.60	10.01	10.43	10.85	11.26	11.68	12.10	12.52	12.93	13.35	14.18	14.60	834.0
110	6.43	6.88	7.34	7.80	8.26	8.72	9.18	9.64	10.10	10.56	11.01	11.47	11.93	12.39	12.85	13.31	13.77	14.23	14.69	15.60	16.06	918.0
120	7.01	7.51	8.01	8.51	9.01	9.51	10.01	10.51	11.01	11.51	12.02	12.52	13.02	13.52	14.02	14.52	15.02	15.52	16.02	17.02	17.52	1001.0
130	7.59	8.14	8.68	9.22	9.76	10.30	10.85	11.39	11.93	12.47	13.02	13.56	14.10	14.64	15.19	15.73	16.27	16.81	17.36	18.44	18.98	1085.0
140	8.18	8.76	9.35	9.93	10.51	11.10	11.68	12.27	12.85	13.43	14.02	14.60	15.19	15.77	16.35	16.94	17.52	18.11	18.69	19.86	20.44	1168.0
150	8.76	9.39	10.01	10.64	11.26	11.89	12.52	13.14	13.77	14.39	15.02	15.64	16.27	16.90	17.52	18.15	18.77	19.40	20.03	21.28	21.90	1251.0
200	11.68	12.52	13.35	14.18	15.02	15.85	16.69	17.52	18.36	19.19	20.03	20.86	21.69	22.53	23.36	24.20	25.03	25.87	26.70	28.37	29.20	1669.0

AMOUNT OF COAGULANT SOLUTION AT VARIOUS STRENGTHS REQUIRED FOR DIFFERENT
VOLUMES OF FLOW

U.S. gal		Gal of chemical solution per min to add 10 parts of chemical per million						
24 hr	Min	1%	2%	3%	4%	5%	6%	10%
250,000	174	0.174	0.087	0.058	0.044	0.035	0.029	0.017
500,000	347	0.347	0.174	0.116	0.087	0.069	0.058	0.035
1,000,000	694	0.694	0.347	0.231	0.174	0.139	0.116	0.069
1,500,000	1,042	1.042	0.521	0.347	0.260	0.208	0.174	0.104
2,000,000	1,389	1.389	0.694	0.463	0.347	0.278	0.232	0.139
2,500,000	1,736	1.736	0.868	0.579	0.434	0.347	0.289	0.174
3,000,000	2,083	2.083	1.042	0.694	0.521	0.416	0.347	0.208
4,000,000	2,778	2.778	1.389	0.926	0.694	0.556	0.463	0.278
5,000,000	3,472	3.472	1.736	1.157	0.868	0.694	0.579	0.347
7,500,000	5,208	5.208	2.604	1.736	1.302	1.042	0.868	0.521
10,000,000	6,994	6.944	3.472	2.315	1.736	1.389	1.157	0.694
20,000,000	13,889	13.889	6.944	4.630	3.467	2.778	2.315	1.389

METRIC TO ENGLISH MEASUREMENT EQUIVALENTS*

Liters per sec	Cu m per hr	Cu m per day	Cu ft per sec	Cu ft per hr	Gal per min	Gal per day, mgd
1	3.6	86.4	0.035	120.6	15.8	0.0227
2	7.2	172.8	0.0706	241.2	31.6	0.0455
3	10.8	259.2	0.1056	361.8	47.4	0.0682
4	14.4	343.6	0.1412	482.4	63.2	0.0911
5	18.0	432.0	0.1765	603.0	79.0	0.1138
6	21.6	518.4	0.2118	723.6	94.8	0.1365
7	25.2	602.8	0.2472	844.2	110.6	0.1594
8	28.8	687.2	0.2825	964.8	126.4	0.1823
9	32.4	775.6	0.3178	1,085.4	142.2	0.2048
10	36.0	864.0	0.3531	1,206.0	158.0	0.227
15	54.0	1,296.0	0.5296	1,809.0	237.0	0.341
20	72.0	1,728.0	0.7062	2,412.0	316.0	0.455
25	90.0	2,160.0	0.8828	3,015.0	395.0	0.568
30	108.0	2,592.0	1.0593	3,618.0	474.0	0.682
35	126.0	3,024.0	1.2358	4,221.0	553.0	0.796
40	144.0	3,456.0	1.4124	4,824.0	632.0	0.910
45	162.0	3,888.0	1.589	5,427.0	711.0	1.023
50	180.0	4,320.0	1.765	6,030.0	790.0	1.038
55	198.0	4,752.0	1.942	6,633.0	869.0	1.251
60	216.0	5,184.0	2.118	7,236.0	948.0	1.465
65	234.0	5,616.0	2.295	7,839.0	1,027.0	1.479
70	252.0	6,028.0	2.4717	8,442.0	1,106.0	1.594
75	270.0	6,480.0	2.648	9,045.0	1,185.0	1.706
80	288.0	6,912.0	2.8248	9,648.0	1,268.0	1.821
85	306.0	7,344.0	3.001	10,251.0	1,343.0	1.934
90	324.0	7,776.0	3.178	10,854.0	1,422.0	2.047
95	342.0	8,208.0	3.354	11,457.0	1,501.0	2.06
100	360.0	8,640.0	3.531	12,060.0	1,580.0	2.275
110	396.0	9,504.0	3.88	13,266.0	1,738.0	2.51
120	432.0	10,368.0	4.237	14,472.0	1,896.0	2.73
130	468.0	11,232.0	4.50	15,678.0	2,054.0	2.95
140	504.0	12,056.0	4.94	16,884.0	2,212.0	3.19
150	540.0	12,960.0	5.296	18,090.0	2,370.0	3.42
160	576.0	13,824.0	5.65	19,296.0	2,536.0	3.64
170	612.0	14,688.0	6.01	20,502.0	2,686.0	3.87
180	648.0	15,552.0	6.35	21,708.0	2,844.0	4.094
190	684.0	16,416.0	6.71	22,914.0	3,002.0	4.12
200	720.0	17,280.0	7.062	24,120.0	3,160.0	4.55
225	810.0	19,440.0	7.945	27,135.0	3,555.0	5.118
250	900.0	21,600.0	8.827	30,150.0	3,950.0	5.558
275	990.0	23,760.0	9.71	35,165.0	4,345.0	6.257
300	1,080.0	25,920.0	10.592	36,180.0	4,740.0	6.84

* Prepared by E. B. Besselievre, August, 1937.

APPENDIX III

GLOSSARY*

Absorption. The taking up of one substance into the body of another.

Action, biochemical. Chemical changes resulting from the metabolism of living organisms.

Activation. The generation, under aerobic conditions, of zoogleal organisms capable of adsorbing organic matter from the sewage in the activated-sludge process.

Adsorption. (1) The adherence of dissolved, colloidal, or finely divided solids on the surface of solid bodies with which they are brought into contact. (2) A change in concentration of gas or solute at the interface of a two-phase system.

Aeration. The bringing about of intimate contact between air and a liquid by one of the following methods: spraying the liquid in the air, bubbling air through the liquid, or agitation of the liquid to promote surface absorption of air.

Aeration, diffused air. The aeration produced in a liquid by passing air through a diffuser (porous tile or tube).

Aeration, mechanical. (1) The mixing, by mechanical means, of sewage and activated sludge, in the aeration tank of the activated-sludge process, to bring fresh surfaces of liquid into contact with the atmosphere. (2) The introduction of atmospheric oxygen into a liquid by the mechanical action of paddles or spray mechanisms.

Aerator. A device that promotes aeration.

Aerofilter. A commercial term applied to a trickling filter containing a relatively coarse filtering material and operating at a high rate which may be maintained, if necessary, at times of low sewage flow by recirculation of the filter effluent or other diluting liquids.

Agglomeration. The coalescence of dispersed suspended matter into larger flocs or particles which settle rapidly.

Agitator. A mechanical apparatus for mixing and aerating.

Alkali. Certain soluble salts, principally of sodium, potassium, magnesium, and calcium, that occur in water or soils.

Alkaline. Pertaining to water or soils that contain a sufficient amount of alkali to raise the pH value above 7.0 or to be harmful in the growth of crops.

Alum. A common name for aluminum sulfate. A coagulant.

Amortization. (1) The payment of a debt, principal and interest. (2) Retirement of capital expenditures by means of an increment allowed from capital, or income, or any other means.

* Definitions adapted from "Glossary—Water and Sewage Control Engineering," American Society of Civil Engineers, 1949.

355

Analysis. (1) The record of an examination of water, sewage, or industrial wastes. In industrial wastes, the determination of chemical composition, concentration, BOD, suspended-solids content, etc.

Apparatus, Dosing. Apparatus for regulating the application of industrial wastes to filters or for applying the required quantity of chemicals (coagulants) to wastes.

Appurtenances. Machinery, appliances, or auxiliary structures attached to a main structure or machine, but not considered an integral part thereof, to enable it to function properly.

Arrestor, flame. A safety device on a gas line which allows gas, but not a flame, to pass.

Back washing. The operation of cleaning a rapid, mechanical, or trickling filter by a reversed flow of liquids.

Bacteria, aerobic. Bacteria which require free (elementary) oxygen for their growth and life.

Bacteria, anaerobic. Bacteria which grow and function in the absence of free oxygen and derive oxygen from breaking down complex substances.

Baffles. Deflector vanes, guides, gratings, or similar devices constructed or placed in the flow of wastes to (1) check or effect a more uniform distribution of velocities; (2) absorb energy; (3) divert, guide, or agitate the liquid; and (4) check or prevent eddy currents.

Banks, sludge. Accumulations on the bed of a waterway of deposits of solids of industrial-waste origin.

Basin, settling. A structure designed to hold wastes in a quiescent state or at a reduced velocity for a sufficient length of time to permit the gravitational deposition of suspended matter, with or without the aid of previous flocculation or coagulation.

Basin, stilling. A structure or excavation that reduces velocity or turbulence in flowing wastes.

Bed, bacteria. A bed of sand, gravel, broken stone, or other medium through which wastes flow or trickle and which depends upon biological action for its effectiveness.

Bed, covered sludge drying. A sludge-drying bed with a glass cover or enclosure for protection against rain or snow and for increasing radiant heating as an aid to evaporation of water in the sludge. Frequently used in built-up sections to remove objections of neighboring residents.

Bed, sludge drying. An uncovered area comprising natural or artificial layers of porous material, usually sand, upon which digested sludge is dried by drainage and evaporation.

Biochemical. Pertaining to biologic growth or activity and measured by, or expressed in terms of, the ensuing chemical change.

Board, scum or baffle. A vertical baffle dipping below the liquid surface of a tank to prevent the passage of floating matter.

Bottom, filter. (1) The underdrainage system for collecting the liquid that has passed through a filter. (2) The underdrainage system supporting the graded mediums of a biological filter bed. It may consist of specially fabricated vitreous tile or concrete blocks containing many waterways or slots to permit the passage of liquid.

Breaker, scum. A device to disintegrate or prevent the formation of surface scum in a sludge-digestion tank.

Bulking, sludge. A phenomenon that occurs in activated-sludge plants wherein the sludge swells and overflows the tanks.

Burner, waste gas. A device for burning the waste gas from a sludge-digestion tank.

By-pass. An arrangement of pipes, channels, etc., whereby the flow may be passed around any unit in the plant.

Cake, sludge. (1) The material resulting from the drying of sludge on open or covered drying beds. (2) The dewatered cake from a vacuum-sludge filter.

Carbon, activated. Carbon particles, usually obtained by carbonization of cellulose material in the absence of air, possessing a high adsorptive capacity. Used in waste treatment for suppressing odors and removing color.

Catcher, grit. (Grit chamber.) A chamber placed at the end of a sewer or at the entrance to a treatment plant to reduce the velocity of the flow sufficiently to permit grit and heavy inorganic matter to settle out.

Centrifuge. A mechanical device utilizing centrifugal force to separate solids from liquids or to separate liquid emulsions.

Chamber, chlorination. A detention basin or tank in which chlorine is diffused through a liquid.

Chamber, detritus. A settling tank designed primarily to remove heavy, settleable solids and inorganic matter. Similar to a grit chamber.

Chamber, mixing. A basin or tank to facilitate the mixing of chemicals with a liquid, usually equipped with mechanical paddles or impellers.

Charges, fixed. The carrying and operating costs of a project which continue to occur whether the plant operates or not. They usually include interest upon the original investment, certain taxes, insurance, payments due on borrowed funds, and in some cases all or a portion of the administrative overhead chargeable to the direct operation. In the case of an industrial-waste-treatment plant on industrial property, they include a charge for rental of the portion of the property occupied by the plant, a proportion of the general overhead for taxes, fire and other insurance, less any credit for materials recovered and sold at a price.

Chlorination. The application of chlorine to wastes, generally for the purpose of disinfection, but also to assist in odor control or, as in cyanide wastes, to produce chemical changes.

Chlorine. An element ordinarily existing as greenish-yellow gas about 2.5 times as heavy as air. Under atmospheric pressure and at a temperature of $-30.1°F$, the gas becomes an amber liquid about 1.5 times as heavy as water.

Clogging, filter. The effect of fine particles filling the voids of biological beds or of growths forming mats (termed "schmutz-decke") on the surface of stone filters, which retard the passage of liquid through the filter.

Cloth, filter. A fabric stretched around the drum of a vacuum filter. May be cotton, wool, rayon, or woven-metal mesh.

Coagulant. A material which, when added to industrial wastes, will combine with certain substances ordinarily present and form a precipitate consisting of more or less gelatinous floc particles and having the capacity to remove colloids from the liquids.

Coagulation. The agglomeration of colloidal or finely divided suspended matter, caused by the addition of appropriate chemical, by biological processes, or by subjecting the material to moderate agitation.

Coils, digester. A system of pipes used for circulating hot water to heat the sludge in digestion tanks.

Collector, grit. A device placed in a grit chamber to collect and convey deposited grit to a common discharge point.

Collector, scum. A mechanical device for collecting and removing scum from the surface of sedimentation tanks.

Collector, sludge. A mechanical device for collecting the sludge deposited on the bottom of a sedimentation tank and conveying it to a sludge hopper from which it can be drawn by hydrostatic pressure or by pumps.

Colloids. Finely divided solids which will not settle but may be removed by coagulation or biochemical action.

Comminution. The process of screening wastes and reducing the retained solids to particles sufficiently fine to pass through the screen openings.

Compact, interstate. A compact or agreement between two or more states to cover the development and utilization of interstate streams, to abate pollution, and to control industrial-waste treatment.

Concentration, hydrogen ion (pH). The weight of hydrogen ions in grams per liter of solution. Commonly expressed as the pH value that represents the logarithm of the reciprocal of the hydrogen-ion concentration. pH 7.0 is neutral. Below pH 7.0 indicates acidity, and above 7.0 indicates alkalinity.

Conditioning, sludge. Treatment of fluid sludge, to facilitate dewatering, by the addition of ferric chloride, alum, lime, etc.

Content, moisture. The quantity of water, usually expressed in percentage by weight, present in sludge from waste treatment, screenings, etc.

Convection currents. The phenomenon occurring when masses of warm liquid rise upward in a tank, the bulk of the volume at lower depths being colder.

Copperas. Common name for ferrous sulfate. A coagulant.

Cubic foot per second. A unit of measurement for flowing liquids, equal to a flow of 1 cubic foot per second past a given section of channel. Also called "second-foot." Known as a "cusec" in Great Britain and other countries.

Decomposition of sewage (*or wastes*). The breakdown of organic matter first by aerobic activity and then by anaerobic oxidation and nitrification.

Degreasing. The process of removing grease or oils from wastes, sludge, etc.

Demand, biochemical oxygen (*BOD*). The quantity of oxygen utilized in the biochemical oxidation of organic matter in a specified time and at a specified temperature. It is not related to the oxygen requirements in chemical combustion, being determined entirely by the availability of the material as a biological food and by the amount of oxygen utilized by the microorganisms during oxidation. It is usually determined for a period of 5 days at 20°C and is expressed in parts per million.

Depth, side water. The depth of a liquid measured along the inside of the vertical exterior wall of a tank.

Detention period. The period of flow through a tank equal to a given number of hours of the hourly volume of flow; *i.e.*, 2 hours detention equals the amount of flow reaching the tank in 2 hours.

Detritus. The sand, grit, and other coarse material removed by gravitational sedimentation in a relatively short period of detention.

Dewatering. The removal of a large part of the occluded water content of sludge by draining or by mechanical means, such as vacuum filters or sludge presses.

Diffuser. A porous tube or plate through which air is forced and divided into minute bubbles for diffusion in liquids. Made of carborundum, alundum, or silica sand.

Digestion. The anaerobic decomposition of organic matter, resulting in partial gasification, liquefaction, and mineralization.

Digestion, mesophilic. Digestion at or below 113°F.

Digestion, separate. The digestion of sludge in two or more tanks arranged in series.

Digestion, sludge. The process by which organic or volatile matter in sludge is gasified, liquefied, mineralized, or converted into more stable organic matter, through the activities of living organisms.

Digestion, stage. The progressive digestion of sludge in several tanks arranged in series.

Digestion, thermophilic. Digestion carried on at a temperature generally between 113 to 145°F.

Dilution. (1) A method of disposing of industrial wastes or plant effluent by discharge into a stream or body of water. (2) The ratio of the volume of a stream to the total volume of wastes or effluent discharged into it.

Distillation. The process of raising the temperature of a liquid to the boiling point and condensing the resultant vapor to liquid form by cooling. It is used to remove substances from a liquid or to obtain a pure liquid from one which contains impurities or which is a mixture of several liquids having different boiling temperatures. Used in the treatment of fermentation products, yeast, etc., and other wastes to remove recoverable products.

Distributor. A device used to apply liquid to the surface of a filter. There are two general types, fixed and movable. The fixed type may consist of perforated pipes or sprinkler nozzles. The movable type may consist of rotating, reciprocating, or traveling perforated pipes or pipe arms fitted with spray nozzles or rotating disks.

Distributor, rotating. A distributor consisting of rotating pipe arms from which the liquid is discharged in the form of a spray or thin sheets.

Dome, gas. In sludge-digestion tanks, a steel cover floating on the gas above the sludge, or a fixed metal dome to contain the gas.

Dose, chlorine.   The amount of chlorine applied to a liquid, usually expressed in parts per million.

Drier, flash.   A device for vaporizing water from partly dewatered and finely divided sludge through contact with a current of hot gas or other vapor.   Usually includes a squirrel-cage mill for separating the sludge cake into fine particles.

Drier, rotary.   A long steel cylinder, lying horizontally, with its long axis on a slight incline, through which sludge passes to be dried in an upgoing current of hot air or gas.

Drier, spray.   A drier in which the liquid containing the solids to be dried is sprayed or atomized into a hot chamber.

Drying, sludge.   The process of removing water from sludge by drainage or evaporation, exposure to the air, the application of heat, or other methods.

Earth, diatomaceous.   Extremely porous earth composed essentially of the siliceous skeletons of diatoms, which are extremely minute unicellular organisms. Used as a coagulant or filter aid in the conditioning of sludge.

Eddy.   A circular movement occurring in flowing water, caused by currents set up in the water due to obstructions or irregularities in a tank or bottom of a channel.

Efficiency.   The relative results obtained in any operation in relation to energy or effort required to achieve such results.   It is the ratio, expressed as a percentage, of the work done by a unit or process.   Thus, a sedimentation unit which removes three-fourths of the suspended solids in a waste liquid would be 75 per cent efficient.

Efficiency, filter.   The operating results of a filter as measured by various criteria, such as percentage reduction in suspended matter, total solids, BOD, bacteria, or color.

Effluent.   The waste water, partially or completely treated, that flows out of a treatment plant; thus, clarifier effluent, filter effluent, final effluent.

Effluent, stable.   A treated waste which contains enough oxygen to satisfy its oxygen demand.

Elutriation.   A process of sludge conditioning in which certain constituents are removed by successive decantations with fresh water or plant effluent, thereby reducing the demand for conditioning chemicals.

Equivalent population.   (1) The calculated population which would normally contribute the same amount of BOD per day.   A common base is 0.17 pound of 5-day BOD per capita per day.   (2) For industrial waste, the estimated number of people that would contribute normal sewage equal in strength to a unit volume of waste or to some other unit used in the production of a commodity.

Feeder, dry chemical.   A mechanical device for applying dry chemicals to wastes at a rate controlled manually, or automatically, by the rate of flow of liquid or by quantity per unit of time.

Film, microbial.   The gelatinous film of zoogleal growths covering the medium of a biological bed, trickling filter, etc.

Filter, high rate, high capacity. A trickling filter operated at a high average daily rate of dosing between 10 million and 30 million gallons per day per acre, sometimes including recirculation of effluent.

Filter, low rate. A trickling filter designed to receive a small load of BOD per unit volume of filtering material and to have a low dosage rate per unit of surface area (usually 1 million to 4 million gallons per day per acre).

Filter, sludge vacuum. A device in which wet sludge, previously conditioned by a coagulant, is partially dewatered by means of a vacuum or pressure. Commonly in the form of a rotating drum, covered with cotton, wool, nylon, or wire cloth or tightly stretched metal springs or strings.

Filter, sprinkling. A trickling filter to which the sewage is applied by sprays from fixed nozzles or rotating arms. An old term, now considered obsolete, trickling filter being preferred.

Filter, trickling. A filter consisting of an artificial bed of coarse material, such as broken stone, clinkers, pebbles, gravel, slate, slats, anthracite coal, or brush, over which wastes are distributed in drops, films, or sprays from moving distributors or fixed nozzles and through which they trickle to the underdrains, giving opportunity for the formation of zoogleal slimes which coat the medium and clarify and oxidize the wastes.

Filter, vacuum. A filter consisting of a cylindrical drum mounted on a horizontal axis, covered with a filter medium (as described in Filter, sludge vacuum), revolving partially submerged in a tank of conditioned sludge. A vacuum is maintained under the filter medium for the greater part of a revolution of the drum to extract moisture. The dewatered cake is continuously removed by a scraper at one side.

Filtration, biological. The process of passing a liquid through a biological filter containing mediums on the surface of which zoogleal films develop, which absorb and adsorb fine suspended, colloidal, and dissolved solids and release the end products of biochemical action.

Float control. A device installed in a channel or tank to operate a screen or pumps. In screening wastes, one form of float control operates on the difference of head between the approaching and discharge side of the screen bars.

Floc. Small, gelatinous masses formed in a liquid by the addition of coagulants, or through biochemical processes, or by agglomeration.

Flocculation. Floc formation by a mechanical unit to stimulate the formation of compact, quick-settling flocs. Usually in the form of revolving shafts with paddle blades operating at slow speed to cause the forming flocs to pass in a multitude of paths through all zones of the flocculation basin.

Flotation. A method of raising suspended matter to the surface of a liquid in a tank in the form of scum—by aeration, the evolution of gas, chemicals, electrolysis, heat or bacterial decomposition, or vacuum.

Flow, radial outward. The flow of liquid in a circular or square tank from an inlet at the center to an overflow weir or apertures at the periphery of the tank.

Flume, Parshall. A device, developed by an engineer by that name, for measuring the flow of liquid in an open channel. It consists of a contracting length, a throat, and an expanding length. At the throat is a sill over which the flow passes. The upper and lower heads are each measured at a definite distance from the sill.

Foaming, sludge. An increase in the gas in separate sludge-digestion tanks causing large quantities of froth, scum, and sludge to rise and overflow from openings at or near the top of the tanks.

Freeboard. The vertical distance between the normal maximum level of the liquid in a tank, channel, etc., and the top of the tank or channel or of a mechanism or structure spanning the tank.

Gas, sludge. The gas produced during the digestion of organic solids from industrial wastes or sewage. Commonly called "sludge-digester gas." May be collected and utilized for heating purposes or for the generation of power for operating vehicles, domestic purposes, etc. The gas normally contains 60 to 65 per cent methane and has an average value of 600 to 650 Btu per cubic foot.

Grinder, screenings. A device for grinding, shredding, or macerating material removed from wastes by coarse or fine screens.

Grit. The heavy mineral matter in sewage or wastes, such as sand, gravel, or cinders.

Head, loss of. The decrease in the level of a liquid.

Head, static. The vertical distance between the free level of the source of supply and the point of free discharge or the level of the free surface.

Head, weir. The distance from the crest of a weir to the water surface at a given point ahead of the weir.

Holder, sludge gas. A tank for the storage of gas collected from sludge-digestion tanks, for the purpose of stabilizing the flow of gas to the burners, or engines, maintaining a nearly constant pressure, and supplying gas at normal volume and pressure when the digestion tanks are out of service for short periods or when gas production drops below normal.

Imhoff cone. A conically shaped graduated glass vessel used to measure the approximate volume of settleable solids in wastes or other liquids.

Index, pollutional. A criterion by which the degree of pollution in a stream may be measured, as indicated by bacterial counts, plankton, BOD, or quantity of dissolved oxygen.

Influent. Sewage, industrial wastes, or other liquids, raw or partially treated, flowing into a treatment plant or unit thereof.

Interstice. A pore or open space in rock or granular material. Also called "void."

Lagoon, sludge. A relatively shallow basin, or natural depression, used for the storage or digestion of sludge and sometimes for its ultimate detention or dewatering.

Level, water. The elevation of the free water or liquid surface of a body of water or liquid above or below a given datum line.

Liquefaction. The changing of the organic matter in wastes from an insoluble to a soluble state effecting a reduction in the solid contents.

Liquid, supernatant. The liquid in a sludge-digestion tank which lies between the sludge at the bottom and the floating scum at the top.

Load, pollutional. The quantity of polluting material discharged into a body of water. The pollutional load imposed on sewage-treatment works is expressed as the equivalent population.

Loading, BOD filter. The pounds of BOD in the applied liquid per unit of filter-bed area or volume.

Matter, suspended. Solids in suspension in wastes or effluent. Commonly, those which can be removed readily by laboratory methods or filtering.

Mixer, flash. A device for dispersing chemicals quickly and uniformly throughout a liquid.

Overflow rate. A criterion for the design of settling tanks in treatment plants; expressed in gallons per day per square foot of the surface area in a tank.

Parts per million. Parts by weight in water and wastes analysis. One ppm is equal to 1 milligram per liter.

Period, aeration. (1) The theoretical time, usually expressed in hours, that the mixed liquor is subjected to aeration in an aeration tank undergoing activated-sludge treatment. It is equal to the volume of the tank divided by the volumetric rate of flow of wastes and return sludge. (2) The theoretical time that liquids are subjected to aeration.

Period, detention. The theoretical time required to displace the contents of a tank or unit at a given rate of flow (volume divided by a rate of discharge in gallons per hour or cubic feet).

Pollution. The addition of industrial wastes or other harmful or objectionable matter to water.

Pooling, filter. The formation of pools of liquid on the surface of biologic filters caused by clogging of the filter medium.

Preaeration. A preparatory treatment of wastes comprising aeration to remove gases, add oxygen, promote flotation of grease, increase the buoyancy of light particles, or aid coagulation.

Precipitation. The phenomenon that occurs when a substance held in solution in a liquid passes out of solution into solid form.

Precipitation, chemical. Precipitation induced by the addition of chemicals.

Presettling. The process of sedimentation applied to a liquid preceding subsequent treatment.

Process, activated sludge. A biological waste-treatment process in which a mixture of wastes and activated sludge is agitated and aerated. The activated sludge is subsequently separated from the treated wastes (mixed liquor) by sedimentation and wasted or returned to the process as needed. The treated wastes overflow the weir of the final settling tank in which separation from the sludge takes place.

Recirculation. (1) The return of all or a portion of the effluent in a high-rate trickling filter for the purpose of maintaining a uniform or nonuniform rate through the filter. (2) The return of effluent to the incoming flow to reduce its strength.

Removal, hydrostatic sludge. The discharge of sludge from a tank by utilizing the pressure of the column of liquid above the sludge outlet.

Sample, composite. A combination of individual samples of wastes taken at selected intervals, generally hourly for 24 hours, to minimize the effect of the variations in individual samples. Individual samples making up the composite may be of equal volume or be roughly apportioned to the volume of flow of liquid at the time of sampling.

Screen, mechanically cleaned. A screen equipped with mechanical cleaning apparatus for removal of retained solids. Usually a rake traveling vertically or in a rotatory manner between screen bars.

Sedimentation. The process of subsidence and deposition of suspended matter in liquids, wastes, etc., by gravity. It is usually accomplished by reducing the velocity of flow of the liquid below the point where suspended material will be transported.

Seeding, sludge. The inoculation of undigested sewage or waste solids with sludge that has undergone or is undergoing decomposition, for the purpose of introducing favorable organisms, thereby accelerating the initial stage of digestion and shortening digestion time.

Sludge. The accumulated settled solids deposited from industrial wastes, raw or treated, in tanks or basins and containing more or less water to form a semi-liquid mass.

Sludge, activated. Sludge floc produced in raw or settled sewage or wastes by the growth of zoogleal bacteria and other organisms in the presence of dissolved oxygen, and accumulated in sufficient concentration by returning floc previously formed.

Sludge, digested. Sludge digested under anaerobic conditions until the volatile content has been reduced, usually, about 50 per cent.

Solids, dry suspended. The weight of suspended matter in industrial wastes after drying for 1 hour at 103°C.

Solids, suspended. Solids that either float on the surface of, or are in suspension in, wastes or other liquids and which are largely removable by laboratory filtering.

Squeegee. The metal blades attached to the lower arms of a sludge-collection mechanism to clean the tank bottom of all settled material.

Tank, sedimentation. A tank or basin in which wastes containing settleable solids are retained for a sufficient time and in which the velocity of flow is sufficiently low to remove a part of the suspended matter by gravity. Usually, in the treatment of decomposable wastes, the detention period must be short enough to avoid anaerobic decomposition.

Tank, sludge digestion. A tank in which the solids resulting from the sedimentation of wastes are stored for the purpose of permitting anaerobic decomposition to the point of rendering the product nonputrescible and inoffensive.

Thickener, sludge. A type of sedimentation tank in which sludge is permitted to settle, usually equipped with scrapers traveling along or around the bottom of the tank to push the settled sludge to a sump. In one form, the mechanism is equipped with a set of vertical fingers or risers which pass through the sludge, releasing occluded water and thickening the mass.

Treatment, preliminary. The conditioning of an industrial waste at its source prior to discharge to remove or neutralize substances injurious to sewers and sewage-treatment processes or to effect a partial reduction in the load on the treatment processes. Unit operations which prepare the liquid for subsequent major operations.

Treatment, primary. The first major treatment and sometimes the only treatment in a waste-treatment works, usually sedimentation and/or flocculation and digestion. The removal of a moderate percentage of suspended matter but little or no colloidal or dissolved matter. May effect the removal of 30 to 35 per cent or more BOD.

Treatment, secondary. The treatment of wastes by biological or chemical methods after primary treatment by sedimentation.

Unloading, filter. The periodic sloughing or unloading of the film on the stones of a trickling filter.

Utilization. The use of the gas produced in the digestion of sludge for heating the sludge-digestion tanks, for heating buildings about the plant, as a fuel in engines for the generation of power, for the incineration of screenings and sludge, and in drying sludge for the production of fertilizer.

Wastes, industrial. The liquid wastes from industrial processes, as distinct from domestic or sanitary sewage.

Water, potable. Water which is considered satisfactory for domestic consumption.

Weir, peripheral. The outlet weir in a settling tank, extending around the perimeter and over which the effluent discharges.

AUTHOR INDEX

A

Adams, C. D., 117
Agar, C. C., 23
Allen, J. H., 345
Anable, A., 92, 345
Anderson, B. G., 117

B

Backmeyer, D., 289
Baffa, J. J., 23
Balmer, R. R., 24
Barnes, G. E., 28, 217
Bartholomew, F. J., 218
Baumann, J. B., 345
Beal, G. D., 85
Beaumont, H. M., 116
Beohner, H. L., 218
Besselievre, E. B., 28, 92, 116, 217, 269, 288, 289, 345
Black, A. P., 345
Bloodgood, D. E., 49, 217, 345
Boruff, C. S., 322
Braley, S. A., 85
Breedham, C. C., 116
Brintzinger, H., 269
Broning, C. F., 16
Brown, C. V., 38
Buswell, A. M., 269

C

Caldwell, D. H., 85
Calvert, C. K., 116
Carpenter, L. V., 269
Childs, J. A., 289
Clark, R. N., 345
Cleary, E. J., 23
Coates, J. J., 269
Coblentz, M. H., 23, 116
Cooper, J. E., 24
Crane, F. W., 289
Croft, H. P., 38

D

Danse, L. A., 33
Demarest, E. L., 260
Del Guercio, V., 217
Devendorf, E., 7, 33
Dickerson, W. H., 322
Doll, B. E., 345

E

Eagles, R. E., 28
Elder, A. L., 269
Eldridge, E. F., 7, 15, 85, 117, 217, 269
Eldridge, W. J., 23
Ellis, M. M., 116
Enslow, L. H., 269
Ettinger, M. B., 85

F

Fair, G. M., 28
Ferguson, R. H., 269
Fischer, A. J., 85, 218
Fisher, L. M., 117
Friel, F. S., 217

G

Garnett, G. R., 85
Gehm, H. W., 23, 322
Glace, I. M., 16
Gorman, A. W., 217
Gray, H. F., 38, 288
Guillot, E. F., 218

H

Hall, G. L., 218
Halperin, Z., 322
Hart, W. B., 6, 217
Hatfield, W. D., 85
Hauck, C. F., 85, 117

SUBJECT INDEX

A

Acceptance of wastes in Worcester, Mass., 15

Accessibility of equipment, 221

Acetone, 107

Acetylene-generator sludge, exclusion from sewers, 95

Acid, hydrochloric, 265–266
    phosphoric, 265
    sulfuric, 265–266

Acid mine wastes, 171–172

Acid wastes, analysis of, in Slough, England, 114
    neutralization of, 214

Acidity, importance of, 56
    test for, 76

Action required by industry, 14

Activated carbon, 265–266

Activated-sludge process, 145–148
    aeration tanks for, 146
    diffusers for, 148
    efficiency of, 84
    horsepower required for, 147
    package plants for, 146
    for packing-house wastes, 167
    for pulp-mill wastes, 188
    in Rubner Packing Co., 169–170
    for slaughterhouse and stockyard wastes, 167
    for sulfite wastes, 188

Adka save-all, 312

Aeration, 253–255
    compressed air for, 253–254
    diffusers for, 254
    Dow Chemical Company system, 254
    jet, 254–255
    swing diffusers for, 254
    volume of air for, 254

Aeration tanks, 146, 254

Aerator-Clarifier, 229

Aerators, types of, 254–255

Aerofilter, 258

Agencies for pollution control, interstate, 44–45
    state, 46–48

Agreements, sanitation, 44–45

Air-conditioning wastes, 104

Alabama Water Improvement Advisory Commission, 46

Alaska health laws and regulations, 333–335

Alcohol wastes, 107
    from distilleries, biofilters for, 142
    recovery of, 311–313
    temperature of, 57

Alkalinity, meaning of, 56
    test for, 76

Allegheny County, Pa., charges for handling wastes in, 284–285

Allis-Chalmers Company centrifugal pumps, 250

Aluminum sulfate, 265–266

American Radiator Company boilers for digesters, 240

American Well Works Company, aerators, 254
    bar screens, 225
    clarifiers, 228
        rectangular, 229
    Dow aeration system, 254
    preaeration units, 238

Ammonia nitrogen, 81–82

Ammonium aluminum sulfate, 266

Analysis of wastes, interpretation of, 72–82
    in Slough, England, 114
    technique of, 68–71

Anderson, Ind., cost of sewage treatment in, 280

Anheuser-Busch, Inc., waste treatment by, 179, 181

Ann Arbor, Mich., cost of sewage treatment in, 281

Anodizing wastes, analysis of, in Slough, England, 114

371

D

Dairy wastes, characteristics of, 84, 105, 202
  methods of treatment of, 202
  recovery from, 317
Dallas, Tex., cost of sewage treatment in, 281
Danville, Ill., cost of sewage treatment in, 281
Dayton, Ohio, regulations for handling wastes, 288
Decatur, Ill., cost of sewage treatment in, 280
  regulations for handling wastes, 288
Dehydration wastes, 172
  regulations on disposal of, in state of Washington, 343–344
Deinking wastes, 109
Deionization, 153–155
DeKalb, Ill., cost of sewage treatment in, 280
DeLaval Company centrifugal pumps, 250
Delaware, pollution-control agencies in, 45–46
Delaware River Basin, Interstate Commission on, 45
Desizing wastes in cotton mills, 110
Detritor, Dorr, 123–124, 237
Devices, protective, for equipment, 223
Dewsbury, England, charges for handling wastes in, 286
Diatomaceous earth as coagulant, 265
Diffusers, swing, 148, 254
Digester gas, for power, 52–53
  use of, 319–322
Digestion, 158–160, 239–244
  BOD reduction by, 141–142, 158–159
  effect of temperature on, 57
  of packing-house wastes, 168–171
  solids suited for, 158
Disintegrator, Dorrco-Sulzer, for screenings, 224
Distillation wastes, acetone and alcohol, 107
Distillery wastes, BOD, 84
  characteristics of, 107
  population equivalent of, 107, 311
  recovery from, 311
  suspended solids in, 84

Distilling grain waste, 107
Distilling molasses waste, 107
District of Columbia, health laws and regulations, 333–335
  in Interstate Commission on Potomac River Basin, 45
Districts for industrial-waste treatment, 50–54
  Chicago Sanitary, 50
  Passaic Valley, 12–13
Domestic Pump and Engine Company sludge pumps, 250
Dorr Company, Aerator-Clarifier, 238
  bar screens, 224
  Clarifiers, 228–229
  Clariflocculator, 232
  Clarigester, 230–232
  conversion factors, 346
  Detritor, 237
  Disintegrator, 224
  distributor, 258
  Dow aeration system, 254
  Duo-Biofilter, 140, 168, 234
  Duo-Clarifier, 232–234
  Duo-Clarigester, 168, 234
  fine screen, 225
  float control, 223
  Flocculator, 244–245, 247–248
  Monorake, 229
  sludge digestion, 240–243
  sludge pump, 229–250
  treatment of pickling liquors, 190–192
  Vacuator, 226, 228–229
Dow Chemical Company, aeration system, 254–255
  treatment of phenol wastes, 175–176
  flow sheet for, 176
Dry-milk waste, 105
Drying, sludge (*see* Sludge Drying)
Duo-Biofilter, 140, 168, 234
Duo-Clarifier, 232–234
Duo-Clarigester, 168, 234
Du Pont Company, research by, 21
  waste treatment by, 175
Durban, Natal, South Africa, charges for handling wastes in, 286
Durham, N.C., regulations for handling wastes, 287
Dyeing wastes, analysis of, in Slough, England, 114